A Peoples Education Lab Manual for
AP*/Honors

Physics B Exam

BY JAMES MOONEY
TAFT SCHOOL
WATERTOWN, CT

Peoples education™
Your partner in student success™

Publisher: Tom Maksym

Executive Editor: Steven Jay Griffel

Vice President of Production: Doreen Smith

Pre-Press and Production Manager: Jason Grasso

Project Manager: Matthew Hjembo

Senior Book Coordinator: Paul Zakrzewski

Production Assistants: Chip Cliffe, Joseph Lisa, Richard Lehmbeck

Designer: Carol Deckert

Copy Editor: Michael O'Neill

Art Director: Amy Rosen

Photo Researcher/Permissions Manager: Kristine Liebman

Technical Art: Chip Cliffe, Matthew Hjembo, Richard Lehmbeck, James Mooney, Paul Zakrzewski

Cover Design: Cristina Castro Pelka, Michele Sakow

Marketing Manager: Kathy Wanamaker

Your partner in student success™

Copyright © 2005

Peoples Education, Inc.

299 Market Street

Saddle Brook, New Jersey 07663

ISBN 978-1-4138-0491-1

ISBN 1-4138-0491-8

Printed in the United States of America.

10   9   8   7

To Catherine:

Thank you for always being there. Your love, support, and encouragement have been the great constants in my life.

Table of Contents

The Advanced Placement Program and AP Exams

Colleges and the AP Exams 1
Which AP Exams to Take 2
Where to Take an AP Exam 2
Registering for AP Exams 3
Receiving and Reporting Your AP Scores 3
Withholding and Canceling AP Grades 3

Content and Format of the AP Physics B Exam

Content 4
Format
    Section I 8
    Section II 10
Weighted and Composite Scores 11
Calculating Your AP Grade 12

Strategies for Taking the AP Physics Exam

Multiple-Choice Strategies 13
Free-Response Strategies 16

Cross-Reference with Popular B-Level Textbooks 19

Chapter 1 Motion in One Dimension

Position and Displacement 21
Velocity 22
Acceleration 24
Constant Acceleration Equations 26
Key Formulas 29
Practice Exercises 30
Answers and Explanations 34

Chapter 2 Vectors and Projectiles

Scalars and Vectors 38
Vector Addition 39
Components of a Vector 41
Vector Multiplication 44
    Dot Product 44
    Cross Product 45
Projectile Motion 46
Key Formulas 50
Practice Exercises 51
Answers and Explanations 53

Chapter 3 Newton's Laws

Inertia and the First Law 57
Types of Forces 58
    Contact Forces 58
    Noncontact Forces 59
Freebody Diagrams 60
Action and Reaction and the Third Law 61
Newton's Second Law 61
Inclines 64
Pulleys 66
Circular Motion 68
Statics 70
    Translational Equilibrium 71
    Rotational Equilibrium 71
Key Formulas 75
Practice Exercises 76
Answers and Explanations 81

Chapter 4 Work and Energy

Work 85
Power 87
Kinetic Energy 88
Conservative Forces 89
Potential Energy 90
Conservation of Energy 91
Graphs of Potential Energy 93
Key Formulas 94
Practice Exercises 95
Answers and Explanations 98

Chapter 5 Impulse and Momentum

Impulse 102
Linear Momentum 103
Conservation of Momentum 104
Collisions 105
    One Dimension 105
    Two Dimensions 107
Center of Mass 109
Angular Momentum and Its Conservation 111
Key Formulas 114
Practice Exercises 115
Answers and Explanations 120

Chapter 6 Gravitation

Newton's Law of Gravity 124
g vs. G 126
Satellites 127
Apparent Weight 130
Key Formulas 131
Practice Exercises 132
Answers and Explanations 133

Chapter 7 Oscillations

Description 135
Simple Harmonic Motion 136
    Spring-Mass 136
    Simple Pendulum 137
    Reference Circle 139
Key Formulas 142
Practice Exercises 143
Answers and Explanations 145

Chapter 8 Fluid Mechanics

Hydrostatic Pressure 149
Buoyancy 152
Fluid Flow 154
    Streamlines 154
    Continuity Equation 155
    Bernoulli's Equation 156
Key Formulas 161
Practice Exercises 162
Answers and Explanations 166

Chapter 9 Thermal Physics

Temperature 169
Internal Energy 172
Work and Heat 172
First Law of Thermodynamics 173
Heat Transfer Mechanisms 173
Ideal Gas 175
    Ideal Gas Law 175
    Kinetic Molecular Theory 177
Work and pV diagrams 179
Second Law of Thermodynamics 182
Entropy 187
Key Formulas 188
Practice Exercises 189
Answers and Explanations 194

Chapter 10 Electric Force and Electric Field

Electric Charge 197
Coulomb's Law 197
Electric Field 199
    Field Due to Point Charge Distributions 200
    Motion of a Charge in an Electric Field 201
Key Formulas 202
Practice Exercises 203
Answers and Explanations 205

Chapter 11 Electric Potential and Electric Potential Energy

Electric Potential 209
    Potential Due to Point Charge Distributions 211
Equipotential Surfaces and Conductors 213
Electric Potential Energy 215
Key Formulas 218
Practice Exercises 219
Answers and Explanations 222

Chapter 12 Electric Circuits

Conductors and Electric Current 224
Batteries 226
Electrical Resistance and Ohm's Law 227
Electric Power 229
Kirchhoff's Laws 230
Resistors in Series and Parallel 232
Terminal Voltage 234
Current Division 235
Simple Circuits 236
Capacitance and Capacitors 237
Capacitors in Circuits 238
    Capacitors in Series and Parallel 239
    Energy and Capacitors 241
Key Formulas 242
Practice Exercises 243
Answers and Explanations 248

Chapter 13 Magnetostatics

Magnetic Field and Force 252
Motion in a Uniform Field 254
Magnetic Force on a Current-Carrying Wire 256
Magnetic Field Due to a Long Wire 258
Force between Long Current-Carrying Wires 259
Key Formulas 260
Practice Exercises 261
Answers and Explanations 266

Chapter 14 Electromagnetic Induction

Motional Induced Voltages 270
Magnetic Flux 272
Faraday's Law 273
Lenz's Law and Flux 274
Faraday's Law Generalized 275
Key Formulas 276
Practice Exercises 277
Answers and Explanations 284

Chapter 15 Waves

Traveling Waves 288
Doppler Effect 291
    Moving Source 292
    Moving Observer 293
Superposition Principle and Interference 293
Wave Reflections 295
Standing Waves 296
    Strings 297
    Air Columns 299
Resonance 300
Beats 301
Key Formulas 301
Practice Exercises 302
Answers and Explanations 305

Chapter 16 Geometrical Optics

Wave Fronts and Rays 307
Index of Refraction 308
Reflection 308
Refraction 309
Total Internal Reflection 311
Mirrors 312
    Plane Mirror 312
    Concave Mirror 313
    Convex Mirror 315
Lenses 316
    Convex Lens 316
    Concave Lens 317
Key Formulas 318
Practice Exercises 319
Answers and Explanations 323

Chapter 17 Wave Optics

Huygens' Principle 327
Diffraction 328
Two-Slit Interference 329
Diffraction Grating 333
Single-Slit Diffraction 333
Thin Film Interference 334
Key Formulas 337
Practice Exercises 338
Answers and Explanations 340

Chapter 18 The Quantum World

Photoelectric Effect 343
The Compton Effect 347
Matter Waves 348
Wave-Particle Duality 349
Atomic Energy Levels 351
Line Spectra 352
Key Formulas 353
Practice Exercises 354
Answers and Explanations 357

Chapter 19 Nuclear Physics

The Nucleus 360
Nuclear Reactions 362
Energy in Nuclear Reactions 363
Key Formula 364
Practice Exercises 365
Answers and Explanations 366

Chapter 20 AP Physics and the Laboratory

Lab Questions on the Exam 368
Practice Exercises 372
Answers and Explanations 372

Appendix

Table of Information 374
Equations 375

Practice Tests

Test 1 377
Test 2 403

Answers and Explanations

Test 1 428
Test 2 441

Glossary
. . . . 456

The Advanced Placement Program and AP Exams

The Advanced Placement (AP) Program was created by the College Board in cooperation with secondary schools around the country. Using course outlines developed by university and high school teachers, secondary schools offer college level courses in a wide range of disciplines. Standardized tests written by a committee consisting of college and high school faculty are administered in each subject area in early May. If you do well on a given test, then you can receive credit at the college you eventually attend. The tests are read and graded, and your scores are reported to your chosen colleges. The scoring scale and interpretation are

> 5—extremely well qualified
> 4—well qualified
> 3—qualified
> 2—possibly qualified
> 1—no recommendation

Colleges and the AP Exams

Most colleges require that you take the SAT. In addition, they usually strongly recommend that you take several SAT II tests as well. AP exams are not a requirement. However, it is fair to say that a high school program that includes one or more AP courses will enhance your chances for acceptance at the college you want to attend. Consider the following points.

- The AP curricula are all demanding and rigorous. Just your enrollment in an AP course sends a signal that you are looking for academic challenge.
- A good grade on the AP exam will provide a standardized measure of your work over the year that will be easy for a college admissions committee to interpret.

Perhaps the prime motivation for the AP program is the college credit that can be earned by high school students. The level of credit earned by a given score on the AP exam is not standardized; it varies from college to college and is usually determined within the particular department that would be granting the credit. For example, the physics department at

Hadron University may give credit for AP Physics B scores of 4 or higher, while the same department at Lepton College may give credit for scores of 3 or better. Even if your score is not high enough to get credit (a few schools require a 5), a solid showing on the test can get you placed into a higher level introductory course.

Which AP Exams to Take

It is difficult to do well in a course that does not interest you, particularly if the course is as rigorous as an AP course. You shouldn't sign up for any AP unless the subject matter really turns you on. However, if you're interested in several disciplines, there's no limit to the number of APs you can take in a given year. Over the first couple of weeks in May, two tests are given each day, one in the morning and one in the afternoon. Obviously, a course load of five APs would be demanding over one year, and the tests could all fall within a narrow time frame depending on which tests you were taking. This is an important consideration, and you can find the test dates for each year at the AP website, http://apcentral.collegeboard.com. If two of the tests you want to take are scheduled for the same time slot, you can arrange to take one of them at a later date. The test will be different from the one given in the usual time slot, but of course it will cover all the same material.

Below are the mean scores in some commonly taken AP exams.

EXAM	MEAN GRADE (in 2001)
Physics B	2.8
Physics C Mech	3.3
Physics C E&M	3.3
Calculus AB/BC	3.0/3.6
Chemistry	2.8
English Literature	3.0
European History	2.9
French	2.8
Latin	2.9
U.S. Government and Politics	2.8
Spanish Language	3.6

Where to Take an AP Exam

AP tests are given at schools that teach the associated AP courses. If you're taking AP Physics B, chances are the test will be held at your school as well. Check with your teacher, guidance counselor, or AP Coordinator. If your school doesn't offer AP courses or tests, you can contact AP Services to find a school nearby that will let you take the tests there.

AP Services
P.O. Box 6671
Princeton, NJ 08541-6671
(609) 771-7300 or toll-free (888) CALL-4-AP [888-225-5427]
Fax: (609) 530-0482
TTY: (609) 882-4118
E-mail: apexams@info.collegeboard.org

Registering for AP Exams

To register for an AP exam, you'll need to fill out several forms and pay a registration fee ($78 in 2004) for each AP exam you want to take. While the fee is considerable, if your AP score gets you placement or credit with the college you attend, you'll probably wind up saving some serious tuition money.

You should register for the AP exam with your AP Coordinator. If your school doesn't have an AP program, you can contact a nearby school that does have an AP Coordinator for all the information.

Receiving and Reporting Your AP Scores

The reading and grading for the exams take the entire month of June. Scores are mailed out over the first half of July. The colleges that you designated will also receive the scores then. If you can't wait the extra week or two, you can pay a fee and find out your score over the phone after July 1.

Withholding and Canceling AP Grades

Suppose you are certain that you did so poorly on the test that you are afraid it will hurt your chances at a particular school. By submitting a signed request to the AP program by June 15, you can prevent a score from being reported to a particular college. You can even have the score permanently canceled so that it will not appear on any record, even the record you receive from the AP program with your other scores. Unfortunately, to withhold or cancel a score, you must do so before you actually know what the score is. Be sure to think it over well before you proceed in withholding or canceling. You will see in the next two chapters that an acceptable grade on an AP exam doesn't always correspond to a high percentage of correct answers.

Content and Format
of the AP Physics B Exam

Many excellent textbooks cover the material essential to the B exam. But publishers usually try to appeal to a larger audience than just AP students, so these books contain quite a bit more material than the AP syllabus warrants. If you've been using one of these books in your school, you may even find that all of the essential material for the test isn't covered in class simply because there's not enough time. This chapter outlines the AP B syllabus, highlighting the specific topics that you need to cover and listing which topics won't appear on the test. Then we'll look at the actual format of the test so that you'll be familiar with how the material appears on the exam.

Content

The B-level course is a broad survey designed to present a wide range of phenomena and the physical laws that explain them. The mathematical level is that of a typical Algebra II course, so you should be comfortable with algebraic manipulations and right triangle trigonometry. At the college level, Physics B is equivalent to an introductory physics course for students who aren't entering the physical sciences. The breadth of the syllabus is daunting, but if you focus on what's essential, you can get through it all, even in a one-year course.

The first column in the following table lists the various topics and subtopics that are typically covered in a B-level textbook. The second column indicates whether the given topic is actually part of the B syllabus, and if it is, what percentage of the total test is drawn from that topic.

	Percentage Goals for Exams
	Physics B
I. Newtonian Mechanics	**35%**
A. Kinematics (vectors, vector algebra, vector components, coordinate systems, displacement, velocity, and acceleration)	7%
1. Motion in one dimension	yes
2. Motion in two dimensions, including projectile motion	yes

B. Newton's laws of motion, including friction and centripetal force	**9%**
1. Static equilibrium	yes
2. Dynamics of a single particle	yes
3. Systems of two or more bodies	yes
C. Work, energy, and power	**5%**
1. Work and work-energy theorem	yes
2. Conservative forces and potential energy	yes
3. Conservation of energy	yes
4. Power	yes
D. Systems of particles and linear momentum	**4%**
1. Center of mass	yes
2. Impulse and momentum	yes
3. Conservation of linear momentum and collisions	yes
E. Circular motion and rotation	**4%**
1. Uniform circular motion	yes
2. Angular momentum and its conservation	
a. Point particles	yes
b. Extended bodies, including rotational inertia	NO
3. Torque and rotational statics	yes
4. Rotational kinematics and dynamics	NO
F. Oscillations and gravitation	**6%**
1. Simple harmonic motion (dynamics and energy relationships)	yes
2. Mass on a spring	yes
3. Pendulum and other oscillations	yes
4. Newton's law of gravity	yes
5. Orbits of planets and satellites	
a. Circular	yes
b. General	NO
II. Fluid Mechanics and Thermal Physics	**15%**
A. Fluid mechanics	**6%**
1. Hydrostatic pressure	yes
2. Buoyancy	yes
3. Fluid flow continuity	yes
4. Bernoulli's equation	yes

B. Temperature and heat | **2%**
1. Mechanical equivalent of heat | yes
2. Specific and latent heat, including calorimetry | NO
3. Heat transfer and thermal expansion | yes

C. Kinetic theory and thermodynamics | **7%**
1. Ideal gases
   a. Kinetic model | yes
   b. Ideal gas law | yes
2. Laws of thermodynamics
   a. First law, including processes and pV diagrams | yes
   b. Second law, including heat engines | yes

III. Electricity and Magnetism | **25%**

A. Electrostatics | **5%**
1. Charge, field, and potential | yes
2. Coulomb's law, and field and potential of point charges | yes
3. Fields and potentials of other charge distributions | yes
   a. Planar | NO
   b. Spherical symmetry | NO
   c. Cylindrical symmetry | NO
4. Gauss's law | NO

B. Conductors, capacitors, and dielectrics | **4%**
1. Electrostatics with conductors | yes
2. Capacitors
   a. Parallel plate | yes
   b. Spherical and cylindrical | NO
3. Dielectrics | NO

C. Electric circuits | **7%**
1. Current, resistance, and power | yes
2. Steady-state direct current circuits with batteries and resistors only | yes
3. Capacitors in circuits | yes
   a. Steady state | yes
   b. Transients in RC circuits | NO

D. Magnetostatics | **4%**
1. Forces on moving charges in magnetic fields | yes
2. Forces on current carrying wires in magnetic fields | yes
3. Fields of long current-carrying wires | yes
4. Biot-Savart and Ampere's law | NO

E. Electromagnetism	**5%**
1. Electromagnetic induction, including Faraday's law and Lenz's law	yes
2. Inductance, including LR and LC circuits	NO
3. Maxwell's equations	NO
IV. Waves and Optics	**15%**
A. Wave motion	**5%**
1. Properties of traveling waves	yes
2. Properties of standing waves	yes
3. Doppler effect	yes
4. Superposition	yes
B. Physical optics	**5%**
1. Interference and diffraction	yes
2. Dispersion of light and the electromagnetic spectrum	yes
C. Geometrical optics	**5%**
1. Reflection and refraction	yes
2. Mirrors	yes
3. Lenses	yes
V. Atomic and Nuclear Physics	**10%**
A. Atomic physics and quantum effects	**7%**
1. Photons and the photoelectric effect	yes
2. Atomic energy levels	yes
3. Wave-particle duality	yes
B. Nuclear physics	**3%**
1. Nuclear reactions, including conservation of charge and mass number	yes
2. Mass-energy equivalence	yes

At the end of each chapter in this book, you'll find practice exercises for both multiple-choice and free-response questions. Some of these practice questions expand on concepts developed in the chapter and are necessary for you to understand the material completely. The free-response questions focus on each chapter's topics, so they aren't always as wide-ranging as those on the AP exam, but they're written at the level of questions on the AP exam.

Format

The AP B Physics test is divided into two sections: Section I is multiple choice, and Section II is free response. Section I consists of 70 questions, and it will account for 50 percent of your grade. You have 90 minutes to complete this section. Section II consists of problems or free response questions. The B level test will usually have 7 or 8 free response questions to be completed within 90 minutes, accounting for 50 percent of your grade. Some of these questions will be worth 10 points and some will be worth 15 points. The total for Section II may add to either 80 or 90 points. This section will account for 50 percent of your grade also.

SECTION I

This section consists of individual questions with five choices. While most questions are self-contained, two or three questions at a time may be linked by a common figure or written description. The questions fall into four basic categories: conceptual, numerical calculation, algebraic calculation, and graphical.

Conceptual Questions

As the name implies, these questions test your understanding of basic concepts without asking you to perform any calculations using the concepts. Here's a sample question:

> Two teams engage in a tug-of-war with a rope held horizontal. Which is true of the winning team?
>
> (A) They were stronger.
> (B) They had more mass.
> (C) They exerted a greater tension force through the rope.
> (D) They exerted a greater force on the ground parallel to the surface.
> (E) They exerted a greater force on the ground perpendicular to the surface.

To answer correctly D, you would need to understand that both tension and friction forces will act in the horizontal direction on each team and that the tension forces acting on each team will always be equal but opposite by Newton's third law. No calculation is needed, however, to arrive at the correct answer.

Numerical Calculation Questions

On Section I of the test, you will *not* be allowed to use a calculator, so it follows that the questions with numerical calculations will involve "nice" numbers. Some questions will even involve using trigonometric functions, but the angles will be 0°, 30°, 37°, 45°, 53°, 60°, and 90°. The sines, cosines, and tangents of these angles, as well as the values of physical constants and some other conventions, will be provided on a Table of Information sheet at the beginning of both Section I and Section II. This information is also included in the appendix to this study guide. You don't need to commit this information to memory, but you should be familiar with what is there and what is not. Of course, calculations involve using the laws of physics in mathematical form, so you'll need to know the many equations that relate the various physical quantities. You will *not* have an equation sheet provided on Section I. Here's an example of a numerical calculation question:

> A 5 kg mass is sliding across a horizontal surface at a constant speed while being pulled by a rope with tension 30 N held at 30° above the horizontal. The force of friction is most nearly
>
> (A) $25\sqrt{3}$ N   (B) $15\sqrt{3}$ N   (C) 25 N   (D) 15 N   (E) 20 N

Because there is no acceleration, the friction force will equal the horizontal component of the tension, 30 cos30. The correct answer, B, includes the square root factor provided in the Table of Information. Since calculators are not allowed for this section, you would not be expected to express the square root as a decimal.

Algebraic Calculation Questions
In this type of question, certain quantities are given symbolically, and you must use them to determine an answer that you express symbolically as well. Here's an example:

> A mass m is accelerated from rest across a smooth horizontal surface by a rope held parallel to the surface. The tension T in the rope is constant. After a time t, the instantaneous power delivered to the mass by the rope is
>
> (A) $\dfrac{T}{m}t$ (B) $\dfrac{T^2}{m}t$ (C) $\dfrac{T}{m}t^2$ (D) $\dfrac{T^2}{m}t^2$ (E) $\dfrac{T^2}{m}$

Here the tension, mass, and time are given, expressed symbolically as T, m, and t, respectively. To determine the correct answer, B, you can apply Newton's second law, one-dimensional kinematics, and the formula relating power, force, and velocity.

$$P = Tv = T(at) = T\left(\frac{T}{m}t\right) = \frac{T^2}{m}t$$

You won't have to do any complex manipulations, but you'll need to be comfortable working with algebraic expressions when you're answering these questions.

Graphical Questions
This type of question comes in two varieties. In the first, you may be asked to identify the behavior of a specific property while one of the parameters that describes it is allowed to vary. You might, for example, need to identify the graph that best depicts the magnetic field due to a long wire as a function of R, the distance from the center of the wire. In the second variety of question, you may work with graphs depicting the time dependence of physical quantities. You could be given a choice of five graphs, for example, and then be asked which best depicts the kinetic energy as a function of time for a projectile fired horizontally from a given height. Here's a specific example:

A wire of constant length is moved through a uniform magnetic field at a constant velocity, with the velocity vector perpendicular to the field. A graph of the induced voltage V_{in} between the ends of the wire as a function of time would look like:

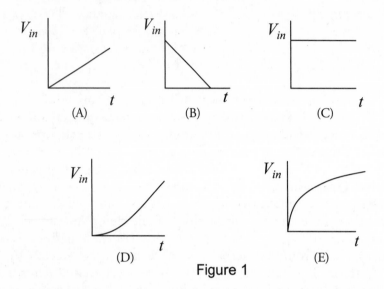

Figure 1

The induced voltage will be a constant with magnitude BLv as long as the field and speed are constant, so C is the correct answer.

A variation of this type of question begins by displaying five graphs. Two or three questions then require that answers be chosen from the five graphs.

SECTION II

On the free response section of the test, you *will* be allowed to use a calculator. Both scientific calculators and more complex graphing calculators are permitted. Calculators with a typewriter QWERTY keyboard aren't allowed, under the assumption that these are closer to computers than calculators. You won't have to clear the memory of your calculator, but since you *will* be provided with a complete equation sheet, there is little need to cram your calculator memory with other information. The equation sheet for the test is included in the appendix of this book. Be sure to look over the information on these sheets carefully. Not every equation is there, but the fundamental ones are, as well as quite a few others.

Three types of free-response questions can appear in Section II: physical situation problems, lab questions, and essays.

Physical Situation Problems

This is a variation of end-of-chapter problems that you're probably quite familiar with. A physical situation is described, often with an accompanying diagram, and you're asked a series of questions about the situation and its development. These problems can be completely numerical, so that you're calculating a numerical answer at the end of each section, or completely algebraic, so that your answers are all expressed in terms of symbols.

Unlike the typical end-of-chapter problem, the AP free-response problem doesn't usually deal with just one topic. It would be rare, for example, to encounter a problem that covers just one-dimensional kinematics. You're more likely to have to solve a problem that begins with questions about kinematics and then brings in concepts like force, energy, or momentum. While each problem usually has a particular focus area, questions within the problem sometimes touch on topics that might be considered well outside the focus area. A question on induction, for example, might bring in concepts from mechanics, and a question on electrostatics might require the use of Newton's second law.

Lab Questions

Since 1996, the AP Physics Committee has included questions that specifically test a student's lab experience. The question may be self contained, or it may be part of a larger question. Chapter 20 looks at these questions in detail. To do well on these questions, you should have performed the basic labs usually included with an introductory physics course. In addition to being familiar with measuring apparatus and the measuring process, you should be able to

1. devise an experiment to measure a basic property
2. explain in words and equations how an experiment achieves the desired result
3. analyze an experiment for sources of error

You may be asked to report data to an appropriate level of precision, so you may need knowledge of significant digit arithmetic. It's only on this type of question, though, that you'll ever have to worry about significant digits.

Essay Questions

On rare occasions, the B-level exam includes a question that asks you to describe a historically important experiment and explain its significance. Typically, you're given a choice among three famous experiments, such as the photoelectric effect, the Milliken oil drop experiment, and Young's two slit experiment. More commonly, you'll be asked to explain something about one of your answers in a section of a larger problem. In a problem dealing with two slit interference, for example, you might be asked to describe what happens to the pattern when the slit separation is changed or if one of the slits is covered. These smaller essays should be expected on every B-level exam.

Weighted and Composite Scores

Section I and Section II are weighted equally when your AP grade is calculated. The B test has 70 multiple-choice questions in Section I. To find your weighted score for Section I, AP counts the number of points you earned using the criteria:

- 1 point awarded for each correct answer
- $\frac{1}{4}$ point subtracted for each incorrect answer
- 0 points awarded for each question left blank

The total number of points earned is then multiplied by $\frac{90}{70} = 1.286$. This is your weighted score for Section I. The last step is needed to make the total number of points in Section I the same as the 90 points of Section II.

The weighted score for the free response section is just the number of points you earned. No points are subtracted for wrong answers.

Finally, your composite score is the sum of the weighted scores for the two sections.

Calculating Your AP Grade

Your composite score on the test is then converted to an AP grade. The cutoff points for the different AP grades are determined by a statistical analysis of the composite scores. There is some variation in these cutoff points from year to year, but not a lot. The following table shows the distribution for the AP Physics B Exam given in 1998, results that are typical of other years as well.

Composite Scores and AP Grades, B Test

Composite Score	AP Grade	Qualification
106–180	5	Extremely Well Qualified
83–105	4	Well Qualified
54–82	3	Qualified
40–53	2	Possibly Qualified
0–39	1	No Recommendation

What should grab your attention in this table is the range of composite scores that receive a qualified or better AP grade. While a student who gets 90 percent of the total points available gets a 5, a student who only got 60 percent correct will also get a 5. Indeed, a student scoring just 30 percent will get a 3.

It is essential that you have a strategy for maximizing your score on the test. You want to be sure that you get to all the questions that you can answer correctly. You need to know how much time should be invested in a given question. You need to know about intelligent guessing. We'll talk about these strategies in the next chapter.

Strategies for Taking the AP Physics Exam

The best way to succeed on the AP exam is to put in the time learning the material. Using this book with its practice exercises and tests will help you sharpen your focus, but even the best of students will encounter questions on the test that they're not sure about. In this chapter, we'll look at strategies for dealing with test situations where you're either uncertain or simply don't know how to proceed. It's important to recognize ahead of time that you'll face these situations on the test, so you'll need to have an organized approach for handling them that doesn't take too much of your allotted time. Remember that you don't have to get everything correct to get a good AP grade—far from it. As you saw in the last chapter, a composite score of about 60 percent of the total points will get you a 5, and a composite score that's less than 50 percent can still get you a 4.

Multiple-Choice Strategies

The scantron will read your multiple-choice answer sheet and tabulate all the correct, incorrect, and unanswered questions. It doesn't question how you arrived at your answers. If you actually understood the material in a question but got the wrong answer because you didn't read the question carefully, you won't get partial credit. On the other hand, if you made an intelligent guess to arrive at the correct answer, you'll get full credit even though you didn't know the answer exactly. Let's look at some of the specific ways you can get this machine to record the highest possible score for you.

GRID YOUR ANSWERS CAREFULLY

If you make mistakes while entering your answers into the grid, it can cost you dearly. This is most likely to happen after you skip a question. If you left question 20 blank and then mistakenly put the answer to question 21 in the space for question 20, a chain of incorrect answers could follow. Don't do it.

Perhaps the best way to avoid this is to recite a complete sentence to yourself as you fill in the oval: "Question 21: answer is A." As you recite this, look at the number of the question and verify that it is the correct one.

MAKE THE MOST OF THE TIME YOU HAVE INVESTED

As you work through the multiple-choice section, you'll want to choose the answer that you think is correct. That's obvious. But what do you do if you can't decide between two or more of the choices? There are two things to keep in mind:

1. An incorrect answer carries with it a quarter-point penalty, as described in the last section. If you answered five questions randomly, chances are you'd get one correct since there are five possible answers to each question. This one point gained would be exactly canceled by the four quarter points lost as a result of the other four incorrect answers. Random guessing neither helps you nor hurts you if there are enough questions that statistics can be applied in the analysis. But if you can eliminate some of the answers, it greatly increases your odds for guessing the correct answer, and the quarter-point penalty will not even the score. If you could eliminate 3 of the 5 answers in each of 5 questions, statistically you would expect to get 2 or 3 of the 5 correct. With the penalty taken into account, your score on these 5 questions would be $2 - 3(\frac{1}{4}) = 1.75$ or $3 - 2(\frac{1}{4}) = 2.5$. Both results are obviously much better than the 0 points you'd get for not answering at all. It's always to your advantage to guess if you can eliminate at least one answer.

2. You have to read and answer questions at the rate of about one every ninety seconds to be sure you'll get a chance to attempt every question. You'll find questions for which you won't be able to eliminate all the answers, even though you may be sure that with just a little more time you'll figure it out. You'll feel the urge to put the question aside so that you can come back to it later. *This is a flawed strategy.* By reading the question and eliminating some of the answers, you have invested a certain amount of time in the question, and you have improved your odds at getting it correct. If you don't answer it now, you can't count on having the time later to return to it, and if you don't answer it at all, then you'll have lost your investment. Any question that you can understand well enough to eliminate at least one answer should be answered right then. If you *do* have time at the end, you can come back and erase your answer if you change your mind, but time is at a premium. Your goal is to achieve the highest possible score from the machine, not to answer every question that you might be able to figure out eventually.

All this being said, if a question looks totally unfamiliar, skip it. Don't waste precious time trying to eliminate answers when you're not even sure what the question is all about.

ELIMINATING ANSWERS

Certain types of questions lend themselves to a systematic testing procedure that will help you determine if an answer could possibly be correct.

Dimensional Analysis

Applying dimensional analysis will be useful on questions involving algebraic calculations. You'll be asked to determine a certain quantity from some givens, and if you know the dimensions of the quantity you're trying to determine, you can check the possible answers to see if they have the correct dimensions. If the dimensions aren't right, the answer can't be correct. Let's reconsider the question used as an example in the last chapter:

A mass m is accelerated from rest across a smooth horizontal surface by a rope held parallel to the surface. The tension T in the rope is constant. After a time t, the instantaneous power delivered to the mass by the rope is

(A) $\dfrac{T}{m}t$ (B) $\dfrac{T^2}{m}t$ (C) $\dfrac{T}{m}t^2$ (D) $\dfrac{T^2}{m}t^2$ (E) $\dfrac{T^2}{m}$

Since power has the units of (force) • (velocity), you could analyze the dimensions of the possible answers to see if any have the wrong dimensions. A could not be correct since $\frac{T}{m}$ has the dimensions of acceleration, and (acceleration) × (time) has the dimensions of velocity. Using this tactic, you could eliminate all the answers except B.

Order of Magnitude
It helps to be aware of the order of magnitude of various phenomena. If you're answering a question that asks for a speed and one of your choices is 4×10^9 m/s, you can eliminate it immediately since it is faster than the speed of light. If you're asked to determine the gravitational force between two objects, the size of $G \cong 10^{-11}$ should pop into your mind. If the masses aren't too big, the force will be small, and you can eliminate large answers. Remember that physical constants are available to you on the Table of Information sheet, and on this type of question these values will be useful to you. If you see a question that has a choice of answers that vary over several orders of magnitude, thinking in terms of orders of magnitude may get you to the answer quickly. Consider the following question:

A current of 3.2 A flows in a segment of copper wire. The number of electrons crossing the cross-sectional area of the wire every second is most nearly

(A) 3.2 (B) 2×10^{19} (C) 2×10^{-19} (D) 3.2×10^{19} (E) 3.2×10^{-19}

If you have a basic understanding of how many electrons are involved when even a modest current is established in a wire, you could eliminate all the answers except B and D. Of course, to distinguish between these two, you'd have to use more than order of magnitude thinking, but if you were stuck at this point, you'd have a 50 percent chance of getting the correct answer.

Limiting Behavior
Graphical questions lend themselves to analysis using limiting behavior. In this approach, you need to have some knowledge about what happens when one of the variables takes on limiting values. For example, the magnetic field outside a long wire decreases as $1/R$, so if you had a choice of graphs supposedly describing this field, you would look for this behavior. Electric field and electric potential become infinite at the position of a point charge, so you can easily eliminate graphs inconsistent with this situation. Here's an

example of this type of question:

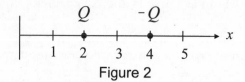

Figure 2

Two equal and opposite charges lie along the *x*-axis as shown in the figure. The graph of the electric potential as a function of *x* is closest to which of the following?

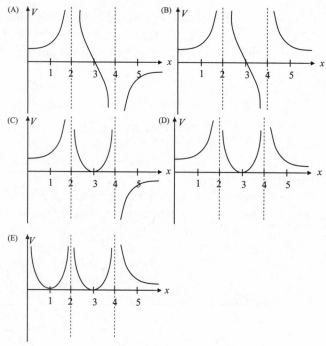

The potential approaches $+\infty$ near the positive charge and $-\infty$ near the negative charge, so only A could be correct.

Free-Response Strategies

Unlike Section I, which is read and graded by a machine, Section II is read by a real person, either an AP teacher or a college professor involved in the AP Program. To do your best on this section of the test, you should know something about how the test is written and graded. A well-written test question must be able to differentiate among the various levels of students. A question in which 90 percent of the students received 12 or more out of 15 points would not adequately differentiate between the student who had weaknesses on related material and the student who really knew her stuff. Similarly, a question in which 90 percent of the students received 7 or fewer out of 15 points would not be well designed. The best questions have a spread in the point distribution centered on 7 out of 15 points, achieved through a process that can be called "front loading" a problem. Easier parts of the question are put up front in Parts a, b, and c. Usually a student with even a little knowledge about what the question asks can get points here. Most questions include Parts d, e, and beyond, and these get progressively more difficult. It's important to remember that the last part to a question, which may totally stump you, is probably worth no more than two or three points.

Some questions may be intimidating when you first look at them. For example, suppose a question on the B test starts with a diagram that shows a Carnot cycle on a pV diagram. Perhaps your teacher never got to this material, and in your self-study you found concepts like adiabatic and isothermal difficult. Resist the urge to skip the question. Remember, front loading means there should be some easy stuff at the beginning. A pV diagram gives the pressure and volume of the gas used as the working substance in the cycle, and typically the questions at the beginning just require you to use the ideal gas law, perhaps to find the temperature at one vertex of the graph. Most questions start out by asking for the most basic answers, so don't let a diagram scare you off. You'll maximize your score by getting most of the points on the questions you're really comfortable with and by getting as many points as you can on the questions that you know you're not going to be able to complete. Getting those extra points at the beginning of the tough problems can make all the difference to your AP grade.

You should also be familiar with how the free-response section is graded. The AP Physics reading takes place in early June. A significant force of AP teachers, college professors, and aides work together for about six days to read through the exams and assign scores to the tests. Before the reading begins, a set of standards is developed for each free-response question. The standards identify the points to be awarded on each section of a problem. They also identify how partial credit is to be awarded if your answer is incorrect.

Let's see how this works in practice. A reader will typically handle just one problem over the course of the reading. Because each reader must grade literally thousands of exams, as he looks at a given problem, he is scanning for correct answers. A well-designed problem will not allow a correct answer to be reached by an incorrect method, so if the reader sees the correct answer, you get the points for that section. (There are rare exceptions to this in problems that specifically ask you to derive something, showing your assumptions and the intermediate steps. In these cases, more than just a correct answer will be needed for full credit.)

So what happens if your answer is not correct? Each reader keeps her copy of the standards right next to her, showing the solution to the problem worked out and the points to be awarded for various steps done correctly. If your answer to a given section was incorrect, the reader looks through the section to see how many of the steps you did correctly. If certain things appear on your paper, you get a certain amount of partial credit. The idea is to make the grading process as objective as possible, so that two readers reviewing the same test would assign the same partial credit.

How can this knowledge help you maximize your grade? First, show your work clearly, including all intermediate steps. Make it simple for the reader to see the logic of your work. It's very easy to make a math or algebra error so that your answer to a given section is wrong, but this will cost you only one point, the so-called answer point, if all the other steps are there and they're correct. If they're not present, a wrong answer means you lose all points for that section, a harsh but ultimately fair penalty. What's more, if you use your incorrect answer in subsequent sections of the problem, you won't be further penalized as long as these steps are done correctly. This means a single calculation error will cost you a total of only one point if you show the steps leading to it.

As you prepare for the AP test, practice your free-response writing. When in doubt, write down a step. Try to avoid leaps that go from initial equation to final answer with nothing in between.

What if you're stumped on a given section? If you know nothing about what is asked, don't waste time. Move on. But what if you have some ideas? Perhaps you know what equations are involved, or perhaps you can get a little way toward the answer. Put it all down. Even when the reader sees that you don't have the correct answer, he's still looking for very specific things, and if they're present, you will get some points. You can almost think of the reader with his standards as being an approximation of a scantron: If equation A is present, 1 point is awarded; if number X is substituted correctly, 1 point is awarded, and so on.

When a free-response question involves numerical calculations, 1 point may be awarded if all your answers have the correct units, even if the answers themselves are wrong. These problems will assign a total of 14 points (or 9 points on a shorter B question) to the various answers to each section. The "units point" is awarded for the problem as a whole if all answers have correct units. You can get the units point even if you don't answer all sections, as long as the sections that you do answer have the correct units.

RECAP

Let's look at the composite score/AP grade chart again.

Composite Scores and AP Grades, B Test

Composite Score	AP Grade	Qualification
106–180	5	Extremely Well Qualified
83–105	4	Well Qualified
54–82	3	Qualified
40–53	2	Possibly Qualified
0–39	1	No Recommendation

You will have done quite a bit of preparation for the exam by the time you're ready to take the test. You may have enjoyed studying physics and have come to appreciate its power and precision, but as you enter the test, you have to take on a different mind set: Your goal is to maximize your composite score, to get the highest point total possible. This means thinking of test taking as a skill with specific strategies to be followed—and followed rigorously. Get through the three hours of the test with your goal and strategy never far from your thoughts, and try not to get flustered. Being flustered is not part of the strategy. If you feel as if you're ready to crack, think of the table above. You can be far from perfection and still get a respectable AP grade.

Cross-Reference
with Popular B-Level Textbooks

The Study Guide for AP Physics B is targeted specifically to the topics of the B-level syllabus. There are several excellent textbooks that are appropriate for use in a B-level course, but none of them is designed *just* for a B-level course. As such they cover more material than required for the AP test and sometimes the coverage of a given topic is more general than would be required. Still, the problems, diagrams, and extended conceptual descriptions of these textbooks are an excellent resource that complements this Study Guide. The Table below lists the subject chapters of this Study Guide and the corresponding sections of several excellent B-level texts. In some cases a section listed will contain some material that is not part of the AP syllabus as well as some that is part of the syllabus. When in doubt compare the content of the textbook section to the material in the Study Guide.

Title	Author	Edition	Publisher
Physics	Cutnell and Johnson	6th	Wiley
Physics	Giancoli	5th	Prentice Hall
College Physics	Serway and Faughn	6th	Brooks Cole
Physics	Walker	2nd	Prentice Hall

Study Guide for AP Physics B	Cutnell & Johnson	Giancoli	Walker	Serway & Faughn
Ch 1 Motion in One Dimension	2.1–2.8	2.1–2.8	2.1–2.7	2.1–2.7
Ch 2 Vectors and Projectiles	1.5–1.9; 3.3	3.1–3.7	3.3–3.5; 4.1–4.5	3.1–3.6
Ch 3 Newton's Laws	4.1–4.6; 4.8–4.13; 5.1–5.4, 5.7–5.8; 9.1–9.3	4.1–4.9; 5.1–5.3; 8.4; 9.2–9.3	5.1–5.7; 6.1–6.5; 11.1,11.3–11.4	4.1–4.6; 7.4,7; 8.1–8.4
Ch 4 Work and Energy	6.1–6.10	6.1–6.10	7.1–7.4; 8.1–8.5	5.1–5.8
Ch 5 Impulse and Momentum	7.1–7.6; 9.6	7.1–7.10; 8.8	9.1– 9.7; 11.6–11.7	6.1–6.4; 8.7

Study Guide for AP Physics B	Cutnell & Johnson	Giancoli	Walker	Serway & Faughn
Ch 6 Gravitation	4.7; 5.5–5.6	5.6–5.8; 5.10	12.1–12.2	7.8
Ch 7 Oscillations	10.1–10.4	11.1–11.4	13.1–13.6, 13.8	13.1–13.4, 13.6
Ch 8 Fluid Mechanics	11.1–11.10, 11.12	10.1–10.9	15.1–15.8	9.3–9.8
Ch 9 Thermal Physics	12.1–12.3, 12.6; 13.1–13.3; 14.1–14.3, 14.5;15.1–15.5; 15.7–15.9, 15.11, 15.13	13.1–13.3, 13.7–13.11; 14.1–14.3, 14.7–14.9; 15.1–15.2, 15.4–15.5, 15.7–15.9, 15.11	16.1–16.2, 16.4, 16.6; 17.1–17.2; 18.1–18.3, 18.5–18.6, 18.8–18.9	10.1–10.2, 10.4–10.7; 11.1, 11.5–11.7; 12.1–12.2, 12.4–12.8
Ch 10 Electric Force and Electric Field	18.1–18.8, 18.11	16.1–16.9	19.1–19.6	15.1–15.7
Ch 11 Electric Potential and Electric Potential Energy	19.1–19.4, 19.7	17.1–17.5	20.1–20.4	16.1–16.4
Ch 12 Electric Circuits	20.1–20.4, 20.6–20.11; 19.5; 20.12, 20.15	18.1–18.4, 18.6; 19.1–19.3; 17.7, 17.9, 19.6	21.1–21.6; 20.5–20.6	17.1–17.5, 17.8; 18.1–18.4; 16.6–16.9
Ch 13 Magnetostatics	21.1–21.7, 21.10	20.1–20.6; 20.12	22.1–22.4	19.1–19.4, 19.6–19.7
Ch 14 Electromagnetic Induction	22.1–22.5, 22.10; 24.1–24.3	21.1–21.4; 22.1, 22.3, 22.5	23.1–23.5; 25.1, 25.3	20.1–20.4; 21.8, 21.10
Ch 15 Waves	16.1–16.2, 16.5, 16.9; 17.1–17.6; 17.8	11.7–11.8, 11.11–11.12; 12.1, 12.5, 12.7–12.8	14.1–14.2, 14.4, 14.6–14.9	13.8–13.13; 14.5–14.12
Ch 16 Geometrical Optics	25.1–25.7; 26.1–26.3, 26.5–26.9, 26.15	23.1–23.9	26.1–26.8	22.1–22.5, 22.8; 23.1–23.4, 23.6
Ch 17 Wave Optics	27.1–27.3, 27.5, 27.7, 27.10	24.1–24.6, 24.8	28.1–28.4, 28.6	22.7; 24.1–24.4, 24.6–24.8
Ch 18 The Quantum World	29.1–29.7; 30.2–30.3	27.1–27.6, 27.9–27.10; 28.1–28.2	30.1–30.6; 31.2–31.3	27.1–27.2, 27.4–27.8; 28.2–28.3
Ch 19 Nuclear Physics	31.1–31.3, 32.2–32.3, 32.5	30.1–30.2; 31.1–31.3	32.1, 32.4–32.6	29.1–29.2, 29.6; 30.1, 30.3

1

Motion in One Dimension

Motion is all around us, so it's easy to understand why the earliest physical thinkers focused on describing motion and determining its causes. In this chapter and the next, you'll learn how to describe motion without considering what is actually causing the motion. This study is called **kinematics**. You'll need to understand the nature of the quantities used to describe motion precisely, as well as the relationships these quantities have with each other. With his long inclines and water clocks, Galileo Galilei was the first to study kinematics experimentally. Just as he did, you'll begin with objects constrained to move along a straight line, or one-dimensional motion.

Position and Displacement

To describe where an object is, you must introduce a coordinate system, pick an origin, and choose the positive direction for each axis. In one dimension you need only one axis, frequently labeled the x-axis for horizontal motion or the y-axis for vertical motion. The **position** of an object is its value of x. As the object moves, its position changes. The change in position is called the **displacement** of the object, written as Δx. The delta symbol, Δ, stands for the change in a quantity, with the change always determined using "final–initial." For displacement, the equation is

$$\Delta x = x_f - x_i$$

where x_f is the final position of the body and x_i is the initial position. As an object moves, its position depends on time, and this functional dependence is often written as $x = x(t)$. Position and displacement are both directed quantities, which means they carry a sign that determines their direction relative to the coordinate system. (When you generalize later to more than one dimension, you'll see that such directed quantities are called vectors.) If an object moving in one dimension never changes direction, the magnitude of its displacement will equal the distance traveled. But if the object does change direction, you'll have to carefully break up its path into segments to determine the total distance traveled. When you throw a ball straight up in the air to a height of 7 m, its displacement is 0 when you catch it, but it has traveled a distance of 14 m.

Velocity

Velocity is the rate at which the position of an object changes. The **average velocity** over a time interval is the displacement during the interval divided by the duration of the interval:

$$v_{av} = \frac{\Delta x}{\Delta t}$$

Let's look at the x vs. t graph for the motion (figure 1).

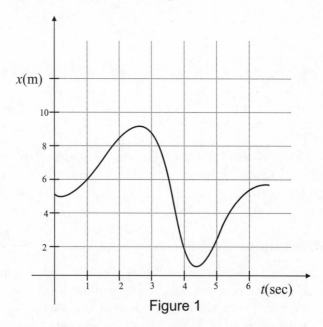

Figure 1

From the graph you can see that at $t = 1$ s, the object is at about $x = 6$ m, and at $t = 4$ s, it is at about $x = 2$ m. During this 3 second interval:

$$v_{av} = \frac{\Delta x}{\Delta t} = \frac{2 - 6}{4 - 1} = -1.33 \, \frac{m}{s}$$

If the function $x = x(t)$ changes considerably, then the average velocity is very sensitive to the interval over which it is averaged. For example, if you had chosen the time interval from 1 to 3 s, then x would have changed from about 6 to about 9 m, for an average velocity of

$$v_{av} = \frac{\Delta x}{\Delta t} = \frac{9 - 6}{3 - 1} = +1.5 \, \frac{m}{s}$$

You'll notice that the average velocity involves a change on the vertical axis divided by a change on the horizontal axis. This is a slope formula, and the average velocity is the slope of the line connecting the two points defining the interval.

Average velocity isn't the most precise way to describe motion because it depends on the particular interval you've chosen to average over. For more precision, you'll need to use instantaneous velocity. You can probably surmise that as an object moves, it has a well defined velocity at every instant. The problem with defining such a quantity is that at each instant it is frozen like a photograph, so how do you determine the displacement and the time interval? You can use the fact that if the interval is small enough, the function will not change much. **Instantaneous velocity** at a given time is the average velocity over a tiny interval (imagine it infinitely small) centered at that time:

$$v = \left(\frac{\Delta v}{\Delta t}\right)_{\text{small}} = \lim_{\Delta t \to 0} \frac{\Delta x}{\Delta t}$$

Because the average velocity is the slope of the line connecting the two endpoints of the interval, the instantaneous velocity will be the slope of the tangent line drawn to the graph at the given time.

EXAMPLE

By drawing a tangent line to the curve at $x = 2$ (figure 2), you can see from the slope that the instantaneous velocity is approximately 1.2 m/s.

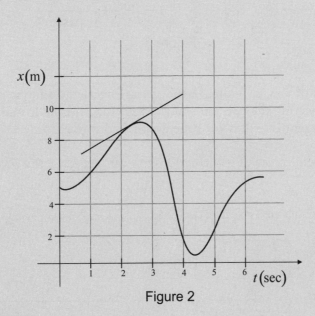

Figure 2

You can always get a good approximation of the instantaneous velocity by choosing a time interval over which the velocity does not change much and finding the average velocity over this interval.

Acceleration

Acceleration is the rate at which velocity changes. Just as you did for velocity, you can define **average acceleration** over an interval or **instantaneous acceleration** at a given time.

$$a_{av} = \frac{\Delta v}{\Delta t} \qquad a = \left(\frac{\Delta v}{\Delta t}\right)_{small} = \lim_{\Delta t \to 0} \frac{\Delta v}{\Delta t}$$

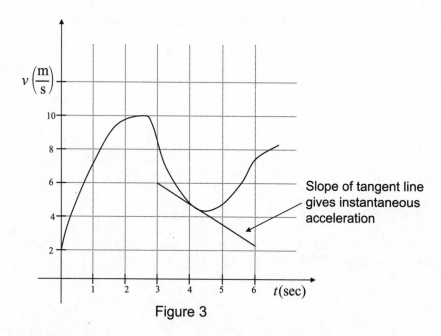

Figure 3

If you look at a graph of v vs. t (figure 3), the average acceleration over an interval is just the slope of the line connecting the two ends of the interval, and the instantaneous acceleration is the slope of the tangent line drawn to the graph at the given time.

There is one other useful piece of information you can get from the v vs. t graph.

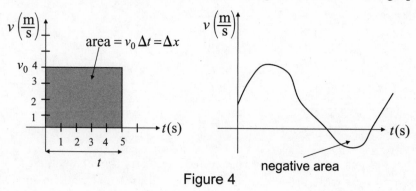

Figure 4

Suppose you have a constant velocity v_0 over a time interval Δt (figure 4). Since $v_0 = \frac{\Delta x}{\Delta t}$, the area under the graph, $v_0 \Delta t$, is just the displacement Δx. Even if the velocity isn't constant, the area under the v vs. t graph will still be the displacement over the interval. Remember that in this context, "area" can be positive (x values increasing) or negative (x values decreasing).

EXAMPLE

Find the displacement over the interval from 0 to 6 s in the two graphs below.

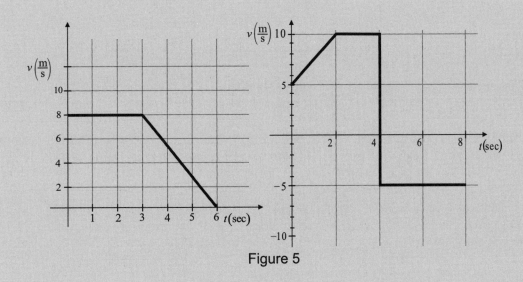

Figure 5

The left graph can be thought of as a rectangle and a triangle, giving

$$area = 8 \cdot 3 + \frac{1}{2}(8 \cdot 3) = 36 \text{ m}$$

In the right graph, you can count the boxes to determine the area. Each box has a value $5 \cdot 2 = 10$ m. From 0 to 4 s, you have 3.5 boxes. From 4 to 6 s, you have 1 box, but the area is negative since it lies below the t-axis and corresponds to decreasing x values. Thus you have a total of 2.5 boxes or 25 m for the displacement.

Constant Acceleration Equations

When acceleration is constant, you can use some simple equations that relate the various kinematic variables. To understand their content, consider the v vs. t graph (figure 6).

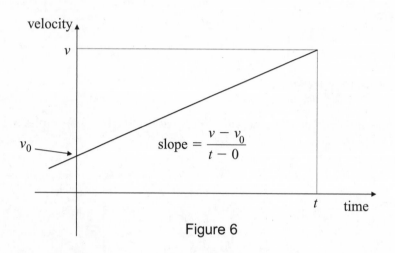

Figure 6

Since the acceleration is the slope of the v vs. t graph, constant acceleration means a straight line. If the interval begins at $t = 0$ and extends to some arbitrary time t, the slope is $a = \frac{\Delta v}{\Delta t} = \frac{v - v_0}{t - 0}$, or you can write

$$v = v_0 + at$$

Since the graph is a straight line, the average velocity over the interval is the median of the velocities at the endpoints: $v_{av} = \frac{1}{2}(v + v_0)$. Since by definition $v_{av} = \frac{\Delta x}{\Delta t}$, you can write

$$\Delta x = \frac{1}{2}(v + v_0)t$$

You can combine these two equations algebraically to eliminate certain variables and obtain other equations. The end result is a set of four equations:

1. $v = v_0 + at$
2. $\Delta x = \frac{1}{2}(v + v_0)t$
3. $\Delta x = v_0 t + \frac{1}{2}at^2$
4. $v^2 = v_0^2 + 2a\Delta x$

You can apply these equations to the motion of an object over an interval where the acceleration a is constant. During this interval, the velocity changes from v_0 to v while a displacement Δx occurs. In a typical problem, you'll be given three of the five quantities v, v_0, a, Δx, and t. You can determine the remaining two by using the four equations. You can usually use several different ways to solve such problems, depending on which equations you decide to use and which quantities you decide to solve for first.

EXERCISE

An automobile moving along a straight road passes an observer who records a speed of 20 m/s. A second observer 100 m from the first records a speed of 30 m/s. Find the value of the acceleration, assuming it is constant, and the time it took to travel the 100 m.

For this interval you have:

$$v_0 = 20 \, \frac{\text{m}}{\text{s}}$$

$$v = 30 \, \frac{\text{m}}{\text{s}} \qquad \Delta x = 100 \text{m}$$

$$a = ? \qquad\qquad t = ?$$

You can use the fourth equation to find the acceleration since it does not involve t:

$$v^2 = v_0{}^2 + 2a\Delta x$$

$$30^2 = 20^2 + 200a$$

$$a = 2.5 \, \frac{\text{m}}{\text{s}^2}$$

You can then use the first equation to find t:

$$v = v_0 + at$$

$$30 = 20 + 2.5t$$

$$t = 4\text{s}$$

One of the most important situations where you can apply one dimensional constant acceleration is the case of an object moving vertically under only the influence of gravity. Gravity causes all masses near the Earth's surface to experience an acceleration of $g = 9.8$ m/s² directed downward. On the AP test, you will always be permitted to replace 9.8 m/s² with 10 m/s² when you're solving numerical problems.

EXAMPLE

A boy on a balcony 25 m above the ground throws a ball straight up with a speed of 20 m/s. The ball misses the balcony on the way down. Neglecting air resistance, determine the maximum height, the total time in the air, and the speed of the ball just before impact with the ground.

First, let's choose the balcony as the origin and make "up" the positive y-direction. To determine the maximum height, select an interval defined by the start of the motion as the ball leaves the boy's hand and the top of the motion where the velocity is instantaneously 0. Over this interval you'll have:

$$v_0 = 20 \; \frac{m}{s}$$

$$v = 0 \qquad \Delta y = \; ?$$
$$t = \; ?$$

$$a = -10 \; \frac{m}{s^2}$$

You know two of the five quantities, so you can solve for the others. Choosing the first equation, you can find t:

$$v = v_0 + at$$

$$0 = 20 - 10t$$

$$t = 2s$$

You could then use the second equation to find Δy:

$$\Delta y = \frac{1}{2}(v + v_0)t$$
$$\Delta y = \frac{1}{2}(0 + 20)(2) = 20m$$

The highest point will be 45 m above the ground.
To find the total time in the air, you could choose an interval beginning with the start of the motion and ending just before the ball hits. For this interval you have:

$$v_0 = 20 \; \frac{m}{s}$$

$$v = \; ? \qquad \Delta y = -25 \; m$$
$$t = \; ?$$

$$a = -10 \; \frac{m}{s^2}$$

You can use the third equation to get t and the first equation to get v:

$$\Delta y = v_0 t + \frac{1}{2}at^2 \qquad\qquad v = v_0 + at$$

$$-25 = 20t - 5t^2 \qquad\qquad v = 20 - 10(5)$$

$$(t - 5)(t + 1) = 0 \qquad\qquad v = -30 \; \frac{m}{s}$$

$$t = 5s$$

This is just one possible path to the solutions. Depending on the intervals you choose to analyze and the variables you solve for first, you could use different equations to end up with the same results.

KEY FORMULAS

Average Velocity $\qquad\qquad v_{av} = \dfrac{\Delta x}{\Delta t}$

Instantaneous Velocity $\qquad\qquad v = \lim\limits_{\Delta t \to 0} \dfrac{\Delta x}{\Delta t}$

Average Acceleration $\qquad\qquad a_{av} = \dfrac{\Delta v}{\Delta t}$

Instantaneous Acceleration $\qquad a = \lim\limits_{\Delta t \to 0} \dfrac{\Delta v}{\Delta t}$

$\qquad\qquad\qquad\qquad\qquad$ 1. $v = v_0 + at$

$\qquad\qquad\qquad\qquad\qquad$ 2. $\Delta x = \dfrac{1}{2}(v + v_0)t$

Constant Acceleration Equations $\qquad$ 3. $\Delta x = v_0 t + \dfrac{1}{2}at^2$

$\qquad\qquad\qquad\qquad\qquad$ 4. $v^2 = v_0^2 + 2a\Delta x$

1. A ball is thrown straight up in the air. When air resistance is ignored, which of the following is true at the ball's highest point?

    I. The velocity is 0.

    II. The acceleration is 0.

    III. The acceleration is directed downward.

    (A) I only (B) II only (C) III only (D) I and II only (E) I and III only

Questions 2 and 3

Objects R and S start at the same origin, and their velocity vs. time graphs are shown on the same set of axes.

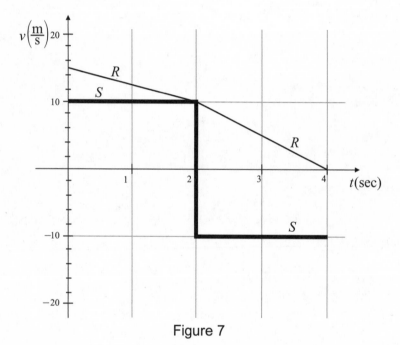

Figure 7

2. After 2 s, the two objects are

    (A) 25 m apart

    (B) at the same position

    (C) 5 m apart

    (D) 20 m apart

    (E) moving at constant speed

3. After 4 s,

(A) R has traveled 35 m
(B) R is instantaneously at rest
(C) S has returned to its original position
(D) A and B only
(E) A, B, and C

Questions 4 and 5

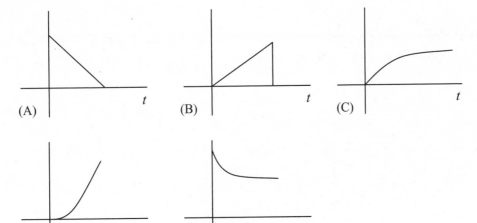

Figure 8

A car with an initial positive velocity slows to a stop with a constant acceleration.

4. Which graph best represents its position vs. time graph?

(A) A (B) B (C) C (D) D (E) E

5. Which graph best represents the velocity vs. time graph?

(A) A (B) B (C) C (D) D (E) E

6. A ball is thrown straight up near the edge of a 25 m cliff with a speed of 20 m/s. If it misses the cliff's edge on the way down, it will hit the ground in a time closest to

(A) 2 s (B) 3 s (C) 4 s (D) 5 s (E) 7 s

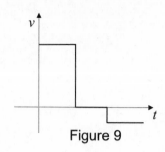

Figure 9

7. An object moves with a velocity vs. time graph as shown above. The position vs. time graph for the same time period would be

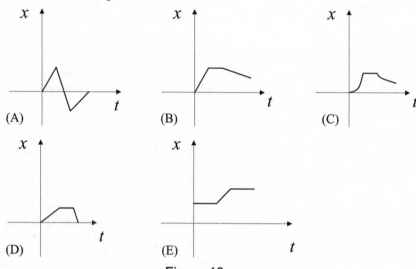

Figure 10

8. A car traveling at 20 m/s can come to a stop after traveling 30 m. If the car is traveling at 40 m/s, how far must it travel to stop, assuming the same acceleration?

(A) 40 m   (B) 30 m   (C) 90 m   (D) 120 m   (E) 60 m

9. Starting from rest, a ball rolls down a long incline with a constant acceleration. After 2 s, it has traveled 2 m. In the next second it will travel

(A) 1.25 m   (B) 2.5 m   (C) 3 m   (D) 1 m   (E) 2 m

10. A rock is dropped from the edge of a cliff 45 m high. One second later, a second rock is thrown straight down with just the right speed to ensure that the two rocks hit the ground at the same time. The initial speed of the second rock is closest to

(A) 5 m/s   (B) 7.5 m/s   (C) 10 m/s   (D) 12.5 m/s   (E) 15 m/s

CHAPTER 1 PRACTICE EXERCISES

SECTION II FREE RESPONSE

1. A two stage rocket leaves its launch pad moving vertically with an average acceleration of 4 m/s². At 10 s after launch, the first stage of the rocket (now without fuel) is released. The second stage now has an acceleration of 6 m/s².
   (a) How high is the rocket when the first stage separates?
   (b) How fast is the rocket moving upon first stage separation?
   (c) What will be the maximum height attained by the first stage after separation?
   (d) What will be the distance between the first and second stages 2 s after separation?

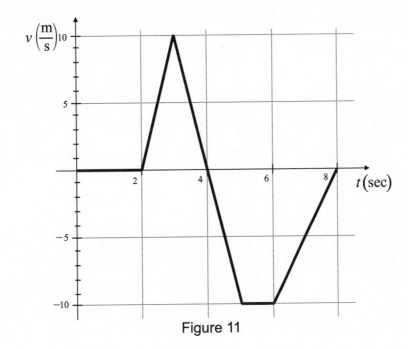

Figure 11

2. A vehicle moves in one dimension with the velocity vs. time graph shown.
   (a) Over what time intervals is the velocity increasing?
   (b) Over what time intervals is the velocity decreasing?
   (c) Determine the displacement during the interval from $t = 2$ to $t = 5$ s.
   (d) On the axes below, sketch the acceleration vs. time graph of the vehicle over the entire time.

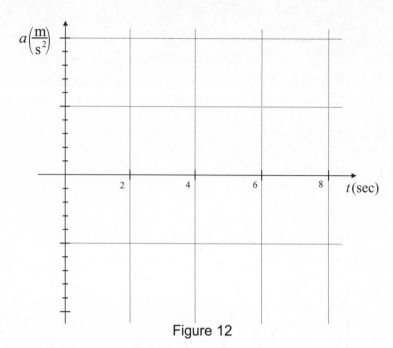

$a\left(\dfrac{m}{s^2}\right)$

2   4   6   8 $t(\text{sec})$

Figure 12

3. A red car is stopped at a traffic light waiting for it to turn green. Meanwhile, a blue car moving at 15 m/s is approaching the same stop light. When the blue car is still 20 m from the light, it turns green, and both cars accelerate, the red one at 6 m/s², the blue one at 2 m/s².
   (a) How far apart are the two cars after 1 s?
   (b) How far has the red car traveled when the blue car passes it?
   (c) Can the red car eventually overtake the blue car again without exceeding the speed limit of 30 m/s?

Answers and Explanations

MULTIPLE CHOICE

1. The answer is E. The acceleration of an object moving only under only the influence of gravity near Earth's surface is 9.8 m/s² directed downward. This is true at the highest point, where the velocity is 0.

2. The answer is C. The area under the graphs will be the displacements of each. For S, you have a rectangle and an area of 20 m, while for R you have a rectangle and triangle with an area of 25 m. Since they begin at the same position, they will be 5 m apart.

3. The answer is E. After 4 s, the area under R is 35 m, and its velocity is instantaneously 0. S has 0 displacement because the areas above and below the *t*-axis are equal.

4. The answer is C. The graph must approach a constant *x*-value. Both C and E do this, but the tangents to E have a negative slope, indicating negative velocity before stopping.

5. The answer is A. Constant acceleration means a straight-line *v* vs. *t* graph. B does not approach 0 velocity continuously as described in the problem.

6. The answer is D. Use equation 1 to quickly find the time to the highest point:

$$v = v_0 + at$$
$$0 = 20 - 10t \qquad \Rightarrow t = 2s$$

Symmetry of the motion then means it takes 4 s to return to the same level, where it is now moving down at 20 m/s with another 25 m to go. Even with no acceleration, this would take only a little more than 1 s more, so with acceleration, you can expect D. Of course, you could use motion equations entirely, but estimations like this are useful on the multiple-choice section.

7. The answer is B. Since velocity is the slope of the *x* vs. *t* graph, you need a large positive slope followed by a 0 slope, followed by a smaller negative slope. C is not consistent with constant velocities within the three intervals.

8. The answer is D. At 40 m/s the second car is traveling at twice the speed of the first. From motion equation 4, you can write $0 = v_0^2 + 2a\Delta x \Rightarrow v_0^2 = -2a\Delta x$. Taking the ratio of this equation in the two cases yields

$$\frac{v_{20}^2}{v_{10}^2} = \frac{2^2}{1} = \frac{-2a\Delta x_2}{-2a(30)} \Rightarrow \Delta x_2 = 120 \text{ m}$$

9. The answer is B. Starting from rest, the displacement of the ball increases as the square of the time as can be seen by the third motion equation, $\Delta x = \frac{1}{2}at^2$. Thus the total displacement over the full 3 s must be $\frac{3^2}{2^2} = \frac{9}{4}$ times the displacement after 2 s. This is 4.5m. Subtracting the 2 m displacement gives 2.5 m traveled in the third second.

10. The answer is D. The first rock will hit in 3 s, as can be seen from $\Delta y = 45 = \frac{1}{2}(10)t^2$. Thus the second rock must reach the bottom in 2 s. Using the third motion equation, you have

$$\Delta y = 45 = v_0(2) + \frac{1}{2}(10)(2)^2 \Rightarrow v_0 = 12.5 \tfrac{\text{m}}{\text{s}}$$

FREE RESPONSE

1. (a) Use equation 3 with $v_0 = 0$.

$$\Delta y = v_0 t + \frac{1}{2}at^2$$
$$\Delta y = 0 + \frac{1}{2}(4)(10)^2 = 200 \text{ m}$$

(b) Use equation 1.

$$v = v_0 + at$$

$$v = 0 + (4)(10) = 40\frac{m}{s}$$

(c) The first stage now moves under only the influence of gravity with the initial position and velocity given in A and B. At the maximum height, the velocity is 0, so use equation 4.

$$v^2 = v_0^2 + 2a\Delta y$$
$$0 = 40^2 + 2(-10)(y - 200)$$
$$y = 280m$$

(d) You need to find the position of each object 2 s after separation and subtract. You can use equation 3 in each case.

First Stage

$$\Delta y = v_0 t + \frac{1}{2}at^2$$

$$y - 200 = 40(2) + \frac{1}{2}(-10)(2)^2$$

$$y = 260m$$

Second Stage

$$\Delta y = v_0 t + \frac{1}{2}at^2$$

$$y - 200 = 40(2) + \frac{1}{2}(6)(2)^2$$

$$y = 292m$$

The two stages are 32 m apart.

2. The slope of the v vs. t graph is the acceleration, and if the acceleration is positive, the velocity is increasing. If the acceleration is negative, the velocity is decreasing.
   (a) Velocity is increasing over the intervals 2–3 s and 6–8 s since the slope (acceleration) is positive over these intervals.
   (b) Velocity is decreasing over the interval 3–5 s since the slope is negative.
   (c) You can get the displacement from the area under the graph. From 2–4 s is a triangle with area $= \Delta x = \frac{1}{2}(2)(10) = 10$ m. From 4–5 s is another triangle with area $= \Delta x = \frac{1}{2}(1)(-10) = -5$. The total displacement is 5 m.

(d)

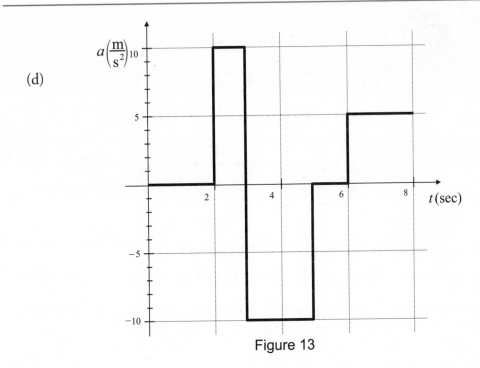

Figure 13

You can find the slopes of the various segments on the v vs. t graph. The discontinuous jumps on this graph are not physical, because in a real world situation, the v vs. t graph wouldn't have sharp corners but would be rounded. This would make the corresponding a vs. t graph continuous.

3. (a) Use the third motion equation to find the displacement of each car.

$$\Delta x_R = \frac{1}{2}(6)(1)^2 = 3 \text{ m} \quad \Delta x_B = (15)(1) + \frac{1}{2}(2)(1)^2 = 16 \text{ m}$$

Since the blue car started 20 m behind the red, the separation S of the two is given by

$$S = \Delta x_R - (\Delta x_B - 20) = 7 \text{ m}$$

(b) The two cars are passing each other when $S = 0$. The time for this to occur satisfies

$$S = 0 = \frac{1}{2}(6)t^2 - (15t + \frac{1}{2}(2)t^2 - 20)$$

$$2t^2 - 15t + 20 = 0 \Rightarrow t = 1.73 \text{ s and } 5.77 \text{ s}$$

Thus the blue catches up to the red after 1.73 s. The red car will have traveled

$$\Delta x_R = \frac{1}{2}(6)(1.73)^2 = 8.98 \text{ m}$$

(c) After 5.77 s, the red car eventually catches the blue one. Use the first motion equation to find its speed then.
$$v = 0 + (6)(5.77) = 34.6 \frac{\text{m}}{\text{s}}$$

This is over the speed limit, so the answer is no.

2

Vectors and Projectiles

In the previous chapter you learned how to describe motion in one dimension. In this chapter you'll find out how to extend this knowledge to two or more dimensions. By using vectors and their components, you'll discover that describing multidimensional motion can be reduced to combining several one-dimensional descriptions. You can easily adapt all the work from the past chapter to handle the more complicated motion.

Scalars and Vectors

The quantities you will study in AP Physics fall into two basic categories: scalars and vectors. A **scalar** needs only one number to completely quantify it. Examples of scalars are time, temperature, mass, and energy. Because it exists in two or three dimensions, a **vector** needs two or three numbers, respectively, to quantify it completely.

The big difference between vectors and scalars is that vectors have a direction associated with them. In two dimensions two numbers that can describe a vector are its magnitude (how big it is) and its direction. You can specify direction most precisely with an angle, measured in degrees or radians in relation to one of the coordinate axes. Vectors are labeled by using boldface—**A**—or by putting an arrow on top of the label—$\vec{A}$. You can specify the magnitude of the same vector by using just the label A without the boldface or arrow. Vectors are depicted graphically with arrows; the length of the arrow indicates the relative size or magnitude of the vector, and the direction of the arrow indicates the direction of the vector (figure 1).

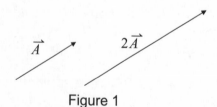

Figure 1

A vector can be multiplied by a scalar. This process will change the magnitude of the vector but not its direction. The vector $2\vec{A}$ is in the same direction as $\vec{A}$ but is twice as big. Examples of vectors are displacement, velocity, acceleration, and force. If you describe an object moving in two dimensions by saying it has a speed of 20 m/s, for example, you have given only the magnitude of the velocity. If you explain that the vector is directed at 30° above the $+x$-axis, then you have completely specified its velocity.

Vector Addition

Let's say you're traveling in a railroad car along a straight section of track at 10 m/s, and you throw a ball at 10 m/s relative to you in the same direction as the train is traveling. A person standing next to the tracks watching you and the train go by would say that the ball has a velocity of 20 m/s in the direction of the train motion. If you threw the ball out the window of the train at the same speed, however, what would the observer say about the speed and direction of the ball now? Such a question requires vector addition of the two velocities. You will see in later chapters that vector addition is common, so let's explore how to add and subtract vectors.

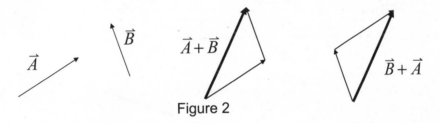

Figure 2

Consider two arbitrary vectors, $\vec{A}$ and $\vec{B}$ (figure 2). To find the sum of the two vectors, move one of them, $\vec{B}$, so that its tail sits on the head of $\vec{A}$. The sum of the two vectors, called the **resultant**, is the vector that extends from the tail of $\vec{A}$ to the head of $\vec{B}$. You can easily see that this process doesn't depend on the order of the vectors, because $\vec{A} + \vec{B} = \vec{B} + \vec{A}$. If you need to add three or more vectors, just continue the process, making a "train" of vectors with the resultant extending from the tail of the first to the head of the last (figure 3).

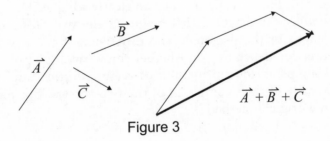

Figure 3

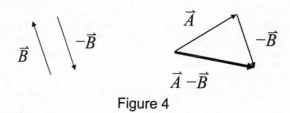

Figure 4

The negative of a vector, $-\vec{B}$, is a vector with the same magnitude as $\vec{B}$ but pointing in the opposite direction (figure 4). This means that you can subtract two vectors by adding one vector to the negative of the other: $\vec{A} - \vec{B} = \vec{A} + (-\vec{B})$.

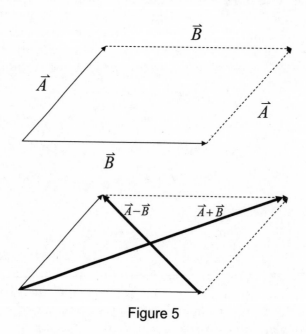

Figure 5

If you draw the two vectors $\vec{A}$ and $\vec{B}$ so that they are tail to tail, you can imagine completing a parallelogram (figure 5). From the figure you can clearly see that the sum of the two vectors $\vec{A} + \vec{B}$ is directed along the diagonal that begins at the two tails and that it is equal in magnitude to the length of the diagonal. The difference of the two vectors is the other diagonal, with the direction depending on whether you want $\vec{A} - \vec{B}$ or $\vec{B} - \vec{A}$. This process is sometimes called the parallelogram method of vector addition and subtraction. Because the parallelogram is made of sides composed of the two vectors, this method is really just a different name for the original method.

Components of a Vector

These graphical methods can help you conceptualize the resultant of two vectors, but to be more precise you need an analytic method that doesn't depend on the imprecision of making scale drawings. Keep in mind that an arbitrary vector $\vec{A}$ can be written in a unique way as the sum of two special vectors: One is directed along the x-axis, and the other is directed along the y-axis (figure 6).

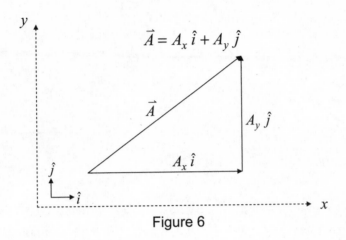

Figure 6

Vectors of length one unit that point in either the x or y direction are called **unit vectors**. The unit vector pointing along the x-axis is labeled $\hat{i}$, and the unit vector pointing along the y-axis is labeled $\hat{j}$, using a caret instead of an arrow. An arbitrary two-dimensional vector can be written like this:

$$\vec{A} = A_x \hat{i} + A_y \hat{j}$$

Here A_x and A_y are called the x and y components of the vector $\vec{A}$. You can think of the vector as the sum of two vectors: The first is A_x units along the x-axis, and the second is A_y units along the y-axis. Using components to describe a vector makes it simpler to perform vector arithmetic. You can apply this concept to the magnitude-and-direction approach using basic right triangle trigonometry. Consider the vector $\vec{B}$ with magnitude B, making an angle θ with respect to the +x-axis (figure 7).

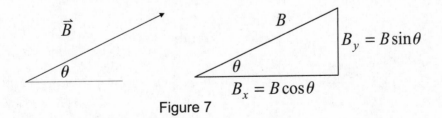

Figure 7

From the definition of sine and cosine, you can write

$$B_x = B\cos\theta \qquad B_y = B\sin\theta$$

You can work in the other direction as well. Given the components B_x and B_y, you can find the magnitude and direction of the vector:

$$B = \sqrt{B_x^2 + B_y^2} \qquad \tan\theta = \frac{B_y}{B_x}$$

EXERCISE

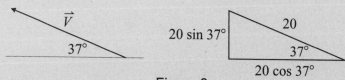

Figure 8

Find the components of a velocity vector $\vec{V}$ with magnitude $20\frac{m}{s}$, making an angle of $37°$ with the negative x-axis (figure 8).

$$V_x = -20\cos37 = -16\frac{m}{s} \qquad V_y = 20\sin37 = 12\frac{m}{s}$$

EXERCISE

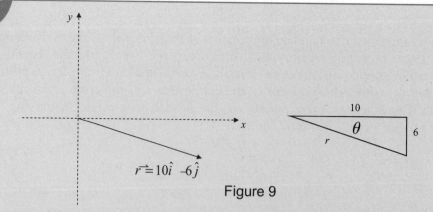

Figure 9

Find the magnitude and direction of the position vector $\vec{r} = 10\hat{i} - 6\hat{j}$.

$$r = \sqrt{r_x^2 + r_y^2}$$

$$\tan\theta = \frac{-6}{10} \Rightarrow \theta = -31° \ (31° \text{ below} + x\text{-axis})$$

$$r = \sqrt{10^2 + (-6)^2} = 11.7 \text{ m}$$

Vector addition is particularly simple in the language of components. The components of vector $\vec{C} = \vec{A} + \vec{B}$ are just the sums of the two vectors being added (figure 10):

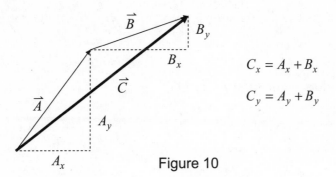

$$C_x = A_x + B_x$$
$$C_y = A_y + B_y$$

Figure 10

$$C_x = A_x + B_x \qquad C_y = A_y + B_y$$

EXERCISE

Given the vectors $\vec{A} = -7\hat{i} + 4\hat{j}$ and $B = 5\hat{i} + 9\hat{j}$, find the vector $\vec{C} = \vec{A} + \vec{B}$.

$$C_x = A_x + B_x \qquad\qquad C_y = A_y + B_y$$
$$C_x = -7 + 5 = -2 \qquad C_y = 4 + 9 = 13$$
$$\vec{C} = -2\hat{i} + 13\hat{j}$$

Vector Multiplication

You can calculate the product of two vectors in one of two basic ways. One method produces a scalar from the two vectors, called the scalar product or the **dot product**. The other method produces a new vector from the original two vectors, called the vector product or the **cross product**. Vector products usually are shown graphically with their tails touching, "tail to tail."

DOT PRODUCT

Consider the two vectors $\vec{A}$ and $\vec{B}$ (figure 11).

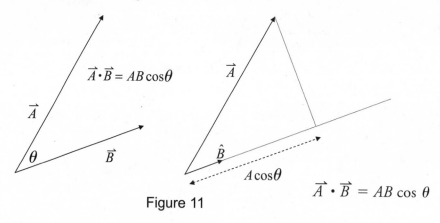

Figure 11

The dot product of these two vectors is defined as:

$$\vec{A} \cdot \vec{B} = AB \cos \theta$$

The magnitude of the dot product is controlled by the angle between the two vectors. It's a maximum for parallel or antiparallel vectors and a minimum for vectors that are perpendicular. What does the dot product really tell you? If you divide both sides of the preceding equation by B, you get

$$\vec{A} \cdot \frac{\vec{B}}{B} = \vec{A} \cdot \hat{B} = A \cos \theta$$

where $\hat{B}$ is a unit vector in the direction of $\vec{B}$. From the figure you can see that $A \cos \theta$ is simply the component of $\vec{A}$ that lies in the direction of $\vec{B}$, so the dot product tells you to what extent the two vectors are in the same direction. If the two vectors are perpendicular, then $\theta = 90°$ and $\vec{A} \cdot \vec{B} = 0$; they have no component along each other. If the two vectors are the same, $\theta = 0$ and $\vec{A} \cdot \vec{A} = A^2$.

CROSS PRODUCT

As mentioned earlier, it's possible to multiply two vectors together in such a way that a third vector is formed. The cross product $\vec{C}$ is written as

$$\vec{C} = \vec{A} \times \vec{B}$$

The magnitude of this vector is

$$C = AB \sin \theta$$

The magnitude is the area made by the parallelogram formed by $\vec{A}$ and $\vec{B}$ (figure 12).

$$\text{area} = AB \sin\theta$$

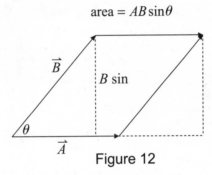

Figure 12

The direction of $\vec{C}$ is defined as perpendicular to both $\vec{A}$ and $\vec{B}$. Since two vectors always define a plane, there are two directions, opposite to each other, that are perpendicular to both $\vec{A}$ and $\vec{B}$. These directions are called $\hat{n}$ and $-\hat{n}$ (figure 13).

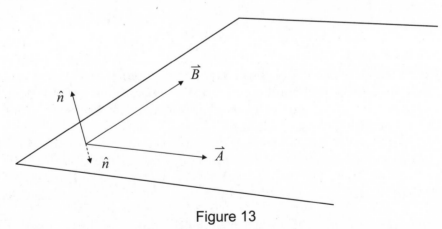

Figure 13

To define the direction of the cross product uniquely, you must choose one of these two possibilities. You'll use the **right-hand rule** (figure 14) to make your choice:

Place the two vectors tail to tail. Align your right hand along the first vector in the product, $\vec{A}$, so that the base of your palm is at the tail of the vector and your fingertips are pointing tow ard the head. Then curl your fingers via the small angle toward the second vector, $\vec{B}$. If $\vec{B}$ is in a clockwise direction from $\vec{A}$, you'll have to flip your hand over to make this work. The direction in which your thumb is pointing is the direction of $\vec{C}$.

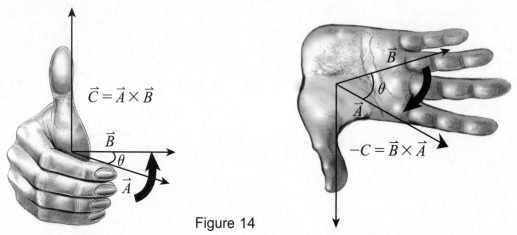

Figure 14

According to this rule and the figure, $\hat{n}$ is the direction of the cross product, so

$$\vec{C} = AB \sin \theta \, \hat{n}$$

You'll notice that if you reverse the order of the cross product, the magnitude stays the same but the direction reverses:

$$\vec{A} \times \vec{B} = -\vec{B} \times \vec{A}$$

Two vectors that are parallel or antiparallel will have a cross product of 0, as you can see from calculating $\sin 0 = \sin 180° = 0$ or thinking in terms of a parallelogram with 0 area. While there is a formula for the components of $\vec{C}$ in terms of the components of $\vec{A}$ and $\vec{B}$, you won't need this level of analysis for the AP test.

Projectile Motion

An object moving near the surface of the Earth under the influence only of gravity is called a **projectile**. When you're working with a projectile, your calculations start after it has been projected. For example, a baseball hit with a bat becomes a projectile after it leaves the bat, and a cannonball becomes a projectile after it leaves the barrel of the cannon. Objects remain projectiles until some other influence, such as the ground, acts upon them. If you ignore air resistance, the only acceleration experienced by the projectile is $g = 9.8 \text{ m/s}^2 \cong 10 \text{ m/s}^2$ directed straight down. Since the projectile doesn't accelerate horizontally, the x-component of the velocity doesn't change. While the projectile does accelerate in the y-direction, it is constant acceleration. You have learned how to handle constant acceleration in the previous chapter.

Ultimately, you can think of projectile motion as two separate motions occurring simultaneously: constant velocity in the x-direction and uniformly accelerated motion in the y-direction. In describing a projectile, you can use all the equations from the last chapter, but be careful about the kind of notation you use. Because the displacement and velocity have two components, you'll need to label them with the appropriate subscripts. With the notation defined in figure 15, you can write the following equations:

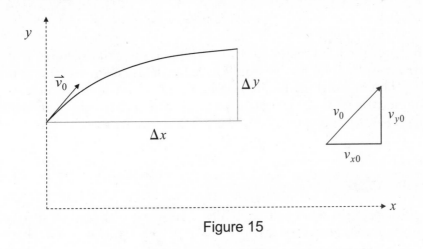

Figure 15

Horizontal	Vertical

Horizontal

$$\Delta x = v_{x0}t$$

$$v_x = v_{x0}$$

Vertical

$$v_y = v_{y0} - gt$$

$$\Delta y = \tfrac{1}{2}(v_y + v_{y0})t$$

$$\Delta y = v_{y0}t - \tfrac{1}{2}gt^2$$

$$v_y^2 = v_{y0}^2 - 2g\Delta y$$

For these equations, assume the positive directions are as shown in the figure, so that $a_y = -g$. Keep in mind that these equations are the basic constant acceleration equations of the last chapter; they look more complex because of the vector labeling, but that is required when you leave the world of one dimension.

EXAMPLE

A ball rolls off a table 1 m high with a speed of 4 m/s. How far from the base of the table does it land?

The object leaves the table moving horizontally, so $v_{y0} = 0$.

Since $v_{x0} = 4$ m/s, the horizontal equation gives you $\Delta x = 4t$. You can get t from the third vertical equation because you know $\Delta y = -1$m.

$$\Delta y = -1 = -\tfrac{1}{2}(10)t^2 \Rightarrow t = 0.45 \text{ s}$$

Substituting, you get $\Delta x = 4(0.45) = 1.79$ m.

Notice that the time the ball took to fall had nothing to do with the horizontal speed. If the object had been released from rest, it would have hit the floor in the same time. In general, the vertical motion of a horizontally projected object is identical to the motion of an object released from rest. If you ignore air resistance, a bullet fired horizontally and a bullet released from the same height from rest will hit the ground simultaneously, assuming the bullets travel over a flat surface.

EXAMPLE

An arrow is shot from a castle wall 10 m high. It leaves the bow with a speed of 40 m/s directed $37°$ above the horizontal.
    (a) Find the initial velocity components.
    (b) Find the maximum height of the arrow.
    (c) Where does the arrow land?
    (d) How fast is the arrow moving just before impact?

(a)

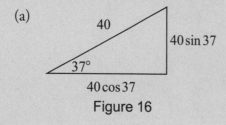

Figure 16

$$v_{x0} = 40 \cos 37 = 32\tfrac{\text{m}}{\text{s}} \qquad\qquad v_{y0} = 40 \sin 37 = 24\tfrac{\text{m}}{\text{s}}$$

(The $37°$ right triangle is a 3-4-5 right triangle, and the AP test uses it frequently.)

(b) Use the fourth vertical equation. At the highest point, the y-component of velocity is 0.

$$v_y^2 = v_{y0}^2 - 2g\Delta y \qquad\qquad \Delta y = 28.8\text{m}$$

$$0 = 24^2 - 20\Delta y$$

The maximum height is 38.8 m.

(c) Use the third vertical equation to find the time in the air. The vertical displacement for the entire motion is -10 m. Use the horizontal equation with this time value to get Δx.

$$\Delta y = v_{y0}t - \tfrac{1}{2}gt^2$$
$$-10 = 24t - 5t^2 \qquad\qquad \Delta x = 32t$$
$$t = 5.2\text{s (use quad eq.)} \qquad \Delta x = 32(5.2) = 166\text{m}$$

(d) The x-component remains 32 m/s until the object hits. Use the first vertical equation and the time from (c) to get the y-component.

$$v_y = v_{y0} - gt$$
$$v_x = 32\tfrac{\text{m}}{\text{s}} \qquad\qquad v_y = 24 - (10)(5.2) = -28\tfrac{\text{m}}{\text{s}}$$
$$v = \sqrt{v_x^2 + v_y^2}$$
$$v = \sqrt{32^2 + (-28)^2} = 42.5\tfrac{\text{m}}{\text{s}}$$

You can derive an interesting equation if you use the horizontal equation to eliminate the time variable in the third vertical equation:

$$\Delta x = v_{x0}t \qquad\qquad\qquad \Delta y = v_{y0}t - \tfrac{1}{2}gt^2$$

$$t = \tfrac{\Delta x}{v_{x0}} \qquad\qquad\qquad \Delta y = v_{y0}\left(\tfrac{\Delta x}{v_{x0}}\right) - \tfrac{1}{2}g\left(\tfrac{\Delta x}{v_{x0}}\right)^2$$

If you choose the origin to be the release point, then $\Delta x = x$ and $\Delta y = y$, and the preceding equation expresses y as a function of x in a quadratic form:

$$y = \left(\tfrac{v_{y0}}{v_{x0}}\right)x + \left(-\tfrac{g}{2v_{x0}^2}\right)x^2$$

This is the equation of a parabola, indicating that the trajectory of a projectile takes this shape if air resistance can be ignored.

KEY FORMULAS

Vector Components

$$A_x = A \cos \theta$$
$$A_y = A \sin \theta$$

Vector Addition $\vec{C} = \vec{A} + \vec{B}$

$$C_x = A_x + B_x$$
$$C_y = A_y + B_y$$

Dot Product

$$\vec{A} \cdot \vec{B} = A \cos \theta$$

Cross Product

$$\vec{C} = \vec{A} \times \vec{B}$$
$$C = AB \sin \theta$$

Projectile Motion

$$v_y = v_{y0} - gt$$

$$\Delta x = v_{x0} t \qquad \Delta y = \tfrac{1}{2}(v_y + v_{y0})t$$

$$v_x = v_{x0} \qquad \Delta y = v_{y0}t - \tfrac{1}{2}gt^2$$

$$v_y^2 = v_{y0}^2 - 2g\Delta y$$

PRACTICE EXERCISES

SECTION I MULTIPLE CHOICE

Questions 1 and 2

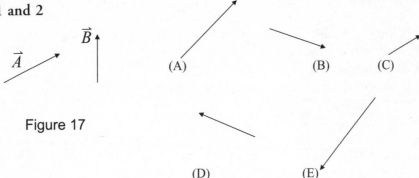

Figure 17

1. The vector representing $\vec{A} - \vec{B}$ most closely is

   (A) A   (B) B   (C) C   (D) D   (E) E

2. The vector $\vec{X}$ that would satisfy the equation $\vec{A} + \vec{B} + \vec{X} = 0$ most closely is

   (A) A   (B) B   (C) C   (D) D   (E) E

3. The dot product of two vectors
   I. is a scalar
   II. is 0 if the two vectors are perpendicular
   III. lies perpendicular to the plane defined by the two vectors

   (A) I only   (B) II only   (C) III only   (D) I and II only   (E) I, II, and III

4. The vectors $\vec{A}$ and $\vec{B}$ both have a magnitude of 5 units. The magnitude of the sum of these two vectors

   (A) has magnitude 10   (B) equals 0   (C) has magnitude 5
   (D) could be A or B but not C   (E) could be A, B, or C

5. Two vectors have their tails connected and their lengths fixed. If the angle between them is now varied, which of the following is true?
   I. The magnitude of the dot product is minimized when the vectors are perpendicular.
   II. The magnitude of the cross product is maximized when they are perpendicular.
   III. Each will always have a component lying along the other.

   (A) I only   (B) II only   (C) III only   (D) I and II only   (E) I, II, and III

6. Three balls are projected from the edge of a cliff. I is fired horizontally, II is fired at an angle of 30° above the horizontal with the same speed as I, and III is released from rest. Which of the following is true?

   (A) I and II hit at the same time, and III hits later.
   (B) I and II hit at the same time, and III hits earlier.
   (C) I and III hit at the same time, and II hits earlier.
   (D) I and III hit at the same time, and II hits later.
   (E) All hit at the same time.

7. At the highest point of its trajectory, a projectile fired at 30° above the horizontal from a starting height of 20 m

   (A) is instantaneously at rest
   (B) has traveled half the distance to its impact point
   (C) has 0 acceleration
   (D) has a horizontal velocity component equal to its initial value
   (E) has more than one of the above properties

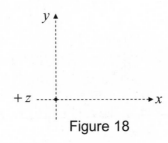

Figure 18

8. Vector $\vec{A}$ points in the $+x$ direction and has a magnitude of 3 units. Vector $\vec{B}$ points in the $+y$ direction and has a magnitude of 4 units. The cross product of these two vectors

   (A) is zero
   (B) is in the x-y plane directed at 45° above the x-axis, with magnitude 5 units
   (C) lies along the $+ z$-axis with magnitude 12 units
   (D) lies along the $- z$-axis with magnitude 12 units
   (E) lies along the $+ z$-axis with magnitude 5 units

CHAPTER 2

PRACTICE EXERCISES

1. A train is moving east at 30 m/s along a long, straight section of track. A person on the train has a dart gun that can shoot rubber-tipped darts at a speed of 10 m/s. If the person aims the gun at an angle of 30° north of east and pulls the trigger, what will be the magnitude and direction of the velocity of the dart as it leaves the gun, relative to a person on the ground watching the train pass by?

2. A projectile is fired from a balcony 20 m high at an angle of 30° above the horizontal. It strikes the ground 10.4 s later.
   (a) Find the initial speed.
   (b) Find the magnitude and direction of the velocity vector after 7 s.
   (c) With the balcony as the origin, find the x and y coordinates of the highest point of the motion.

3. A quarterback throws a pass to a receiver. The release point for the football is 1.8 m above the ground. He projects the ball with a speed of 20 m/s at an angle of 40° above the horizontal.
   (a) If the pass falls incomplete, how long is it in the air?
   (b) If the pass falls incomplete, how far from the quarterback does it land?
   (c) How high above the release point will the ball reach?
   (d) A receiver 15 m from the quarterback is running at a constant speed away from him at the time of release. How fast must the receiver be running to be able to catch the ball, assuming he receives it at ground level (he makes a diving catch)?

Answers and Explanations

MULTIPLE CHOICE

1. The answer is B. Put $-\vec{B}$ at the tip of $\vec{A}$, estimating the lengths. Connect from the tail of $\vec{A}$ to the head of $\vec{B}$ to get the answer.

2. The answer is E. Put $\vec{B}$ at the tip of $\vec{A}$. The vector $\vec{X}$ must connect back to the tail of $\vec{A}$ so that the sum of all three is 0. This leads to E.

3. The answer is D. The dot product is a scalar and doesn't have a direction, so III isn't possible.

4. The answer is E. The magnitude of $\vec{A} + \vec{B}$ can be anywhere between 0 (opposite directions) and +10 (parallel), depending on the angle they make with each other.

5. The answer is D. While the dot product can be negative, its magnitude is always greater than or equal to 0, so A is true. B is true according to the definition. When the two vectors are perpendicular, each has no component along the other, excluding III.

6. The answer is D. Horizontally fired projectiles will hit at the same time as those dropped from rest from the same height because the horizontal speed is not affected by gravity. Object II fired upward will reach some greater height where its speed is purely horizontal. This makes it a horizontal projectile from a greater height, which clearly will take longer to fall.

7. The answer is D. The object will never be at rest until it hits because the x-component of the velocity always stays the same. It is less than halfway to its impact point since it began 20 m off the ground, not at ground level. The acceleration is always 9.8 m/s^2 down, never 0.

8. The answer is C. The magnitude of the cross product is $AB \sin \theta = (3)(4) \sin 90 = 12$. The right-hand rule tells you that the direction is along the $+ z$-axis.

FREE RESPONSE

1. The velocity observed by a person at rest with the tracks will be the vector sum of the train velocity and the velocity of the dart with respect to the train. If you have difficulty seeing this, think of the limiting cases where the dart is fired in the same direction as the train velocity or in the opposite direction to the train velocity. In the first case, it should be clear that the final velocity is 40 m/s in the train direction, while in the second case it is 20 m/s in the train direction. These cases are both consistent with the vector addition of the two velocities. For the current situation, let east be the $+ x$ direction, and north the $+ y$ direction.

$$v_x^{\text{train}} = 30$$

$$v_y^{\text{train}} = 30$$

Relative to the train, the dart velocity is $v_x^{\text{dart/train}} = 10 \cos 30 = 8.7 \frac{\text{m}}{\text{s}}$

$$v_y^{\text{dart/train}} = 10 \sin 30 = 5 \frac{\text{m}}{\text{s}}$$

The velocity of the dart relative to the tracks is the sum of the two vectors, and you can find the components of the sum by adding the components of each vector.

$$v_x^{\text{dart/track}} = v_x^{\text{train}} + v_x^{\text{dart/train}} = 30 + 8.7 = 38.7 \frac{\text{m}}{\text{s}}$$

$$v_y^{\text{dart/track}} = v_y^{\text{train}} + v_y^{\text{dart/train}} = 0 + 5 = 5 \frac{\text{m}}{\text{s}}$$

To find the magnitude and direction, use the basic right triangle trigonometry.

$$v^{\text{dart/track}} = \sqrt{38.7^2 + 5^2} = 39.0\tfrac{\text{m}}{\text{s}} \quad \tan\theta = \tfrac{5}{38.7} = 0.13$$

$$\theta = 7.4°$$

2. (a) The final vertical displacement is -20 m, so given the time and angle, you can use the third vertical equation to find the initial speed.

$$\Delta y = v_{y0}t - \tfrac{1}{2}gt^2$$
$$-20 = (v_0 \sin 30)(10.4) - 5(10.4)^2$$
$$v_0 = 100\tfrac{\text{m}}{\text{s}}$$

(b) The x-component of the velocity is $v_x = v_0 \cos 30 = 100(0.87) = 87$ m/s. This stays the same for the entire motion. The initial y-component of the velocity is $v_{y0} = v_0 \sin 30 = 100(0.5) = 50$ m/s. Use the first vertical equation to find the value after 7 s:

$$v_y = v_{y0} - gt \qquad\qquad v_y = -20\tfrac{\text{m}}{\text{s}}$$

$$v_y = 50 - 10(7)$$

You can find the magnitude and direction of the velocity from basic trigonometry:

$$v = \sqrt{v^2_x + v^2_y} = \sqrt{87^2 + (-20)^2} = 89.2\tfrac{\text{m}}{\text{s}} \qquad \tan\theta = \tfrac{-20}{87}$$

$$\theta = -13°$$

(c) At the highest point, $v_y = 0$. If you find the time it takes to get here, you can then substitute to find the coordinates. Since the balcony is the origin, the coordinates and displacement are identical: $\Delta x = x \quad \Delta y = y$.

$$v_y = v_{y0} - gt \qquad x = v_{x0}t \qquad y = \tfrac{1}{2}(v_y + v_{y0})t$$

$$0 = 50 - 10t \qquad x = 87(5) \qquad y = \tfrac{1}{2}(0 + 50)(5)$$

$$t = 5s \qquad\qquad x = 435m \qquad y = 125m$$

3. (a) First find the components of the initial velocity.

$$v_{x0} = 20 \cos 40 = 15.3 \tfrac{m}{s} \qquad\qquad v_{y0} = 20 \sin 40 = 12.9 \tfrac{m}{s}$$

When the pass lands incomplete, the vertical displacement will be -1.8 m. Using the third motion equation, you have

$$-1.8 = 12.9t - \tfrac{1}{2}(10)t^2 \Rightarrow t = 2.7\text{s (use quadratic formula)}$$

(b) $\Delta x = v_{x0}t = 15.3(2.7) = 41.3$ m

(c) The maximum height y is attained when $v_y = 0$. Use the fourth motion equation.

$$v_y^2 = 0 = v_{y0}^2 - 2g\Delta y = (12.9)^2 - 20(y - 1.8)$$

(d) The receiver must travel $41.3 - 15 = 26.3$ m to catch the ball, and he must do this in 2.7 s. His constant speed over this interval must be

$$v = \tfrac{\Delta x}{\Delta t} = \tfrac{26.3}{2.7} = 9.7\tfrac{m}{s}$$

CHAPTER 3

Newton's Laws

Mechanics is the branch of physics that deals with the description and causes of motion. Galileo was the first person to study motion scientifically, discovering what are now called kinematic relations among the quantities used to describe motion. You have seen these relations expressed in the basic equations used to describe one-dimensional, uniform accelerated motion and projectile motion. But while Galileo was the first to develop a quantitative description of motion, the remarkable Isaac Newton created an entire framework for linking the causes of motion to the motion itself. The foundation of this framework lies in what are called Newton's three laws of mechanics. Central to these laws is the concept of force. In fact, you can use the three laws to precisely define force and to directly relate it to the motion of objects.

Inertia and the First Law

You are probably familiar with what happens when an object in space, far away from any outside influence, is given an initial velocity: It continues undeflected at constant speed forever or until something interferes with it. A physicist would say that this behavior is a basic property inherent in all matter, a property called inertia. **Inertia** means that matter stays in a state of rest if it is currently at rest and it stays in a state of constant speed in a straight line if it is moving. The measure of inertia is mass, with units of kilograms in the SI system. The more massive an object is, the more inertia it has. Newton's first law is sometimes called the law of inertia:

An object at rest will remain at rest, or if it is in uniform motion (constant speed in a straight line), it will continue as such unless acted upon by a net (unbalanced) force.

The concept of force first appears in the first law; a force must be present to cause an object to deviate from its state of either rest or uniform velocity. But you know from kinematics that such a deviation, a change in velocity, has to mean acceleration is present, so you can conclude that forces will be related to accelerations. Inertia itself, however, is not a force, and no force is needed to keep an object moving. A nonzero net force is needed to change an object's velocity.

Types of Forces

When two systems interact, they exert forces on each other. In terms of Newton's first law, each system changes its velocity; it doesn't simply continue in a straight line at constant speed. Two systems must always be present for a force to occur: A ball hits a wall; your hand pushes on a desk; Earth attracts the moon. Forces are categorized in terms of how the two systems interact. **Contact forces** involve two systems actually touching. **Noncontact forces** involve interactions between two systems that aren't actually touching.

CONTACT FORCES

When an object, such as a brick, rests upon another surface, such as a table, the table supports the brick with a force that is directed perpendicular to the surface of the table (figure 1).

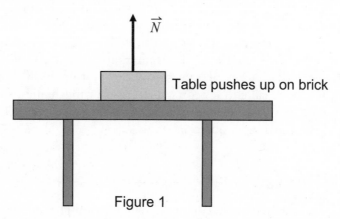

Figure 1

This is the **normal force**, $\vec{N}$, the force between two surfaces that acts perpendicular to the surface. The origin of this force lies in the electric forces that hold together the materials. When the brick is placed on the table, the table sags slightly as the molecules adjust their positions, much like the effect on a mattress when you lie down. If the brick slides across the table, a component of force exerted by the table will act parallel to the surface, in this case opposing the motion of the brick. This is a **friction force**, f, the force exerted between two surfaces that acts parallel to the surface.

You can trace the origin of friction to electrical interactions between the materials. There are two types of friction: static friction, $\vec{f_s}$, when the two surfaces experience a sliding stress but don't actually move, and kinetic friction, $\vec{f_k}$, when the two surfaces do slide over each other. The amount of friction produced will depend on the degree to which the two surfaces are pushed into each other, or the normal force. Over a wide range of conditions, the magnitude of the kinetic friction force is directly proportional to the normal force:

$$f_k = \mu_k N$$

Here, μ_k is the coefficient of friction between the two surfaces, and it will depend on the nature of the interacting surfaces.

For static friction, the situation is different. A brick at rest on a level surface such as a table experiences no friction, but if you tilt the table (figure 2), it won't move until some maximum angle is reached.

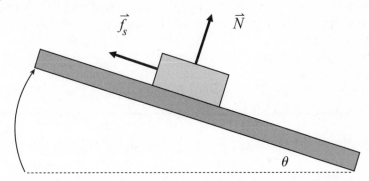

Static friction force can range between zero and a maximum value.

Figure 2

The static friction force will vary from 0 to some maximum value, but this maximum value will depend on the nature of the interacting surfaces and how the surfaces are pushed together, or the normal force:

$$f_s \leq \mu_s N = f_s^{\max}$$

Here μ_s is the coefficient of static friction between the two surfaces. Usually, $\mu_s > \mu_k$.

The force exerted by ropes or rods attached to objects is called **tension** $\overrightarrow{T}$. When you pull on one end of an ideal, massless rope, the rope transmits this force to the object, but it is the rope that is in direct contact with the object. You cannot push with a rope, but you can push something with a rigid rod, and this force is called compression. Once again, the origin of these forces lies in the electrical interactions of the molecules.

NONCONTACT FORCES

Magnetic, electric, and gravitational forces do not require direct contact between the interacting systems. As you'll see later, such forces are transmitted by the fields created in the surrounding space, and each object interacts directly with the field of the other object. When you're using a force law relating two objects, you can apply Newton's laws, treating these types of forces no differently from tension, friction, or any other force.

For mechanics, the only force you need to consider from this category is gravitational attraction. The gravitational attraction between the Earth and an object near its surface is called the **weight**, W, of the object. You'll also look at the more general case of gravitational interaction in a separate chapter.

Freebody Diagrams

You'll find it much easier to apply Newton's laws if you can draw accurate freebody diagrams. A **freebody diagram** is a properly oriented representation of the system removed from its surroundings but showing all interactions as force vectors, represented as arrows coming out of the body. You'll need to give the vectors appropriate descriptive labels, but you don't need to labor over your drawing. Usually a simple box or even a point will work just fine, unless you're dealing with rotation, which will be covered at the end of this chapter.

Let's look at a couple of examples.

A boy is using a rope to pull a sled up an incline, keeping the rope parallel to the incline surface. Draw a freebody diagram for the sled (figure 3).

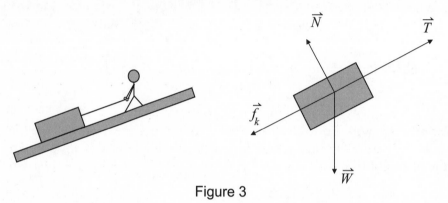

Figure 3

Two weights connected by a rope are lifted by a second rope connected to the upper weight. Draw a freebody diagram for each weight (figure 4).

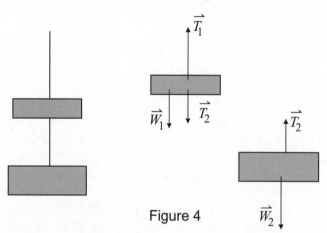

Figure 4

Notice that the last example uses subscripts to differentiate between the different weights and the different tensions.

Action and Reaction and the Third Law

As you've learned, it takes two systems for an interaction to occur. Newton's third law addresses this interaction in a general way:

When an interaction takes place between two systems, each system exerts a force on the other, and these two forces are equal in magnitude and opposite in direction.

The two forces are sometimes called an action-reaction pair. When a bat hits a baseball, for example, the bat exerts a force on the ball, and the ball exerts an equal and opposite force on the bat. It doesn't matter which of these forces you call "action" and which you call "reaction," because neither is more fundamental than the other.

If you don't understand the third law completely, it's easy to become confused. In the example, for instance, you might argue that the two forces couldn't be equal because the ball obviously receives a much greater acceleration than the bat, but this argument ignores the difference in the inertia of the bat and ball. This point will become clearer when you read about the second law.

Another argument is that the forces couldn't be equal and opposite because then they would cancel each other out and nothing would accelerate. But each member of the action-reaction pair acts on a different object, so there's no question about the force on the ball or the bat canceling out with anything. Action-reaction pairs never act on the same object.

Finally, it's possible for two forces to be equal in magnitude and opposite in direction, and yet not be action-reaction pairs. The brick resting on a flat surface is a good example. Intuition probably tells you that the normal force acting up is just equal to the weight acting down. But this is not an action-reaction pair. The normal force results from an interaction between the brick and the table. Its reaction partner is a force exerted on the table (causing it to sag). The weight force is an interaction between the brick and the entire Earth. Its reaction partner is a force exerted on the entire Earth by the brick!

Newton's Second Law

Newton's second law is a quantitative statement that relates the vector sum of all forces acting on a system, the **net force**, to the acceleration of the system:

$$net\vec{F} = m\vec{a}$$

Keep in mind that for a fixed mass, the net force and acceleration are directly proportional: Doubling the force will double the acceleration. But the same force will produce different accelerations on systems with different masses. This equation sets the units of force in the SI system to be $\frac{\text{kg} \cdot \text{m}}{s^2}$, which is called a Newton (N). Because this is a vector equation, it is actually a separate equation for each component:

$$netF_x = ma_x \qquad netF_y = ma_y$$

Analyzing a physical system with this law is a four-step process:

Step 1.   For each object, draw a freebody diagram with the forces properly labeled. If numerical values are given for the forces, include them. Otherwise, use symbolic notation such as T and W.

Step 2.   For each object and each direction, determine the sum of all the force components using the symbols and numbers in Step 1. This will be $netF_x$ or $netF_y$ for each object.

Step 3.   Equate your result from Step 2 to ma for each component: for example, $netF_x = ma_x$.

Step 4.   Use these equations to determine any unknown factors.

Although you'll need to focus on these four steps when you're first learning, eventually they should become second nature. After you're familiar with the technique, you won't always need to state the obvious, but be careful. Faulty intuition often leads to errors that you could have avoided by considering the facts more carefully.

EXAMPLE 1

A mass m falls freely. Find the relation between the mass and the weight of the object. Because all motion is in y-direction, you can drop the x and y labels.

Step 1.

$\vec{W}$

Figure 5

Step 2. $netF = W$

Step 3. $W = ma$

Step 4. Because the mass falls freely, $a = g \Rightarrow W = mg$

This example leads to the important equation that relates mass and weight near the surface of Earth:

$$W = mg$$

EXAMPLE 2

A horizontal rope with tension 30 N pulls a 5 kg mass across a horizontal surface where the coefficient of kinetic friction is 0.4. Find the acceleration of the mass.

Step 1.

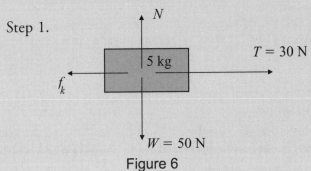

Figure 6

Step 2. y-direction: $netF_y = N - W = N - 50$
x-direction: $netF_x = T - f_k = 30 - (0.4)N$

Step 3. $N - 50 = 5a_y$
$30 - (0.4)N = 5a_x$

Step 4. There is no vertical acceleration, so $a_y = 0 \Rightarrow N = 50$ Newtons
$30 - (0.4)(50) = 5a_x \Rightarrow a_x = 2\dfrac{\text{m}}{\text{s}^2}$

In numerical problems, be sure to include units in your answers. On the AP test, sometimes you can receive points for having correct units in all answers within a given problem.

EXAMPLE 3

A 200 kg beam is connected by a cable to a 300 kg beam below it. The two are raised with an acceleration of 0.5 m/s^2 by another cable attached to the 200 kg beam. Ignoring the masses of the cables, find the tension in each.

With all motions vertical, you can again drop the x, y subscripts.

Step 1.

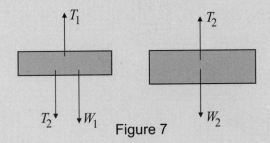

Figure 7

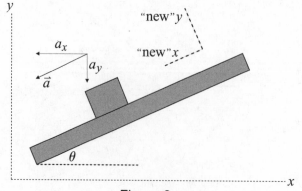
Step 2. On 200 kg mass: $netF_{top} = T_1 - T_2 - 2{,}000$
On 300 kg mass: $netF_{bot} = T_2 - 3{,}000$

Step 3. $T_1 - T_2 - 2{,}000 = 200(0.5)$
$T_2 - 3{,}000 = 300(0.5)$

Step 4. $T_2 = 3{,}150\text{N} \Rightarrow T_1 = 5{,}150 \text{ N}$

In Step 4 you had to solve for the tensions in the two equations simultaneously. But there's another approach you could have used in this problem that will be useful in other multiple-object problems where the objects all have the same acceleration. You can apply Newton's second law to the system as a whole:

Step 1. same as above

Step 2. $netF_{sys} = T_1 - T_2 - 2{,}000 + T_2 - 3{,}000 = T_1 - 5{,}000$

Step 3. $T_1 - 5{,}000 = 500(0.5)$

Step 4. $T_1 = 5250\text{N}$

Note that in Step 2, the T_2 tension force canceled out. For the ideal massless cables, the two T_2 forces were action-reaction pairs. Whenever you look at the entire system, the internal forces exerted by one part of the system on another part will always occur in pairs like this and will cancel out in the overall system equation. Notice also that this approach would not allow you to determine T_2, an internal force. You would have to apply the second law to one of the individual objects to find T_2.

Inclines

When an object is constrained to move on an incline (figure 8), its description is complicated by the fact that its acceleration has both vertical and horizontal components.

Figure 8

But since you know that it has an acceleration component only along the incline, it makes sense to change the coordinate system so that the new x-axis lies parallel to the incline surface and the new y-axis is perpendicular to the surface. Doing this also simplifies the description of the surface forces: Friction will have only an x-component, and the normal force will have only a y-component. The downside is that the weight will have both x- and y-components. Given the angle of the incline, however, the decomposition of the weight force into its components is the same every time (figure 9).

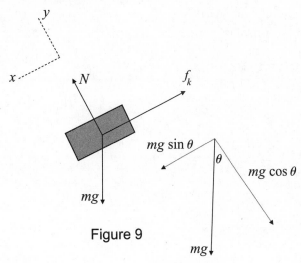

Figure 9

With some practice, you should be able to analyze inclines easily.

EXAMPLE

A 5 kg mass is placed on a plank where the coefficients of friction are $\mu_s = 0.6$, $\mu_k = 0.4$. The plank is raised slowly until the mass just starts to slide. Find the angle at which sliding occurs and the acceleration of the mass as it slides.

The angle where sliding just begins is called the angle of repose. As you approach this angle, you reach the maximum value of static friction that can be supplied by the surfaces: $f_s = \mu_s N$. The acceleration will be 0 until you reach this limiting angle.

Step 1.

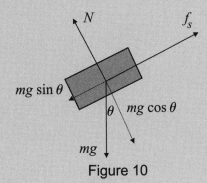

Figure 10

Step 2. $netF_x = mg\sin\theta - f_s = mg\sin\theta - \mu_s N$ $netF_y = N - mg\cos\theta$

Step 3. $mg\sin\theta - \mu_s N = ma_x = 0$ $N - mg\cos\theta = ma_y = 0$

Step 4. $mg\sin\theta = \mu_s N = \mu_s mg\cos\theta \Rightarrow \mu_s = \tan\theta$ $N = mg\cos\theta$
$\tan\theta = 0.6 \Rightarrow \theta = 31°$

To find the acceleration down the incline, change f_s to f_k, use the 31° result from the first part of the problem, and recognize that a_x is no longer 0.

Step 1. same but with friction type changed

Step 2. $netF_x = mg\sin\theta - f_k = 50\sin31 - (0.4)N$
$netF_y = N - mg\cos\theta = N - 50\cos31 = N - 43$

Step 3. $50\sin31 - (0.4)N = 5a_x$ $N - 43 = 5a_y = 0 \Rightarrow N = 43N$

Step 4. $25.8 - 17.2 = 5a \Rightarrow a = 1.7 \text{ m/s}^2$

Pulleys

On the B-level AP test, pulleys are idealized: They are frictionless and add no inertia to the system. They serve as agents that redirect forces without otherwise affecting the dynamics.

Consider two masses connected over an idealized pulley, the so-called Atwood's machine (figure 11).

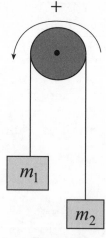

Figure 11

Before you analyze the system, let's look at two important points:

1. A real pulley will not allow for the masses to accelerate if the tensions are equal on each side of the pulley. In the limit of the idealized pulley, however, these two tensions can be considered equal, so the tension is the same throughout the rope.

2. You'll need to adopt a sign convention to determine positive and negative quantities. One approach is to focus on the pulley rotation, arbitrarily calling counterclockwise rotation positive. Forces that tend to cause this type of rotation will be positive, while those that oppose it will be negative. Similarly, accelerations that increase the rate of counterclockwise rotation will be considered positive. In figure 11, the curved arrow indicates positive direction.

Now, on to the analysis:

Step 1.

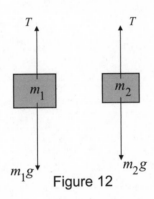

Figure 12

Step 2. $netF_1 = m_1g - T$
$netF_2 = T - m_2g$

Step 3. $m_1g - T = m_1a$
$T - m_2g = m_2a$

Step 4. $a = \dfrac{m_1 - m_2}{m_1 + m_2}g$ $\qquad$ $T = \dfrac{2m_1m_2}{m_1 + m_2}g$

Since each mass has the same acceleration, you could have found the acceleration quickly by analyzing the system as a whole. Because the tensions are internal to the system, they cancel out.

Step 2. $netF_{sys} = m_1g - T + T - m_2g$

Step 3. $m_1g - m_2g = (m_1 + m_2)a$

Step 4. $a = \dfrac{m_1 - m_2}{m_1 + m_2}g$

Circular Motion

When an object moves in a circle, it's accelerating even if its speed stays the same. This is because the velocity vector is changing direction. Consider a ball of mass m moving in a horizontal circle of radius R with a constant speed v (figure 13).

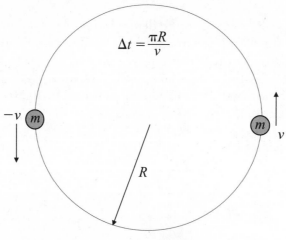

Figure 13

If you calculate the average acceleration over the time it takes to execute half a rotation, you'll see:

$$a_{av} = \frac{\Delta v}{\Delta t} = \frac{v - (-v)}{\frac{\pi R}{v}} = \left(\frac{2}{\pi}\right)\frac{v^2}{R}$$

If you had taken the average over a different interval, your result would have differed by only the factor in parentheses: $a_{av} = (different)\frac{v^2}{R}$. If you make the averaging interval very small, you'll approach the instantaneous acceleration, and in this limit the (different) factor approaches 1. For the instantaneous acceleration of an object moving at a constant speed in a circle, you have:

$$a_{cp} = \frac{v^2}{R}$$

This acceleration is directed toward the center and is called the **centripetal acceleration**. Since there is acceleration, there must be a nonzero net force present as well. The force that produces the acceleration depends on the system in question: For a ball on a string moving in a horizontal circle, it will be tension, for example, and for the Earth moving around the sun it will be gravity. But the generic name for the net force acting toward the center of an object moving in a circle is the **centripetal force**.

Keep in mind that the centripetal force is supplied by such real forces as tension and gravity. When you draw a freebody diagram for an object moving in a circle, you will still draw the usual forces present; never draw the centripetal force as a separate force. The only difference between analyzing a circular motion problem and other second law problems is that you know the direction of the acceleration immediately (toward the center), and you can express the acceleration in terms of v and R. Your first step in this analysis is to identify the center of the circle. The sum of all forces along the line connecting the object to the center will provide the centripetal force. The sum of all forces perpendicular to this direction often just adds up to 0, but if it doesn't, you can apply the second law in that direction to determine this component of the acceleration.

EXAMPLE 1

A 2 kg ball is rotated in a vertical circle by a light, rigid rod of length 3 m attached to a motor that keeps the ball moving at a constant speed of 12 m/s (figure 14). Find the tension in the rod at the highest and lowest points.

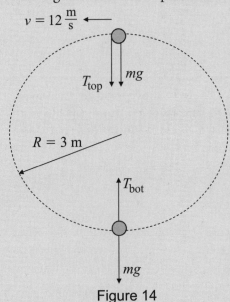

$$v = 12 \frac{m}{s}$$

$T_{top} \quad mg$

$R = 3\ m$

T_{bot}

mg

Figure 14

Top

Step 1. see figure

Step 2. $netF_{top} = T_{top} + mg$

Step 3. $T_{top} + mg = ma_{cp} = m\dfrac{v^2}{R}$

Step 4. $T_{top} = m\dfrac{v^2}{R} - mg = 76\ N$

Bottom

Step 1. see figure

Step 2. $netF_{bot} = T_{bot} - mg$

Step 3. $T_{bot} - mg = ma_{cp} = m\dfrac{v^2}{R}$

Step 4. $T_{bot} = m\dfrac{v^2}{R} + mg = 116\ N$

Choose the direction toward the center as the positive direction, and pay careful attention to the signs.

A highway curve can be banked at just the right angle so that when a car moves through the curve at just the right speed, no friction is needed between the road and tires to turn the car while it maintains the same height on the bank. Find the relation between speed and banking angle (figure 15).

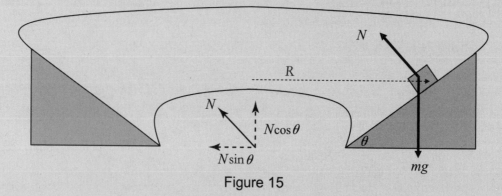

Figure 15

Note that the center of the circle is above ground level, with the circle radius parallel to the ground. You'll need to find force components along this line and perpendicular to it, since you know the accelerations along these directions.

Step 1. See figure 15.

Step 2. $netF_x = N\sin\theta$ $netF_y = N\cos\theta - mg$

Step 3. $N\sin\theta = ma_{cp} = m\dfrac{v^2}{R}$ $N\cos\theta - mg = ma_y = 0$

Step 4. $\dfrac{N\sin\theta}{N\cos\theta} = m\dfrac{\frac{v^2}{R}}{mg}$

$\tan\theta = \dfrac{v^2}{Rg}$

Statics

Statics is the study of systems in equilibrium. Often the systems to be analyzed will be at rest, although they don't have to be. There are two types of equilibrium: translational equilibrium and rotational equilibrium. You already have all the tools needed to understand translational equilibrium, but you'll need to learn the concept of torque to understand rotational equilibrium. This section presents a simple approach to torque that will enable you to analyze rotational equilibrium for the B-level AP test.

TRANSLATIONAL EQUILIBRIUM

A system is in **translational equilibrium** if the net force on the system is 0: $net\vec{F} = 0$. To analyze the system, just proceed as in any second-law problem, but use the fact that the acceleration is 0.

EXAMPLE

A 5 kg traffic light is hung from two wires as shown in figure 16. Find the tension in the wires.

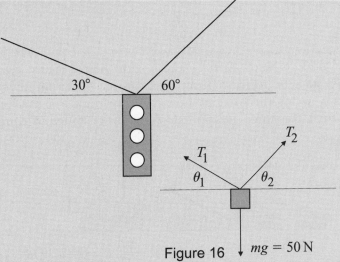

Figure 16 $mg = 50\,\text{N}$

Step 1. See figure 16.

Step 2. $netF_x = T_{1x} + T_{2x}$ $netF_y = T_{1y} + T_{2y} - mg$

$\qquad = T_1\cos\theta_1 - T_2\cos\theta_2$ $\qquad = T_1\sin\theta_1 + T_2\sin\theta_2 - mg$

Step 3. $T_1\cos\theta_1 - T_2\cos\theta_2 = 0$ $T_1\sin\theta_1 + T_2\sin\theta_2 - mg = 0$

Step 4. $T_1(0.87) - T_2(0.80) = 0$ $T_1(0.50) + T_2(0.60) - 50 = 0$

$\qquad\qquad\qquad\qquad\qquad\qquad T_1 = 43.4\,\text{N and } T_2 = 47.8\,\text{N}$

ROTATIONAL EQUILIBRUIM

Imagine a rigid rod pivoted about its left end so that it can rotate freely in a horizontal plane. You can apply a 10 N force (figure 17) in a variety of ways, and your intuition should tell you that not all of them are equally efficient in causing rotation to begin.

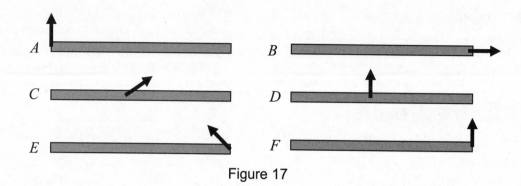

Figure 17

A and B will not work at all. D is better than C, and F is the best, because it will most easily get the rod out of its rest state to begin rotating. You can see that a number of factors are involved in this analysis: how big the force is, how far from the pivot the force is applied, and the direction in which the force is applied. A quantity called **torque** reflects this information (figure 18).

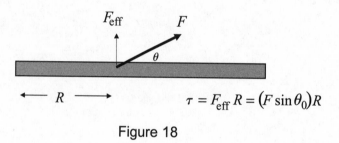

Figure 18

$$\tau_F = (F \sin\theta_0)R = F_{eff} R$$

Here F_{eff} is the component of F that is effective in causing rotation. F_{eff} is perpendicular to the line drawn from the pivot to the point where the force acts. The length of this line is R. Torques that tend to cause counterclockwise rotation are said to be positive, while negative torques will tend to cause clockwise rotation. In the preceding example, A and B had 0 torque, while F had the largest value, and in this case it was positive. When several forces act on an object, they all will exert torques about a given pivot or axis. But if the sum of all the torques, the net torque, adds up to 0, you might expect that there would be no tendency to rotate. In fact, this is the condition for **rotational equilibrium**: $net\tau = 0$ about any axis. While the axis you choose could be anywhere in principle, in practice a given problem will usually have a clear best choice. If there is no clear pivot point, choose a place where several forces act. Since their distance from the axis will be 0, their contribution to the torque will be 0.

When you're dealing with rotational equilibrium, you have to address the torque exerted by gravity. In general, to work with this, you'll need to use the concept of center of mass. To handle basic equilibrium problems involving regular shaped objects, however, it's enough to know that the object's center of mass lies at the geometric center and that the weight can be considered as acting at this point when you calculate torques. Gravity will exert 0 torque about this point.

Finally, there's another way to think of torque that can be useful in some problems. You can rearrange the formula for torque this way:

$$\tau_F = (F\sin\theta)R = F(R\sin\theta) = FR_{\text{eff}}$$

Here R_{eff}, also called the lever arm, is the perpendicular distance from the axis to the line of action (figure 19) of the force.

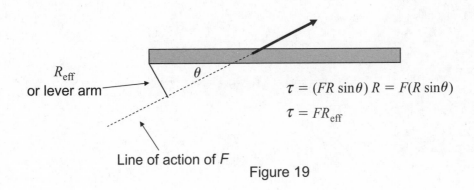

$\tau = (FR\sin\theta)\,R = F(R\sin\theta)$

$\tau = FR_{\text{eff}}$

Figure 19

EXAMPLE

A uniform rod of mass 12 kg and length 6 m is attached at one end to a wall and is partially supported by a guy wire attached at the end as pictured (figure 20). A 20 kg mass is suspended by a rope wrapped around the rod, 4 m from the wall. Find the tension in the guy wire.

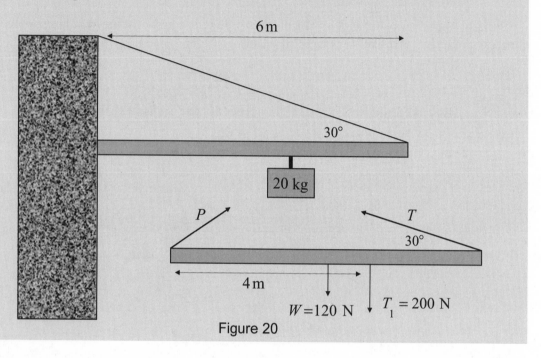

Figure 20

The strategy will be to analyze the rod, applying the condition of rotational equilibrium to it. You'll need to draw a freebody diagram (see figure 20). Notice that the diagram must reflect the different points where forces are applied: A single point is not enough to represent the object. A force $\overline{P}$, probably a result of normal and frictional forces, acts at the wall-rod connection, but if you choose this as your axis, it will exert 0 torque. For a uniform rod, the force of gravity can be considered as acting at the center of the rod. For this axis, you can write:

$$net\tau = (T\sin30)(6) - 200(4) - 120(3) = 0$$
$$T = 387 \text{ N}$$

KEY FORMULAS

Newton's Second Law	$net\vec{F} = m\vec{a}$
Kinetic Friction	$f_k = \mu_k N$
Static Friction	$f_s \leq \mu_s N$
Weight	$W = mg$
Translational Equilibruim	$netF_x = netF_y = 0$
Torque	$\tau = RF_{\text{eff}} = R_{\text{eff}}F = RF\sin\theta$
Rotational Equilibrium	$net\tau = 0$
Centripetal Acceleration	$a_{cp} = \dfrac{v^2}{R}$

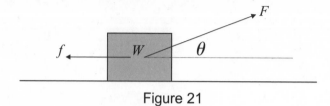

Figure 21

1. A weight W is pulled by a rope at an angle θ across a horizontal surface where the coefficient of kinetic friction is μ. Which of the following is true for the friction force f acting on the mass?

   (A) $f = \mu W$
   (B) $f = \mu(W + F\sin\theta)$
   (C) $f = \mu(W + F\cos\theta)$
   (D) $f = \mu(W - F\sin\theta)$
   (E) $f \leq \mu(W - F\cos\theta)$

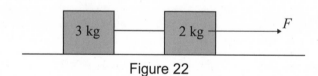

Figure 22

2. A tension T exists in the rope connecting the two masses. The value of F is

   (A) $\dfrac{3}{2}T$

   (B) $\dfrac{3}{5}T$

   (C) T

   (D) $\dfrac{5}{3}T$

   (E) $\dfrac{5}{2}T$

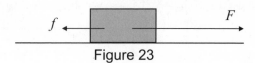

Figure 23

3. When $F = 8$ N, the 4 kg mass accelerates to the right at 1 m/s². If F is doubled to 16 N, the acceleration will be

(A) $1\dfrac{m}{s^2}$

(B) $2\dfrac{m}{s^2}$

(C) $3\dfrac{m}{s^2}$

(D) $4\dfrac{m}{s^2}$

(E) $0.5\dfrac{m}{s^2}$

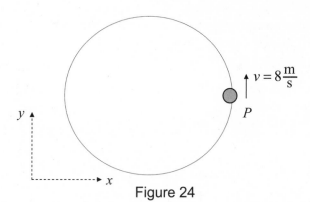

Figure 24

4. A 3 kg mass is moving in a vertical circle of radius 4 m at a constant speed of 8 m/s. At point P, the magnitude and direction of the centripetal acceleration are given by

(A) $16\dfrac{m}{s^2} + y$

(B) $48\dfrac{m}{s^2} - x$

(C) $16\dfrac{m}{s^2} - y$

(D) $16\dfrac{m}{s^2} - x$

(E) $48\dfrac{m}{s^2} + y$

5. Two teams engage in a tug-of-war with a rope held horizontal. Which is true of the winning team?

   (A) They were stronger.
   (B) They had more mass.
   (C) They exerted a greater tension force through the rope.
   (D) They exerted a greater force on the ground parallel to the surface.
   (E) They exerted a greater force on the ground perpendicular to the surface.

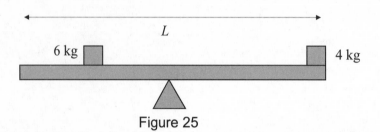

Figure 25

6. A 10 kg uniform plank of length L is pivoted at its center. A 4 kg mass is to be placed on the right end. How far from the pivot must a 6 kg mass be placed to keep the plank in equilibrium?

   (A) $\dfrac{L}{2}$

   (B) $\dfrac{L}{4}$

   (C) $\dfrac{3L}{4}$

   (D) $\dfrac{L}{3}$

   (E) $\dfrac{2L}{3}$

7. A 3 kg mass moving at 6 m/s is brought to rest in 2 s. The magnitude of the net force acting on the mass is

   (A) 18 N
   (B) 9 N
   (C) 6 N
   (D) 12 N
   (E) 36 N

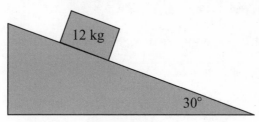

Figure 26

8. A 12 kg mass is at rest on a 30° incline where the coefficient of static friction is 0.8. The friction force exerted on the mass is most nearly

(A) 120 N
(B) 104 N
(C) 83 N
(D) 60 N
(E) 96 N

9. A pendulum consists of a rope of length 2 m and a bob of mass 4 kg. It moves through its lowest point with a speed of 6 m/s. The tension in the rope is most nearly

(A) 40 N
(B) 72 N
(C) 32 N
(D) 112 N
(E) 48 N

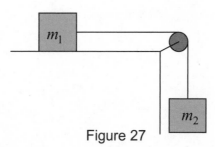

Figure 27

10. Assuming no friction, to double the current value of the system acceleration, you can
    I. double the value of m_2
    II. halve the value of m_1
    III. halve the value of $(m_1 + m_2)$ by adjusting m_1 only

(A) I only
(B) II only
(C) III only
(D) I and II
(E) I and III

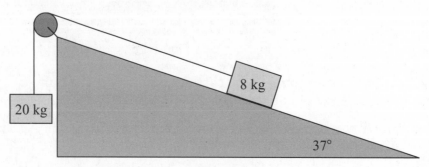

Figure 28

1. In the diagram, the 8 kg mass moves up the incline where the coefficient of kinetic friction is 0.4. Assume an ideal pulley.

    (a) Determine the friction force acting on the 8 kg mass.

    (b) Determine the acceleration of each mass.

    (c) Determine the tension in the connecting rope.

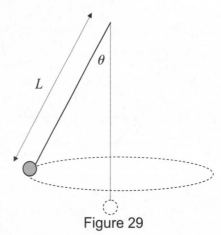

Figure 29

2. A mass m is attached to a length L of string and hung straight down from a pivot. Small vibrations at the pivot set the mass into circular motion, with the string making an angle θ with the vertical.

    (a) Draw and label all forces acting on the object.

    (b) Obtain an expression for the speed v of the mass in terms of θ, L, and g.

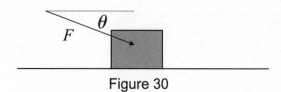

Figure 30

3. A force is applied at an angle θ below the horizontal to a mass m resting on a horizontal surface where the coefficients of friction are μ_s and μ_k. The magnitude of F is slowly increased until the mass just starts to move. At this point its acceleration is a_0. Calculate the following in terms of μ_s, μ_k, θ, m, and g.

(a) Determine the value of F where movement just begins.

(b) Determine a_0.

Answers and Explanations

MULTIPLE CHOICE

1. The answer is D. The vertical component of F is $F\sin\theta$. In the y-direction you then have $netF_y = 0 = N + F\sin\theta - W \Rightarrow N = W - F\sin\theta$.

2. The answer is D. $T = (3m)a \Rightarrow a = \frac{T}{3m}$. For the system you have: $F = (5m)a \Rightarrow F = \frac{5}{3}T$.

3. The answer is C. Applying the second law, you have: $netF = 8 - f = 4(1) \Rightarrow f = 4$ N. When F is doubled, the friction force doesn't change, so you have $netF = 16 - f = 12 = 4a \quad a = 3\frac{m}{s^2}$.

4. The answer is D. At P the center is in the $-x$ direction and $a_{cp} = \frac{8^2}{4} = 16\frac{m}{s^2}$.

5. The answer is D. The tension force is the same for each team as a result of the third law, so only by pushing harder parallel to the ground can a team win. Strength and mass need not be a factor; imagine a football team on in-line skates.

6. The answer is D. Choose the center of the plank to calculate torques, because here the weight of the plank exerts no torque. Then $0 = net\tau = 40\frac{L}{2} - 60x \Rightarrow x = \frac{L}{3}$.

7. The answer is B. Find the acceleration: $a = \frac{\Delta v}{\Delta t} = \frac{0 - 6}{2} = -3\frac{m}{s}$. Applying the second law, you have $netF = ma = 3(-3) = -9$ N.

8. The answer is D. The component of weight down the incline is $mg\sin\theta = 120(0.5) = 60$ N. For equilibrium, the static friction must just supply this value.

9. The answer is D. At the lowest point you have $netF = T - mg = m\frac{v^2}{R}$
$$T = 4\frac{6^2}{2} + 40 = 112N$$

10. The answer is E. For the system as a whole, you have from the second law $netF = m_2 g = (m_1 + m_2)a \quad a = \frac{m_2 g}{(m_1 + m_2)}$. The answer follows from inspecting the formula.

FREE RESPONSE

1. Apply the solution steps to each object (figure 31).

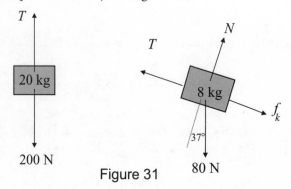

Figure 31

8 kg   20 kg

Step 1. See figure 31.   Step 1. See figure 31.

Step 2. $netF_y = N - 80\cos37$ Step 2. $netF = 220 - T$

$netF_x = T - 80\sin37 - 0.4N$

Step 3. $N - 64 = 0 \Rightarrow N = 64$ Step 3. $200 - T = 20a$

$T - 48 - 0.4(64) = 8a$

Note that the friction force is 25.6 N, the answer to part a.

Step 4. Add the equations: $-48 - 25.6 + 200 = 28a \Rightarrow a = 4.5$ m/s^2.

Substitute to find T: $200 - T = 10(4.5) \Rightarrow T = 110N$.

2. (a) See figure 32.

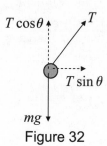

Figure 32

(b) Only the tension has a component toward the center, so

$$netF_x = m\frac{v^2}{R} \qquad\qquad netF_y = T\cos\theta - mg = 0$$

$$T\sin\theta = m\frac{v^2}{L\sin\theta} \qquad\qquad T\cos\theta = mg$$

Dividing the two equations eliminates T, and you have $v = \sqrt{g\tan\theta(L\sin\theta)}$

3. (a) Apply the basic steps to the object, remembering that when the object is just about to slide, the static friction force is at its maximum value.

Step 1. See figure 33.

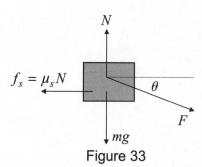

Figure 33

Step 2. $netF_x = F\cos\theta - \mu_s N$ $\qquad\qquad netF_y = N - mg - F\sin\theta$

Step 3. $N - mg - F\sin\theta = 0$

$F\cos\theta - \mu_s N = 0$

Step 4. $N = mg + F\sin\theta$

$F\cos\theta - \mu_s(mg + F\sin\theta) = 0 \Rightarrow F = \dfrac{\mu_s mg}{\cos\theta - \mu_s\sin\theta}$

(b) As acceleration begins, this is the value of F, and now it is kinetic friction acting. The analysis in steps 1, 2, and 3 is the same except for the friction name change and the fact that there is a nonzero horizontal acceleration. You can then move to Step 4 to write

$$N = mg + F\sin\theta$$

$$F\cos\theta - \mu_k(mg + F\sin\theta) = ma \Rightarrow a = \frac{F}{m}\cos\theta - \mu_k\left(g - \frac{F}{m}\sin\theta\right)$$

CHAPTER 4

Work and Energy

While Newton's laws provide a complete description of mechanical systems, applying $F = ma$ directly isn't always the easiest way to approach a problem. In this chapter and the next, you'll see that often you can determine the properties of a system directly from the initial properties, without knowing all the details of the motion between the initial and final states. This approach involves using **conservation laws**, which tell you when certain physical properties remain constant throughout the motion. Knowing how and when to apply the conservation laws is essential to doing well on the AP test. In this chapter you'll learn about mechanical energy and the conditions for its conservation.

Work

When a force acts on an object while a displacement occurs, the force has done **work** on the object. Work is a scalar quantity that has no direction associated with it, but it can be positive or negative. The magnitude of the work done will depend on the magnitude of the force, how much of it is applied along the direction of the displacement, and the magnitude of the displacement. For a constant force, you'll use the following definition (figure 1):

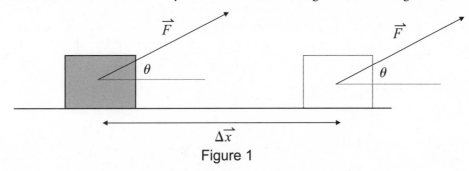

Figure 1

$$W_F = F\cos\theta\Delta x = \vec{F} \cdot \Delta\vec{x}$$

The units of work are $N \cdot m$, which is called a Joule (J).

Work and Energy 85

Determining the sign of the work done by a force is easy. If the force has a component in the direction of the displacement—for example, if the force tended to make the object undergo the displacement—then the work done by the force is positive. If the force opposes the motion, then the work done is negative. If the force acts perpendicular to the displacement, then it does zero work.

EXERCISE

Find the work done by all forces as a 4 kg mass slides 5 m down a 30° incline where the coefficient of kinetic friction is 0.3. (figure 2)

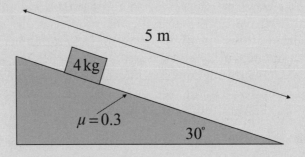

5 m

4 kg

$\mu = 0.3$

30°

Figure 2

$W_N = 0$ since it acts perpendicular to the motion

$W_{\text{grav}} = + (mg\sin\theta)\Delta x = (40)(0.5)(5) = 100 \text{ J}$

$W_{\text{fric}} = - (\mu N)\Delta x = - (\mu mg\cos\theta)\Delta x = - (0.3)(40)(0.87)(5) = -52 \text{ J}$

If you look at a graph (figure 3) of a one-dimensional constant force as a function of position, the work done has a simple interpretation: It is the area under the graph.

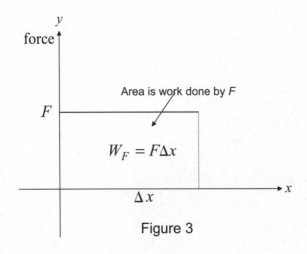

y

force

Area is work done by F

F

$W_F = F\Delta x$

Δx

x

Figure 3

When the force isn't constant but varies with the position, the work done will still be the area under the graph (figure 4). If the graph is a simple shape, you can use geometry to find the area.

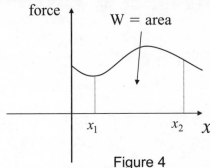

Figure 4

An important example of a nonconstant force is the elastic force exerted by a spring either in tension or in compression. Hooke's law states that the force exerted by a spring displaced an amount x from its equilibrium position is calculated as $F = -kx$. Here k is called the **spring constant**, and it measures how stiff the spring is. Since a graph of F vs. x is a straight line through the origin, the area under the graph from 0 to some point x is just the area of a triangle (figure 5). This means the magnitude of the work done by a spring displaced x from the equilibrium point will be as follows:

$$W_{spring} = \frac{1}{2}kx^2$$

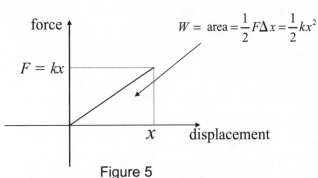

Figure 5

Power

Power is the rate at which work is done. For a force doing an amount of work ΔW_F over a time interval Δt, the average power delivered is

$$P = \frac{\Delta W_F}{\Delta t} \quad \text{The units of power are } \frac{J}{s} = \text{Watt}$$

To determine instantaneous power delivered, you'll need to average over a very small interval. For a constant force, $P = \frac{F\cos\theta \Delta x}{\Delta t} = F\cos\theta v = \vec{F} \cdot \vec{v}$. Letting the interval be infinitesimally small, v is the instantaneous speed, and P is then the instantaneous power delivered.

EXAMPLE

Find the instantaneous power delivered by gravity to a 4 kg mass 2 s after it has fallen from rest.

The force and velocity are collinear, so $\cos\theta = 1$.

$$v = gt = 20\frac{m}{s} \qquad P = Fv = (mg)v = (40)20 = 800 \text{ W}$$

Notice that the instantaneous power delivered by gravity is not a constant even though the force is constant. Of course, this is because the velocity is changing.

Kinetic Energy

Up to this point, "work" has been just a new definition. If you look at the work done by the net force on the system, however, you can derive a relation that will be equivalent to Newton's second law but without the explicit appearance of acceleration. Let's consider a one-dimensional example (figure 6) in which a mass is accelerated through some displacement by the constant net force acting on it.

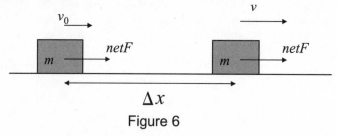

Figure 6

$$W_{netF} = netF \cdot \Delta x = ma\Delta x$$

You can use a motion equation to obtain

$$W_{netF} = ma\left(\frac{v^2 - v_0^2}{2a}\right) = \frac{1}{2}mv^2 - \frac{1}{2}mv_0{}^2$$

(Note that the acceleration cancels out.)

With the **kinetic energy** of an object defined as $K = \frac{1}{2}mv^2$, this relation becomes

$$W_{netF} = \Delta K$$

This relation is called the **work-energy theorem**.

EXAMPLE

Figure 7: A 10 kg mass is moving at 5 m/s over a rough surface. A 50 N horizontal tension force causes it to accelerate to 8 m/s while traveling 6 m. Find the coefficient of kinetic friction.

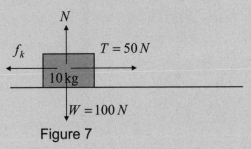

Figure 7

$$N - 100 = 0 \Rightarrow N = 100N$$

$$W_{netF} = (50 - f_k)(6) = (50)(6) - (F_k)(6) = W_T + W_f$$

$$300 - \mu(100)6 = \Delta K = \tfrac{1}{2}(10)(8)^2 - \tfrac{1}{2}(10)(5)^2 = 195J$$

$$\mu = \frac{105}{600} = 0.18$$

In the second step, note that the work done by the net force equals the sum of the works done by each individual force acting:

$$W_{netF} = W_T + W_f = W_{total}$$

This will always be the case because the two sides of the equation differ only in the order in which math operations are performed. On the left side you add the force components first, then multiply by the displacement; on the right side you multiply each force component by the displacement, then add them up.

Conservative Forces

Suppose a mass is moved from ground level to a height H. You can calculate the work done by gravity for this process, assuming that the mass is raised directly to the final height (figure 8).

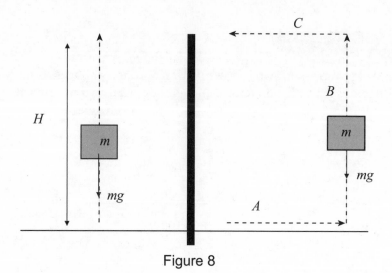

Figure 8

Since the constant force of gravity acts opposite to the displacement, the result is $W_{grav} = -mgH$. Now suppose the mass doesn't move directly to the final height but follows the paths A→B→C. Since gravity does no work along paths A and C and the work done along path B is the same as the direct path, then the work done in this process is the same. In fact, no matter what path you choose between two points, the work done by gravity will always be the same. Forces that meet this condition are called **conservative forces**, and gravity is an example of a conservative force. The elastic forces associated with springs are also conservative. Because the work done by these forces is path-independent, the work can depend on only the endpoints of the path. This means that the work done by such forces is always 0 for a path that ends at the beginning point (closed path), since the work is obviously 0 if there is no displacement at all.

Forces also can be nonconservative, meaning that the work they do *does* depend on the path taken between the endpoints. Dissipative forces such as friction and air resistance are examples of nonconservative forces. For example, the work done by kinetic friction as a mass moves over a horizontal surface depends on the total length of the path: $W_f = -f(\text{length})$. Obviously, an infinite number of possible paths of different lengths can connect two points on the surface. Similarly, the work done by the tension in a rope will depend on the path taken.

Potential Energy

It's possible to do work on an object and never change the kinetic energy. For example, you could very slowly lift a mass to some height above the ground. You'd have to perform work $W = mgH$ to get the mass there, because you'd apply a force just equal to mg to keep the mass moving up at a very slow but constant speed. Intuitively, you might expect that the work done could be "retrieved" by letting the mass fall and gain kinetic energy.

You can apply the same analysis to stretching a spring-mass system. If you slowly pull the mass out an amount x from the equilibrium position, you must do work $W = \frac{1}{2}kx^2$. Once again, you might expect that this work could be "retrieved" by releasing the mass and letting the spring contract. In these cases, the work you put into the system is stored as **potential energy** (PE). Potential energy is energy associated with the position of the system.

Not all work that's put into slowly positioning a system, however, is "retrievable." If you slowly push a mass in a straight line across a rough horizontal surface, you do work $W = f_k\Delta x$. But when you release the mass, it just sits there; the work you put into positioning it does not reappear as kinetic energy (KE). Only with conservative forces can you get back in KE the work you put into positioning, so it is only for these forces that you can meaningfully define the potential energy.

For conservative forces, the change in PE, ΔU, is the amount of work it takes to slowly change the position of the system. Since slow change implies that the agent doing the positioning applies a force just opposite to the conservative force F, it follows that

$$\Delta U = -W_f$$

Only the change in the PE is defined because only changes in energy can be measured. You are free to choose the zero point of PE associated with a force at any convenient point. For example, if you're dropping objects to the floor, it makes sense to call the floor the zero point of gravitational PE. On the other hand, if you're dropping objects onto a desk, you might decide to call the desktop the zero point.

The definition of potential energy now leads to two important formulas for PE:

$$U_{\text{grav}} = mgh \quad \text{where } h \text{ is measured from the arbitrary zero point}$$

$$U_{\text{spring}} = \frac{1}{2}kx^2 \quad \text{where } x \text{ is measured from the equilibrium point}$$

Conservation of Energy

Suppose a single conservative force F does work on a mass. The work-energy theorem is $W_F = \Delta K$. But because the force is conservative, you'll have $W_F = -\Delta U$. Combining them, you get

$$-\Delta U = \Delta K$$
$$0 = \Delta K + \Delta U = \Delta(K + U)$$

This means that the quantity $K + U$, the sum of the kinetic and potential energies, doesn't change. This quantity is called the **total mechanical energy** E.

$$E = K + U$$

If several conservative forces are acting, U is just the sum of each potential energy, and if only conservative forces are doing work on the system, you can apply the law of **conservation of mechanical energy:**

$$E_i = E_f$$

As the system moves under the influence of conservative forces, the individual amounts of kinetic and potential energies change, but the sum of all of them stays the same.

EXAMPLE

A 4 kg mass is fired from ground level with a speed of 50 m/s at an angle of 37° with the horizontal. A smooth horizontal platform is placed at the correct position so that the mass will land on it at the highest point of its motion.
It then slides into a spring with $k = 1,600$ N/m.
  (a) Find the total energy of the mass.
  (b) Find the height of the platform.
  (c) Find the maximum spring compression.

(a) After the mass is fired, only gravity and elastic spring forces do work on the mass. The normal force exerted by the platform does no work as it acts perpendicular to the motion. At the initial projection, $E_i = \frac{1}{2}(4)(50)^2 = 5,000$ J, and this will remain constant over the motion.

(b) At the highest point of the motion, only the x-component of the velocity is present, $v_x = 50\cos37 = 40$ m/s. To find the height of the platform, you can use energy conservation:

$$E_1 = E_2$$

$$5,000 = \frac{1}{2}mv^2 + mgh = \frac{1}{2}(4)(40)^2 + (4)(10)h$$

$$h = 45\text{m}$$

(c) Upon full compression, the energy is all potential, and you can apply energy conservation again.

$$E_1 = E_2$$

$$5,000 = mgh + \frac{1}{2}kx^2 = (4)(10)(45) + \frac{1}{2}(1,600)x^2$$

$$x = 2\text{m}$$

Graphs of Potential Energy

Many systems in mechanics can be described by a potential energy function that depends on only one variable. With a graph of this potential energy, you can make some specific statements about the motion of the system. Consider the graph of the spring PE: $U = \frac{1}{2}kx^2$ (figure 9).

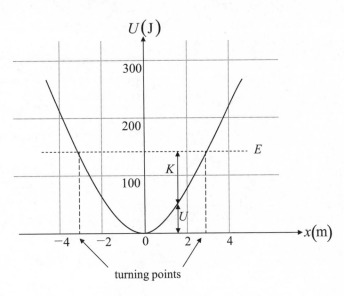

Figure 9

The following statements apply to any such graph:

1. For a given total energy E, turning points of the motion will occur where the energy is all potential. This happens where the graph intersects the horizontal total energy line. In this case, you have

$$E = \frac{1}{2}kx^2 \Rightarrow x = \pm \sqrt{\frac{2E}{k}}$$

2. The vertical separation between the curve and the total energy line is the KE of the system at that point, based on $K = E - U$.

3. Where the graph reaches maxima or minima, the force will be 0, and stable equilibrium points will be located at the minima. For this graph, $x = 0$ is a point of stable equilibrium. Here a small displacement in either direction will result in a force that tends to restore the object to $x = 0$ again.

In describing the motion of an object moving under the influence of a potential, imagine a bead sliding along the curve. It would slow down and speed up in the same way the system would.

KEY FORMULAS

Work	$W_F = F\cos\theta\Delta x \qquad W_F = \vec{F} \cdot \vec{\Delta x}$
Power	$P_F = \dfrac{\Delta W_F}{\Delta t} = F\cos\theta v = \vec{F} \cdot \vec{v}$
Kinetic Energy	$K = \dfrac{1}{2}mv^2$
Work-Energy Theorem	$W_{\text{total}} = \Delta K$
Potential Energy	$\Delta U = -W_F$
PE Gravity	$U_{\text{grav}} = mgh$
PE Spring	$U_{\text{spring}} = \dfrac{1}{2}kx^2$
Total Mechanical Energy	$E = K + U$
Conservation of Energy	$E_i = E_f$

PRACTICE EXERCISES

SECTION I MULTIPLE CHOICE

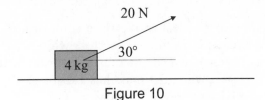

Figure 10

1. A 4-kg mass accelerates 6 m across a frictionless surface under the influence of a 20 N force as shown in figure 10. The work done over this interval is

   (A) $10\sqrt{3}\,$J   (B) $60\sqrt{3}\,$J   (C) $10\frac{\sqrt{3}}{2}\,$J   (D) 60 J   (E) 120 J

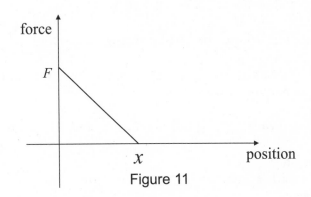

Figure 11

2. Starting from the origin with speed v_0, a mass m moves in one dimension under the influence of the force shown in the figure. When the mass reaches x, its kinetic energy will be

   (A) $\frac{1}{2}Fx + \frac{1}{2}mv_0^2$

   (B) $\frac{1}{2}Fx$

   (C) $Fx + \frac{1}{2}mv_0^2$

   (D) Fx

   (E) $\frac{1}{2}Fx - \frac{1}{2}mv_0^2$

3. Starting from rest and a height of 10 m, a 2 kg mass slides down a 30° incline, reaching the bottom with a speed of 10 m/s. What is the approximate work done by friction?

    (A) 0   (B) $-10\sqrt{3}$ (C) -100 J   (D) -200 J
    (E) cannot be determined without the coefficient of friction

4. A mass is attached to an ideal spring on a smooth horizontal surface. It is displaced an amount Δx_0 and released. Which of the following is true?
    I. The KE is largest when the mass passes through the equilibrium point.
    II. The PE is largest when the mass has a displacement of $\pm \Delta x_0$.
    III. The PE and KE will never be equal.

    (A) I only   (B) II only   (C) III only   (D) I and II only   (E) I and III only

5. A 2-kg mass is raised 6 m at a constant speed of 3 m/s by a vertical rope. The power supplied by the rope is most nearly

    (A) 120 W   (B) 360 W   (C) 6 W   (D) 36 W   (E) 60 W

6. When is total mechanical energy of a system conserved?
    I. always
    II. when nonconservative forces are present but do no work
    III. when nonconservative forces are not present

    (A) I only   (B) II only   (C) III only   (D) I, II, and III   (E) II and III only

Questions 7 and 8
    A 4-kg mass with a total energy of 150 J moves under the influence of the potential energy shown below.

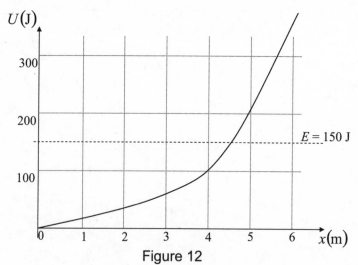

Figure 12

7. At $x = 4$, the speed of the mass is closest to

    (A) 4 m/s   (B) 5 m/s   (C) 25 m/s   (D) 50 m/s   (E) 100 m/s

8. When the mass is at $x = 4$, the displacement it must undergo to reach its maximum x-coordinate is closest to

    (A) 0   (B) 4.5 m   (C) 0.5 m   (D) 2 m   (E) -4.5 m

9. A 4-kg mass initially moving at 5 m/s slides across a horizontal surface where the force of kinetic friction on the mass is 12 N. After 1 s, the rate at which the mass loses mechanical energy is

    (A) 50 W   (B) 12 W   (C) 60 W   (D) 24 W   (E) 0

10. A 3-kg mass is attached to a light string 2 m long and hung vertically to make a simple pendulum. The pendulum is displaced until the string is horizontal and then released. What is the approximate speed of the pendulum at its lowest point?

    (A) 5 m/s
    (B) 6 m/s
    (C) 7 m/s
    (D) 8 m/s
    (E) cannot be determined because the tension is a nonconservative force

CHAPTER 4 PRACTICE EXERCISES

SECTION II FREE RESPONSE

Figure 13

1. A 2-kg mass is pushed 0.5 m into a spring with spring constant 200 N/m on a frictionless horizontal surface. Upon release, the mass travels across the surface until it encounters a rough incline. The mass moves up the incline and stops at a height of 1 m above the horizontal surface.
   (a) How much work must be done to compress the spring initially?
   (b) Find the speed of the mass at the base of the incline.
   (c) How much work was done by friction on the incline?

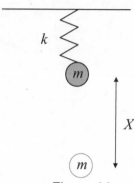

Figure 14

2. A spring with spring constant k is hung vertically. A mass m is gently attached to it and released in such a way that the spring is unstretched upon release. The mass descends to a maximum spring extension X. Respond to the following in terms of m, k, and g.

(a) Determine X.
(b) Determine the speed of the mass at $\frac{1}{4}X$, where the mass has moved through $\frac{1}{4}$ the maximum extension.
(c) Determine the maximum speed of the mass.

3. A mass m is dropped from a height H onto a hard, flat surface. When it collides with the surface, it rebounds with the same speed it had before the collision. However, there is a constant force of air resistance f acting on the mass as it undergoes this motion. Answer the following in terms of f, m, H, and g.

(a) How fast is the mass moving just before it hits for the first time?
(b) How high does the mass after the first collision?
(c) After many bounces, the ball comes to rest on the surface. While its overall displacement was $-H$, it traveled a considerably larger distance. Determine the total distance traveled by the ball.

Answers and Explanations

MULTIPLE CHOICE

1. The answer is B. The component of the force in the direction of the displacement is $20\cos 30 = 10\sqrt{3}$. The work done is $60\sqrt{3}$.

2. The answer is A. The work done is the area of the triangle $\frac{1}{2}Fx$. According to the work energy theorem, $\frac{1}{2}Fx = \Delta K \Rightarrow K = \frac{1}{2}Fx + \frac{1}{2}mv_0{}^2$

3. The answer is C. Using the work-energy theorem, you get

$$W_{total} = \Delta K$$

$$\Rightarrow W_{fric} = -100J$$

$$W_{grav} + W_{fric} = \frac{1}{2}mv^2 - 0$$

$$(2)(10)(10) + W_{fric} = \frac{1}{2}(2)(10^2)$$

4. The answer is D. III is not true because there will always be two places where KE = PE, one on either side of the equilibrium point.

5. The answer is E. The tension force must equal 20 N, the weight, since there is no acceleration; then $P_T = Tv = (20)(3) = 60$ W.

6. The answer is E. If nonconservative forces such as friction or tension are present, then the mechanical energy will, in general, not be conserved. An exception, however, is when the nonconservative forces don't do any work. One example of this is the tension force supplying centripetal force. It acts at right angles to the motion and so does no work.

7. The answer is B. At $x = 4$, the kinetic energy is 50 J, the difference between the total energy and the potential energy at that point. Then $50 = \frac{1}{2}(4)v^2 \Rightarrow v = 5$ m/s

8. The answer is C. The maximum x-coordinate of the mass occurs at $x = 4.5$ m, when the total energy equals the potential energy. Since the mass is at $x = 4$, it must move only 0.5 m to reach this point.

9. The answer is D. The acceleration of the mass follows from the second law.
$$netF = ma$$
$$-12 = 4a \Rightarrow a = -3\frac{m}{s^2}$$
Using the first motion equation, you see that the velocity after 1 s is $v = 5 - 3(1) = 2$ m/s. Then the instantaneous power delivered by fiction has a magnitude given by
$$P = fv = (12)(2) = 24W$$

10. The answer is B. You can use energy conservation because the tension does no work.

$$E_i = E_f$$

$$\Rightarrow v = \sqrt{2gh} = \sqrt{40} = 6.3 \frac{m}{s}$$

$$mgh = \frac{1}{2}mv^2$$

FREE RESPONSE

1. (a) $W = +\frac{1}{2}kx^2 = \frac{1}{2}(200)(0.5)^2 = 25$ J

   (b) Energy is conserved until the incline is encountered.
   $$E_i = E_f$$
   $$25 = \frac{1}{2}mv^2 = \frac{1}{2}(2)v^2 \qquad \Rightarrow v = 5\,\frac{m}{s}$$

   (c) You could use the work-energy theorem applied from the beginning where the KE is 0, to the end, where the KE is also 0. The spring, gravity, and friction do work, resulting in
   $$W_{total} = \Delta K$$
   $$W_{spring} + W_{grav} + W_{fric} = \quad 0 \Rightarrow W_{fric} = -5\text{ J}$$
   $$+ 25 - (2)(10)(1) + W_{fric} = 0$$

2. (a) Energy will be conserved throughout the motion. For A, call the zero point for gravity the point of maximum extension.
   $$E_0 = E_f$$
   $$mgX = \frac{1}{2}kX^2 \qquad \Rightarrow X = \frac{2mg}{k}$$

   (b) Now call $x = \frac{1}{4}X$ the zero point for gravity. Then, relative to this point
   $$E_0 = E_f$$
   $$mg\left(\frac{1}{4}X\right) = \frac{1}{2}mv^2 + \frac{1}{2}k\left(\frac{X}{4}\right)^2 \qquad \text{plug in X: } v = \sqrt{\frac{7mg^2}{8k}}$$

   (c) As the mass descends, it will gain speed until the spring force is large enough to start slowing it down, when the spring force is just equal to the gravity force: $kx = mg \Rightarrow x = \frac{mg}{k}$. Now you can use energy conservation again, with this point as the zero point for gravity.
   $$E_0 = E_f$$
   $$mg(x) = \frac{1}{2}mv^2 + \frac{1}{2}k(x)^2 \qquad \text{plug in for x: } v = \sqrt{\frac{mg^2}{k}}$$

3. (a) Since energy is not conserved, you could use the work-energy theorem applied over the first drop interval.
   $$W_{total} = \Delta K$$
   $$W_{grav} + W_f = \frac{1}{2}mv^2 - 0$$
   $$mgH - fH = \frac{1}{2}mv^2 \Rightarrow v = \sqrt{2gH - \frac{2fH}{m}}$$

(b) At the peak of the first bounce, the KE is again zero. If Δy is the difference in height from the start to the top of the first bounce, then the work-energy theorem tells you

$$W_{total} = \Delta K$$

$$W_{grav} + W_f = 0 - 0$$

$$mg\Delta y - f(2H - \Delta y) = 0 \Rightarrow \Delta y = \frac{2f}{mg + f} H$$

Then the height reached at the peak is
$$H - \Delta y = \frac{mg - f}{mg + f}$$

(c) Apply the work-energy theorem over the entire time during which the motion occurs. The final and initial KE will both be 0. Letting s be the total distance traveled by the mass, you have

$$W_{total} = \Delta K$$

$$W_{grav} + W_f = 0$$

$$mgH - fs = 0 \Rightarrow s = \frac{mgh}{f}$$

CHAPTER 5

Impulse and Momentum

This chapter introduces the concept of linear momentum. Unlike energy, momentum is a vector quantity, but like energy, momentum has a conservation law. The condition for momentum conservation is different from that for energy, and it's important to learn not only how to apply the law, but also how to recognize when the law can be applied to a particular system. The last section in the chapter includes an introduction to angular momentum at the B level.

Impulse

When a force acts on an object over a certain time period, the force has delivered an **impulse** to the object. For constant forces, the exact definition is

$$\vec{J}_F = \vec{F}\Delta t$$

Here, $\vec{J}_F$ is the impulse delivered by the force F over the time Δt, a vector quantity. For a one-dimensional constant force, a graph (figure 1) of F vs. t over the interval leads to a simple interpretation of the impulse: It is the area under the curve.

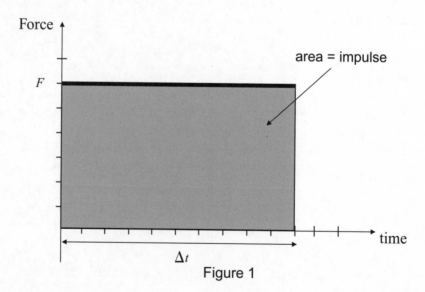

Figure 1

This property is true even if the force isn't constant. In a graph of force component vs. time, for example, the area under the force graph will be the component of the impulse delivered.

Linear Momentum

On its own, impulse isn't that significant. But if you look at the impulse delivered by the net force, you can apply Newton's second law to get a useful relation. In one dimension with constant forces, you have

$$J_{netF} = netF\Delta t = ma\Delta t = m\left(\frac{v - v_0}{\Delta t}\right)\Delta t = mv - mv_0$$

If you define the **linear momentum** to be $\vec{p} = m\vec{v}$, then you have $J_{netF} = \Delta p$, or in two or more dimensions:

$$\vec{J}_{netF} = \Delta\vec{p}$$

This is sometimes called the impulse-momentum theorem. It's really a restatement of the second law in the language of impulse and momentum.

EXERCISE

Find the rebound speed of a 0.5 kg ball falling straight down that hits the floor moving at 5 m/s, if the average normal force exerted by the floor on the ball is 205 N for 0.02 s.

$$J_{netF} = \Delta p$$

$$(N - W)\Delta t = mv - mv_0$$

$$(205 - 5)(0.02) = 0.5v - 0.5(-5) \Rightarrow v = 3\frac{m}{s}$$

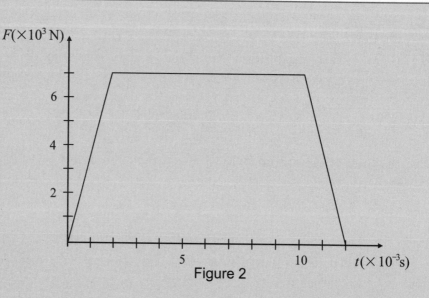

Figure 2

A 5 kg mass moving at 10 m/s in the $+x$ direction is acted upon by a force acting in the $-x$ direction with magnitude given as a function of time by the graph (figure 2). Determine the speed and direction of the mass after the force has stopped acting.

The area under the graph is 70 N s (rectangle and two triangles), so this is the magnitude of the impulse delivered to the mass. Since the force acted in the $-x$ direction, the vector value is -70 N · s. You can write:

$$J_{netF} = \Delta p$$

$$-70 = 5v - 5(10) \Rightarrow v = -4\frac{m}{s}$$

Conservation of Momentum

Now let's look at systems that consist of several objects interacting with each other (for example, collisions). Allow for the possibility that there may be other forces acting on these objects besides the forces they exert on each other. For such a system with internal and external forces acting on it, you can define the total linear momentum as the vector sum of the momentum of each individual object:

$$\vec{P}_{total} = \vec{p}_1 + \vec{p}_2 + \ldots$$

In the Newton's laws chapter, you saw that when you're considering the net force acting on an entire system, you need to include only the forces external to the system. The internal forces that different parts of the system exert on each other always occur in action-reaction pairs that cancel out when added over the entire system. Since the impulse-momentum theorem is just a restatement of the second law, it's not surprising that there's an analogous result for the impulse delivered by the net force. When the entire system is considered, only the impulse delivered by the forces external to the system needs to be included. Internal impulses will cancel out in pairs as a result of the third law.

$$\Delta \vec{P}_{\text{total}} = \vec{J}_{\text{ext}}$$

If there are no external forces to the system or if the impulse they deliver is negligible, then the **conservation of momentum principle** applies:

$$\Delta \vec{P}_{\text{total}} = 0 \Rightarrow \vec{P}^i_{\text{total}} = \vec{P}^f_{\text{total}}$$

In the absence of external forces, the total linear momentum will stay the same. As individual objects in the system interact, their individual momenta change, but the sum of all remains constant. Keep in mind that this is a vector equation; if no external forces are present for a particular direction, the momentum component in that direction is conserved.

Notice the difference between the energy and momentum conservation conditions. For a system's energy to be conserved, external forces may be present, but they have to be of a particular type, the so-called conservative forces. For momentum conservation, no external forces can be present at all on the system.

It's worth mentioning that when the mechanical energy of a system isn't conserved, it doesn't simply disappear. The mechanical energy will be transferred to some other system, perhaps in some other form. For example, the kinetic energy lost by a mass sliding over a rough surface can be accounted for in the internal energy associated with the molecular motions within the mass and the surface. Similarly, when the linear momentum of a system isn't conserved, that linear momentum will be transferred to some other system. It's always possible, however, to extend the system to include all the momentum and energy transfers, so that in this larger sense, energy and linear momentum are always conserved. But if the system has to be extended too much, applying the conservation principles to solve problems may not be the most efficient technique.

Collisions

ONE DIMENSION

Collisions are a common application of this concept. Consider a one-dimensional example: A 4 kg mass moving in the $+x$ direction at 10 m/s collides head-on with a 2-kg mass moving at 6 m/s in the $-x$ direction. Determine the final speeds and directions of the masses.

$$P^i_{total} = P^f_{total}$$

$$m_1 v_{1i} + m_2 v_{2i} = m_1 v_{1f} + m_2 v_{2f}$$

$$4(10) + 2(-6) = 4v_{1f} + 2v_{2f}$$

$$14 = 2v_{1f} + v_{2f}$$

You can't proceed further, however, without more information. If you knew one of the final velocities, you could plug it in to get the other, but in general there are an infinite number of possibilities consistent with momentum conservation. The masses could be bouncy steel balls or mushy balls of clay; even with the same initial velocities, the results would obviously be much different.

Sometimes the extra information is provided as a condition on the kinetic energy in the collision. If the total kinetic energy is conserved, the collision is **elastic**. From the definition of KE you have

$$\frac{1}{2} m_1 v_{1i}^2 + \frac{1}{2} m_2 v_{2i}^2 = \frac{1}{2} m_1 v_{1f}^2 + \frac{1}{2} m_2 v_{2f}^2$$

You can combine this equation with momentum conservation, $m_1 v_{1i} + m_2 v_{2i} = m_1 v_{1f} + m_2 v_{2f}$, to derive a third equation that has a simple interpretation:

$$v_{1i} - v_{2i} = -(v_{1f} - v_{2f})$$

This simple equation says that the relative velocity of the two objects $v_1 - v_2$ changes direction but maintains the same magnitude in an elastic, one-dimensional collision.

EXAMPLE

Suppose the previous collision was elastic. What are the final velocities?

$$14 = 2v_{1f} + v_{2f}$$

$$v_{1i} - v_{2i} = -(v_{1f} - v_{2f})$$

$$10 - (-6) = v_{2f} - v_{1f}$$

$$16 = v_{2f} - v_{1f}$$

Solving simultaneously gives:

$$v_{1f} = -0.67 \frac{m}{s}$$

$$v_{2f} = 15.33 \frac{m}{s}$$

It's possible for two objects to stick together in a collision. This is called a **totally inelastic collision**. Much of the kinetic energy initially in the bodies is lost and goes into the work done by internal forces within the objects as they deform and perhaps get warmer. Since there is only one common final velocity, the momentum conservation condition alone allows you to determine it.

EXAMPLE

Suppose the previous collision was totally inelastic. What is the final speed, and what fraction of the original kinetic energy is lost?

$$P^i_{total} = P^f_{total} \qquad KE_i = \tfrac{1}{2}(4)(10)^2 + \tfrac{1}{2}(2)(-6)^2 = 236 \text{ J}$$

$$4(10) + 2(-6) = 6v \qquad KE_f = \tfrac{1}{2}(6)(4.67)^2 = 65.3 \text{ J}$$

$$v = 4.67 \tfrac{m}{s} \qquad \Delta KE = -170.7 \text{ J}$$

$$\text{Fraction lost} = \frac{170.7}{236} = 0.72$$

TWO DIMENSIONS

Momentum conservation involves a vector equation, equating the initial momentum of the system to the final momentum of the system.

$$\vec{P}_i = \vec{P}_f$$

Since two vectors can't be equal unless their components are separately equal, the law actually provides two separate conditions:

$$P_{xi} = P_{xf} \qquad P_{yi} = P_{yf}$$

To see how this works, consider a mass m_1 moving with velocity $\vec{v}_1$ colliding with a stationary mass m_2 (figure 3).

A Two-Dimensional Collision

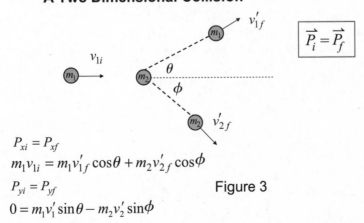

$$P_{xi} = P_{xf}$$
$$m_1 v_{1i} = m_1 v'_{1f}\cos\theta + m_2 v'_{2f}\cos\phi$$
$$P_{yi} = P_{yf}$$
$$0 = m_1 v'_1 \sin\theta - m_2 v'_2 \sin\phi$$

Figure 3

Even if you know the masses and initial velocity, there are still four unknowns, the final speeds and angles. Momentum conservation provides only two conditions, and an elastic collision provides only one more condition on the final velocities, so you need more information about the collision to completely determine the final velocities from the initial velocities. The situation simplifies if the collision is totally inelastic, because then there is only one final velocity, and once again momentum conservation gives all the information needed to obtain a solution.

EXAMPLE

A 4 kg mass moving at 10 m/s in the $-y$ direction collides and sticks to a 2 kg mass moving at 6 m/s in the $+x$ direction. Find the final velocity components.

$$P_{xi} = P_{xf} \qquad\qquad\qquad P_{yi} = P_{yf}$$

$$2(6) = 6v_x \qquad\qquad\qquad 4(-10) = 6v_y$$

$$v_x = 2\tfrac{m}{s} \qquad\qquad\qquad v_y = -6.67\tfrac{m}{s}$$

When the masses are equal, momentum conservation yields a condition on the velocities if one object is initially stationary:

$$m\vec{v}_{1i} = m\vec{v}_{1f} + m\vec{v}_{2f}$$

$$\vec{v}_{1i} = \vec{v}_{1f} + \vec{v}_{2f}$$

The three vectors then form a triangle (figure 4).

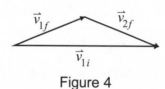

Figure 4

If, in addition, the collision is elastic,

$$\tfrac{1}{2}mv_{1i}^2 = \tfrac{1}{2}mv_{1f}^2 + \tfrac{1}{2}mv_{2f}^2$$

$$v_{1i}^2 = v_{1f}^2 + v_{2f}^2$$

then the triangle is a right triangle $\theta + \phi = 90°$

Center of Mass

When a system consists of several objects, their motion can be quite complex. But one point associated with the system undergoes a particularly simple motion, the **center of mass** (CM). It is the average of each particle coordinate, weighted by the mass of each particle:

$$x_{CM} = \frac{m_1 x_1 + m_2 x_2 + ...}{m_1 + m_2 + ...} \qquad y_{CM} = \frac{m_1 y_1 + m_2 y_2 + ...}{m_1 + m_2 + ...}$$

Here's a simple example: Consider two masses on the x-axis, a 4 kg mass at $x = 18$ and a 2 kg mass at $x = 6$ (figure 5).

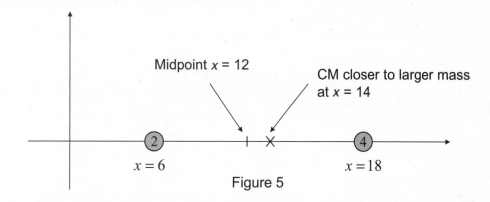

Figure 5

$$x_{CM} = \frac{m_1 x_1 + m_2 x_2 + ...}{m_1 + m2 + ...} = \frac{4(18) + 2(6)}{(4 + 2)} = 14$$

If the two masses were equal, the CM would have been halfway between them at $x = 12$. Since the 4 kg mass is twice the 2 kg mass, the CM is closer to the 4 kg mass, and the CM breaks the distance between the two masses into a 2-to-1 ratio, the same as the ratio of the masses. It's easy to see from the definition that uniform, symmetric objects will have their CM at the geometric center.

Now let's look at the velocity of the CM (in one dimension for simplicity). During a time Δt, the objects will undergo displacements Δx_1, Δx_2 ..., which will lead to a displacement in the CM, Δx_{CM}.

$$\Delta x_{CM} = \frac{m_1 \Delta x_1 + m_2 \Delta x_2 + ...}{m_1 + m_2 + ...} = \frac{m_1 \Delta x_1 + m_2 \Delta x_2 + ...}{M_{total}}$$

Divide by Δt and rearrange:

$$M_{total} v_{CM} = m_1 v_1 + m_2 v_2 + ... = p_1 + p_2 + ... = P_{total}$$

Since the total momentum of the system is the total mass multiplied by v_{CM}, it's as if the CM is moving as a point particle with mass M_{total} and velocity v_{CM}.

To see why the motion of the CM is simple, look at its acceleration and apply Newton's second law. For simplicity, use a one-dimensional situation.

$$a_{CM} = \frac{m_1 a_1 + m_2 a_2 + \dots}{m_1 + m_2 + \dots}$$

$$M_{total} a_{CM} = netF_1 + netF_2 + \dots$$

As you add up all the forces on the system, the internal forces will cancel in action-reaction pairs, leaving only the net external force on the right-hand side.

$$M_{total} a_{CM} = netF^{ext}$$

Generalized to three dimensions, this means that the CM moves as a point particle with mass M_{total}, experiencing only the external forces. If there are no external forces, the CM initially at rest will remain at rest; if the CM initially is moving, it will continue to do so with a constant velocity.

EXERCISE

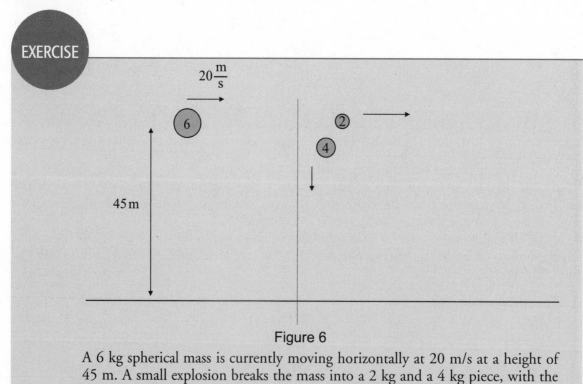

Figure 6

A 6 kg spherical mass is currently moving horizontally at 20 m/s at a height of 45 m. A small explosion breaks the mass into a 2 kg and a 4 kg piece, with the 4 kg piece falling straight down (figure 6). How far does the 2 kg piece travel?

If the explosion had not occurred, the object and its CM would have traveled 60 m before hitting:

$$\Delta y = \tfrac{1}{2}gt^2 \qquad\qquad \Delta x = v_{x0}t$$

$$45 = 5t^2 \qquad\qquad \Delta x = 20(3)$$

$$t = 3 \text{ s} \qquad\qquad \Delta x = 60 \text{ m}$$

With the explosion occurring, the CM will still land here because it continues to move under only the influence of the external force of gravity; the explosion itself exerted only internal forces. Since the 4 kg piece lands 60 m to the left of the CM contact point, the 2 kg piece must land 120 m to the right of the same point. The 2 kg piece, then, travels 180 m horizontally from the explosion.

Angular Momentum and Its Conservation

The concept of angular momentum is intimately linked to the concept of rotation. While the dynamics of rotation are not part of the B-level syllabus, you need to know the basics of angular momentum and its conservation.

Angular momentum is a system property that depends on the system's linear momentum and the orientation of the linear momentum vector with respect to a given origin. More precisely, for a point particle of momentum $\vec{p}$, angular momentum is defined through the cross product:

$$\vec{l} = \vec{r} \times \vec{p}$$

Here $\vec{r}$ is a vector pointing from the origin to the position of the particle (figure 7).

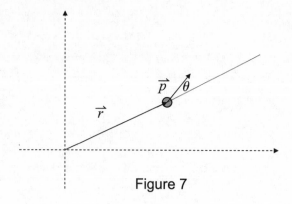

Figure 7

Of course, the direction of $\vec{l}$ is perpendicular to both $\vec{r}$ and $\vec{p}$ in keeping with the right-hand rule. You can think of the magnitude of the angular momentum, $l = rp\sin\theta$, in two ways, depending on how you group the $\sin\theta$ (figure 8).

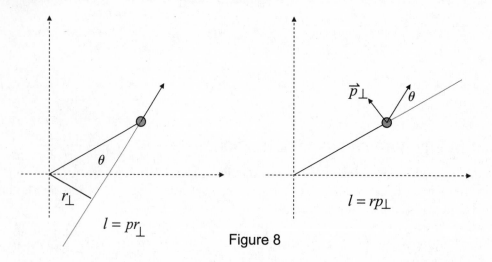

Figure 8

If you write

$$l = (r\sin\theta)p = r_\perp p$$

then the angular momentum is the product of the linear momentum and the distance from the origin to the line defined by the linear momentum vector. If the particle never changed direction, this is the closest approach distance to the origin. You can see immediately that if $r_\perp = 0$ (the object is moving directly at or away from the origin), then the angular momentum about that origin is 0. It also follows that if an object is moving in a circle of radius R, then the angular momentum about an origin at the center of the circle is just $l = Rp$.

You can also write

$$l = r(p\sin\theta) = rp_\perp$$

In this way of thinking, the angular momentum is the product of the distance from the origin and the component of the linear momentum perpendicular to the line connecting the origin and the position of the particle.

Just as you can define the total linear momentum of a system as the sum of the individual contributions of each particle in the system, you can define the total angular momentum of a system as the sum of the angular momenta of each particle in the system:

$$\vec{L} = \vec{l_1} + \vec{l_2} + \dots$$

The total linear momentum of a system is conserved if there are no external forces acting on the system. The analogous statement for angular momentum is the following:

The total angular momentum of a system will be conserved if there are no external torques acting on the system.

Clearly, if there are no external forces, there will be no external torques either. What's interesting is that there are situations where an external force is acting so that linear momentum is *not* conserved, but the force exerts no torque about a particular origin, so the angular momentum about this origin *is* conserved and stays the same. External forces that exert no torque act along the line connecting the point of application of the force to the origin. One common example is the tension in a string connected to a ball. If the string has one end fixed at the origin, the tension acting on the ball exerts no torque about the origin.

EXERCISE

A 0.5 kg mass is moving over a smooth table at a constant speed of 10 m/s in a horizontal circle of radius 1 m by means of a string that passes through a hole in the table. As the mass continues to move, the string is shortened by being pulled through the hole. Find the speed of the mass when the radius is reduced to 0.25 m.

The weight and normal force will have effects on the mass that cancel out. The tension force acts toward the place where the string passes through the table. If you call this the origin, then tension exerts 0 torque, and angular momentum about this origin is conserved.

$$L_i = p_\perp R = mvR = (0.5)(10)(1) = 5 \text{ kg} \cdot \frac{m}{s^2}$$

$$L_f = p_\perp R = mv_f R = (0.5)(v_f)(0.25)$$

$$L_i = L_f$$

$$5 = 0.125 v_f \qquad \Rightarrow v_f = 40 \frac{m}{s}$$

Conservation of angular momentum as illustrated in this example is the reason a spinning ice skater will rotate faster as she draws her arms closer to her.

KEY FORMULAS

Impulse Delivered by a Force $\vec{J}_F = \vec{F}\Delta t$

Linear Momentum of Mass $\vec{p} = m\vec{v}$

Impulse-Momentum Theorem $\vec{J}_{netF} = \Delta \vec{p}$

Total Linear Momentum of System $\vec{P} = \vec{p}_1 + \vec{p}_2 + \ldots$

Conservation of Momentum $\vec{P}_i = \vec{P}_f$

Center of Mass $x_{CM} = \dfrac{m_1 x_1 + m_2 x_2 + \ldots}{m_1 + m_2 + \ldots}$

$y_{CM} = \dfrac{m_1 y_1 + m_2 y_2 + \ldots}{m_1 + m_2 + \ldots}$

Angular Momentum $l = p_\perp r = r_\perp p$

CHAPTER 5 PRACTICE EXERCISES

SECTION I MULTIPLE CHOICE

1. A 2 kg mass moving at 3 m/s hits a vertical wall and rebounds with the same speed. If the contact time with the wall is 0.01 s, the magnitude of the force exerted on the mass is most nearly

   (A) 6 N
   (B) 600 N
   (C) 1,200 N
   (D) 12 N
   (E) 300 N

2. A 1,000 kg vehicle moving at 3 m/s collides with a 2,000 kg stationary vehicle. After the collision, the two move together. The speed of the two just after collision is

   (A) 1.5 m/s
   (B) 1 m/s
   (C) 2 m/s
   (D) 0.5 m/s
   (E) 0.67 m/s

3. A compressed spring is placed between two masses M and m resting on a smooth horizontal surface. When the spring is released, the two fly apart, with M moving at velocity V. The velocity of m is

   (A) $\dfrac{M}{m}V$

   (B) $-\dfrac{M}{m}V$

   (C) $\dfrac{m}{M}V$

   (D) $-\dfrac{m}{M}V$

   (E) $\dfrac{m}{m+M}V$

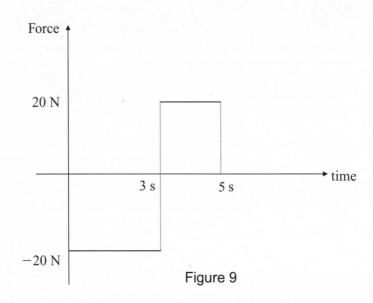

Figure 9

4. A mass M moving with velocity v experiences the force described in the previous question for 5 seconds. The change in momentum of the mass is

(A) $100 \dfrac{\text{kg} \cdot \text{m}}{\text{s}}$

(B) $20 \dfrac{\text{kg} \cdot \text{m}}{\text{s}}$

(C) not calculable until M and v are known

(D) $-20 \dfrac{\text{kg} \cdot \text{m}}{\text{s}}$

(E) $40 \dfrac{\text{kg} \cdot \text{m}}{\text{s}}$

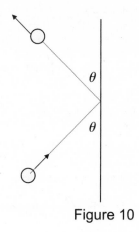

Figure 10

5. A mass rebounds off a wall elastically as shown in the figure. The vector that best represents the impulse delivered by the wall is

(A) ↘   (B) ↖   (C) ←   (D) ↙   (E) ↑

6. A mass m moving east with speed v on a smooth horizontal surface explodes into two pieces. After the explosion, one piece of mass $\frac{3}{4}m$ continues in the same direction with speed $\frac{4}{3}v$. Find the magnitude and direction for the velocity of the other piece.

(A) $\frac{1}{3}v$ to the left
(B) The piece is at rest.
(C) $\frac{1}{4}v$ to the left
(D) $\frac{3}{4}v$ to the left
(E) $\frac{1}{4}v$ to the right

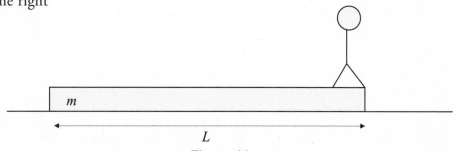

Figure 11

7. A man of mass m stands at the rear of a uniform plank of equal mass and length L that rests on a frictionless surface. The man walks forward to the center of the plank. Relative to the surface, the man has moved

(A) $\frac{L}{2}$ (B) L (C) $\frac{L}{4}$ (D) $\frac{3L}{4}$ (E) $\frac{L}{3}$

8. A 0.5 kg mass moving north at 4 m/s collides head-on with a 10 kg stationary mass in an elastic collision. After the collision, the velocity of the 0.5 kg mass is most nearly
   (A) 1 m/s north
   (B) 2 m/s south
   (C) 3.5 m/s south
   (D) 0
   (E) 4.5 m/s south

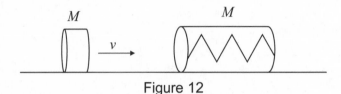

Figure 12

Questions 9 and 10
A mass M moving with speed v collides with a stationary spring gun of equal mass containing an uncompressed spring with spring constant K. Assume all surfaces are frictionless.

9. The maximum compression of the spring will be

   (A) $v\sqrt{\dfrac{M}{K}}$ (B) $v\sqrt{\dfrac{2M}{K}}$ (C) $v\sqrt{\dfrac{M}{4K}}$ (D) $\dfrac{v}{2}\sqrt{\dfrac{M}{K}}$ (E) $v\sqrt{\dfrac{M}{2K}}$

10. After the collision, the gun will be moving with a speed most nearly

   (A) $\dfrac{v}{2}$ (B) $\dfrac{v}{4}$ (C) v (D) $2v$ (E) $\dfrac{v}{3}$

CHAPTER 5 PRACTICE EXERCISES

SECTION II FREE RESPONSE

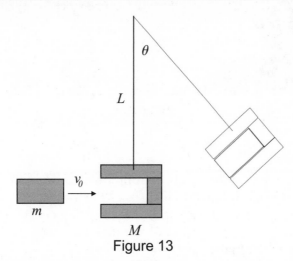

Figure 13

1. A mass m is fired with speed v_0 into a pendulum of length L, mass M. The pendulum mass is specially shaped to catch the incoming mass so that the two move together after the collision. In terms of v_0, m, L, M, and g, determine
   (a) the speed of the two masses after the collision
   (b) an expression for the angle θ through which the pendulum moves after the collision

   Suppose the pendulum is hung so that it can move in a complete vertical circle.

   (c) What is the minimum value of v_0 that will ensure that the pendulum makes one complete revolution?

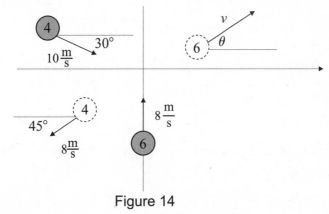

Figure 14

2. A 4 kg mass moving at 10 m/s at an angle of 30° below the horizontal collides with a 6 kg mass moving vertically at 8 m/s. As a result of the collision, the 4 kg mass moves back at 45° below the $-x$-axis at 8 m/s.

   (a) Determine the magnitude and direction of the 6 kg mass velocity.
   (b) Was the collision elastic? Explain.

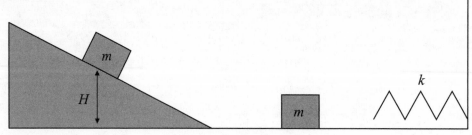

Figure 15

3. A mass m slides down a smooth incline from a height H and collides with a stationary mass M sitting on a smooth horizontal surface. The two masses stick together and move to the right, where they encounter a spring with spring constant k.
   (a) Find the speed of m at the bottom of the incline.
   (b) Find the speed of the masses after the collision.
   (c) Find the maximum compression of the spring.
   (d) After the masses leave the spring moving to the left, a small explosion separates the two masses and causes the mass M to come to rest. How high will m go on the incline?

Answers and Explanations

Multiple Choice

1. The answer is C.
$$\Delta p = 2(3) - 2(-3) = 12 \text{N} \cdot \text{s}$$
$$F\Delta t = \Delta p \Rightarrow F = \frac{\Delta p}{\Delta t} = \frac{12}{0.01} = 1{,}200 \text{ N}$$

2. The answer is B.
$$P_i = P_f$$
$$3(1{,}000) = 3{,}000v \Rightarrow v = 1\frac{\text{m}}{\text{s}}$$

3. The answer is B.
$$P_i = P_f$$
$$0 = mv + MV \Rightarrow v = -\frac{M}{m}V$$

4. The answer is D. The area under the graph is $-60 + 40 = -20 \frac{\text{kg} \cdot \text{m}}{\text{s}}$.

5. The answer is C. The vertical component of momentum doesn't change, so there is no vertical impulse component.

6. The answer is B.
$$P_i = P_f$$
$$mv = (\tfrac{3}{4}m)(\tfrac{4}{3}m) + (\tfrac{1}{4}m)v' \Rightarrow v' = 0$$

7. The answer is C. The CM is initially at rest and halfway between the man and the center of the plank, $\frac{L}{4}$ from the man. No external forces act, so the CM cannot move. When the man walks to the center of the plank, the CM of the system is directly underneath him, so he moves only $\frac{L}{4}$. As he walks to the left, the plank moves to the right as well.

8. The answer is C. An elastic collision reverses the direction of the relative speed. The initial relative speed is 4 m/s. The mass differences between the two objects imply that the 10 kg will not be moving fast, and that the 0.5 kg will reverse direction, so C is the only answer that could work. D violates KE conservation. Of course, you could use equations to get the same result, but it would take longer.

9. The answer is E. At maximum compression, the two masses have the same speed as in a totally inelastic collision. Momentum conservation gives
$$P_i = P_f$$
$$Mv = 2Mv' \Rightarrow v' = \frac{v}{2}$$

The KE lost, $\frac{1}{2}Mv^2 - \frac{1}{2}(2M)v'^2 = \frac{1}{4}Mv^2$ becomes PE in the spring:
$$\frac{1}{2}Kx^2 = \frac{1}{4}Mv^2 \Rightarrow x = v\sqrt{\frac{M}{2K}}$$

10. The answer is C. After the spring is uncompressed again, the collision is elastic. For equal masses, you can apply momentum conservation and the relative speed change formula:
$$P_i = P_f$$
$$Mv = Mv_1 + Mv_2 \qquad v = v_2 - v_1 \quad \text{Combine to get} \quad \begin{aligned} v_2 &= v \\ v_1 &= 0 \end{aligned}$$
$$v = v_1 + v_2$$

FREE RESPONSE

1.(a) $P_i = P_f$

$$mv_0 = (m + M)V$$

$$V = \frac{m}{m + M}v_0$$

(b) After the collision, energy is conserved:

$$E_i = E_f$$

$$\frac{1}{2}(m + M)V^2 = (m + M)gh$$

$$\frac{1}{2}\left(\frac{m}{m + M}v_0\right)^2 = g(L - L\cos\theta)$$

(c) At the top where the mass has risen $2L$, the centripetal force is supplied by the tension and gravity and will be a minimum when the tension is 0 (figure 16).

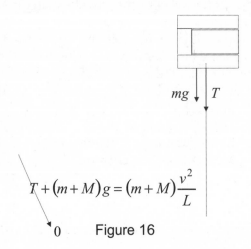

$$T + (m + M)g = (m + M)\frac{v^2}{L}$$

Figure 16

You can then apply energy conservation from just after the collision to the top of the motion.

$$netF_{top} = (m + M)\frac{v^2}{L} \qquad E_i = E_{top}$$

$$(m + M)g = (m + M)\frac{v^2}{L} \qquad \tfrac{1}{2}(m + M)V^2 = \tfrac{1}{2}(m + M)v^2 + (m + M)g(2L)$$

$$v^2 = gL \qquad \tfrac{1}{2}(\tfrac{m}{m+M}v_0)^2 = \tfrac{1}{2}gL + g(2L)$$

$$v_0 = \tfrac{m+M}{m}\sqrt{5gL}$$

2.(a) $P_{xi} = P_{xf}$

$(4)(10)\cos 30 = -(4)(8)\cos 45 + 6v_x$

$v_x = 9.5\frac{m}{s}$

$P_{yi} = P_{yf}$

$-(4)(10)\sin 30 + (6)(8) = -(4)(8)\sin 45 + 6v_y$

$v_y = 8.4\frac{m}{s}$

$v = \sqrt{v_x^2 + v_y^2} = 12.7\frac{m}{s} \quad \tan \theta = \frac{v_y}{v_x} = .88 \Rightarrow \theta = 41.5° \text{ with respect to } +x\text{-axis}$

(b) $KE_i = \frac{1}{2}(4)(10)^2 + \frac{1}{2}(6)(8)^2 = 392$ J

$KE_f = \frac{1}{2}(4)(8)^2 + \frac{1}{2}(6)(12.7)^2 = 612$ J

Kinetic energy increased as a result of the collision, so it clearly wasn't conserved, implying that the collision was not elastic.

3. (a) $E_i = E_f$ (b) $P_i = P_f$ (c) $E_i = E_f$

$mgH = \frac{1}{2}mv^2$ $mv = (m+M)V$ $\frac{1}{2}(m+M)V^2 = \frac{1}{2}kx^2$

$v = \sqrt{2gH}$ $V = \frac{m}{m+M}\sqrt{2gH}$ $x = \sqrt{\frac{m^2(2gH)}{k(m+M)}}$

(d) $P_i = P_f$ $E_i = E_f$

$(m+M)V = mv' + 0$ $mgH_f = \frac{1}{2}mv'^2 = \frac{1}{2}m(2gH)$

$v' = \frac{m+M}{m}V = \sqrt{2gH}$ $H_f = H$

The system ends up with the same energy with which it began. Energy was lost in the first collision, with the lost energy perhaps appearing as internal energy in the masses. Then energy was added to the system with the explosion. Here, stored chemical energy became mechanical energy in the system, just enough to get the total mechanical energy back to its initial value.

6

Gravitation

This chapter focuses on the gravitational attraction between masses. After an introduction to the general force law, we'll look at applications to orbital motion of planets and satellites.

Newton's Law of Gravity

Isaac Newton hypothesized that any two masses exert an attractive force on each other. For point masses, this force is directed along the line connecting the masses. Its magnitude is directly proportional to the product of the two masses, and inversely proportional to the square of their separation. The equation for **Newton's law of gravity** (figure 1) summarizes this:

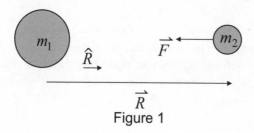

Figure 1

$$\vec{F}_{1on2} = -G\frac{m_1 m_2}{R^2}\hat{R} \qquad\qquad G = 6.67 \times 10^{-11}\frac{N}{kg^2 \cdot m^2}$$

Here $\vec{F}_{1on2}$ is the force exerted on m_2 by m_1, and $\hat{R}$ is a unit vector directed along the line connecting the masses from m_1 to m_2. Since $\hat{R}$ and $\vec{F}_{1on2}$ point in opposite directions, there is a minus sign in the equation. Of course, Newton's third law states that

$$\vec{F}_{1on2} = -\vec{F}_{2on1}$$

This equation is also true for spherical masses, where R is now the separation of the centers and $\hat{R}$ points along this line. To determine the effects of gravity, you can always imagine a spherical mass as a point mass with all its mass concentrated at its center.

Because of the R^2 in the denominator in the force law, Newton's law of gravity is said to be an **inverse square law**. As masses are separated, the force between them weakens. Should they increase their separation to twice the original value, the force becomes one-fourth its original value. Similarly, should the masses get closer so that they are separated by just one-third the original separation, the force increases to nine times the original value (figure 2).

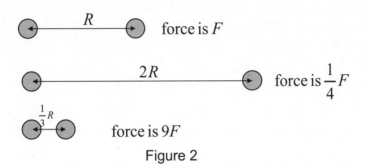

Figure 2

The quantity G is called the **universal gravitational constant**. The fact that it is so small indicates that gravitational force is inherently weak. In fact, of all the basic forces of physics, the force of gravity is by far the weakest. The weakest force in nature being responsible for planetary and galactic motions may seem like a contradiction, but gravity acts over large distances and it's always attractive. Gravity can be the dominant force on the large scale because electric force gets contributions from equal numbers of positive and negative charges that cancel out.

EXERCISE

Find the attractive force between two 1 kg masses separated by 1 m.

Using the inverse square law, you get $F = G\frac{(1)(1)}{1^2} = 6.67 \times 10^{-11}\text{N}$. Obviously, this weak force will have no noticeable effect on two masses sitting on a table.

Find the force exerted on the Earth by the Sun.

$M_e = 5.98 \times 10^{24}$ kg

$M_s = 1.99 \times 10^{30}$ kg

$R = 1.5 \times 10^{11}$ m

$F = G\frac{M_e M_s}{R^2} = 6.67 \times 10^{-11}\frac{(5.98 \times 10^{24})(1.99 \times 10^{30})}{(1.5 \times 10^{11})}$

$F = 3.5 \times 10^{22}\text{N}$

Because of the very large masses involved, you shouldn't be surprised that this large force has a very noticeable effect.

g vs. G

You've already seen one constant associated with gravity, the acceleration due to gravity near the Earth's surface: $g = 9.8 \frac{m}{s^2}$. But if you think about it, this isn't a constant at all. If you traveled to another planet or even moved a fair distance from the Earth's surface, the local acceleration due to gravity would be different. On the other hand, the G in Newton's law of gravity is a true constant. Its value is the same whether you measure the force between two bugs or two galaxies.

Remember, however, that G is not an acceleration. It is a very small number that sets the scale of the force when you express quantities in SI units. Since weight on Earth is just the force of gravity between an object and the entire Earth, you can combine the second law formula for weight, $W = mg$, with the law of gravity, recognizing that "close to the Earth's surface" means a separation between the Earth and the object of one Earth radius, R_e (figure 3).

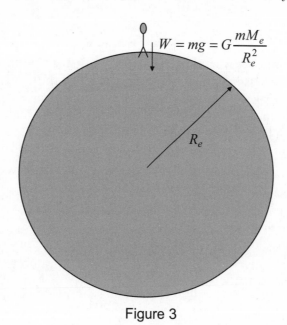

$$W = mg = G\frac{mM_e}{R_e^2}$$

Figure 3

$$mg = G\frac{mM_e}{R_e^2} \quad \Rightarrow \quad g = G\frac{M_e}{R_e^2}$$

You can generalize this to any spherical planet with mass M_p and radius R_p:

$$g_p = G\frac{M_p}{R_p^2}$$

The local acceleration due to gravity, then, is determined by multiplying the universal G by a factor that depends on the mass and radius of the planet.

EXERCISE

If you weigh 800 N on Earth, what will you weigh on a planet with half the mass of Earth and a radius that is twice the radius of Earth?

Since the weight on the planet is $W_p = mg_p$, you can determine the overall factor of change using the relation for g_p. Halving the mass reduces g_p by $\frac{1}{2}$, while doubling the radius reduces g_p by a factor of $\frac{1}{4}$. The overall change is a factor of $\frac{1}{8}$, so your weight on the planet is 100 N.

Satellites

Gravitational force can supply the centripetal force needed to cause an object to move in a circular orbit. Examples abound, from man-made communication satellites to the Moon as it moves around the Earth to the Earth itself as it moves around the Sun. Let's apply the second law to a mass m circling another mass M (figure 4).

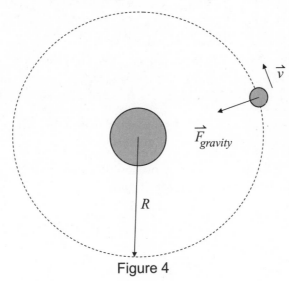

Figure 4

$$F_{cp} = ma_{cp} = m\frac{v^2}{R}$$
$$G\frac{mM}{R^2} = m\frac{v^2}{R} \qquad \Rightarrow v = \sqrt{\frac{GM}{R}}$$

Notice that the speed is independent of the orbiting mass and that the speed decreases by the square root of R as the radius gets bigger; at $4R$, the orbital speed is half the orbital speed at R.

EXERCISE

Communications satellites are often put into **geosynchronous** orbits. Such an orbit takes exactly one day to complete, so a satellite circling over the equator will always be above the same point on Earth. Determine the radius of a geosynchronous orbit.

The time it takes a satellite to travel one full circumference of its orbit is called the period T of the orbit. For a geosynchronous satellite, the period is one day, or 86,400 s. That means:

$$2\pi R = vT \Rightarrow v = \frac{2\pi R}{T}$$

Substitute into the relation for the orbital speed:

$$v = \sqrt{\frac{GM}{R}}$$

$$\frac{2\pi R}{T} = \sqrt{\frac{GM}{R}} \qquad \Rightarrow R = \left(\frac{GMT^2}{4\pi^2}\right)^{\frac{1}{3}}$$

Substituting G, T, and $M = 6 \times 10^{24}$ kg, you get $R = 4.23 \times 10^7$ m, corresponding to a distance of a little more than 26,000 miles. Since Earth's radius is about 4,000 miles, this is more than 22,000 miles above Earth.

Orbits of satellites and planets can be elliptical. In fact, a circle is a "degenerate" ellipse. The ellipse of an orbit due to the gravitational attraction of a satellite to a large mass will always have the large mass at one of the foci of the ellipse (figure 5).

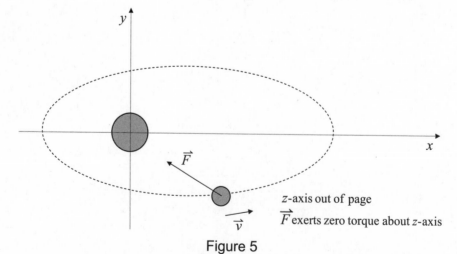

z-axis out of page

$\vec{F}$ exerts zero torque about z-axis

Figure 5

Whether the orbit is truly circular or elliptical, the force on the orbiting mass will always act directly toward the large mass. Let's describe the motion with the large mass at the origin and the x-y plane determined by the plane of the orbit. Because the gravitational force is acting directly at the origin, it will exert no torque about this point. This means the angular momentum of the satellite is conserved. This is a trivial statement for circular orbits since the speed is constant then, but for elliptical orbits it means that the object will change speed as its orbit distance varies.

EXAMPLE

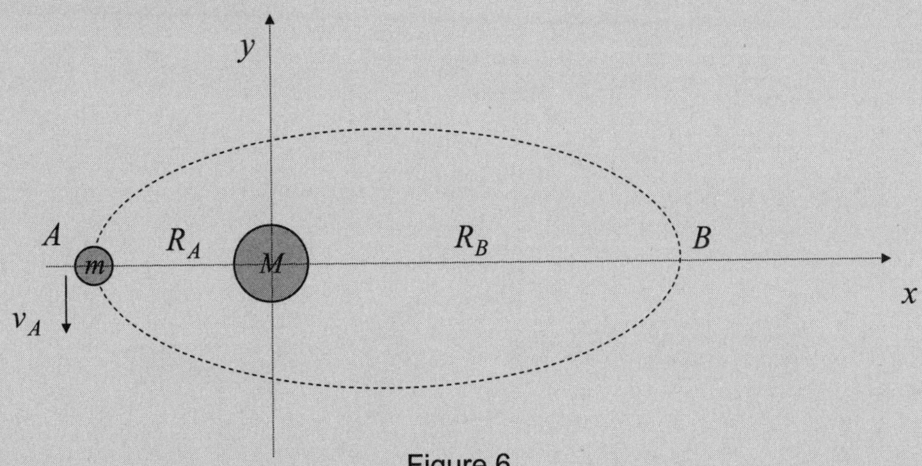

Figure 6

Consider the elliptical orbit shown here (figure 6). At the points A and B, where the object is closest and farthest from M, its velocity vector is perpendicular to the line connecting each point to the center of M, labeled R_A and R_B. If the speed of the object at A is v_A, what will be the speed at B?

Because the gravitational force exerts 0 torque about the axis of rotation, angular momentum is conserved. At any point in the motion $l = mvr_\perp$, and at A and B, $r_\perp$ is just the distance to M, so you get

$$l_A = l_B$$
$$mv_A R_A = mv_B R_B$$

$$\Rightarrow v_B = \frac{R_A}{R_B} v_A$$

The object slows down as it moves from A to B.

Apparent Weight

Weight is the common name for the force of attraction between an object and the Earth. In your everyday life, however, you probably identify your weight with the reading on a bathroom scale. When you stand motionless on the scale, the weight force acting down and the normal force exerted by the scale acting up are equal (figure 7). The reaction force to the normal force acts down on the scale, and the scale registers this force. If you jump around on the scale the reading will change, not because your weight has changed, but because the normal force has changed.

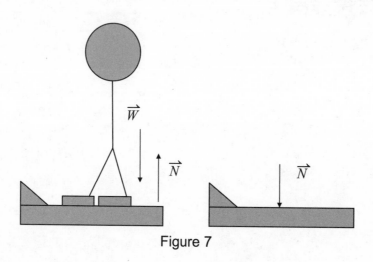

Figure 7

Let's identify the **apparent weight** in several different situations. If you get on an elevator, for example, and it initially accelerates upward, the normal force of the floor must supply a force greater than your weight to accelerate you upward. A bathroom scale on the elevator would show a value larger than your weight, and your apparent weight would increase. The opposite would occur if you initially accelerated downward. If you were to jump out a window and go into free fall, a bathroom scale attached to your feet would read 0, since it too would be in free fall. In this case, your apparent weight is 0. But since $g = 9.8$ m/s^2, your true weight hasn't changed.

Now let's consider an astronaut aboard the space shuttle at a height of 300 miles above the Earth. This makes the orbit radius, measured to the Earth's center, about 6.9×10^6 m. The local value of g there is

$$g_{\text{orbit}} = G \frac{M_p}{R^2_{\text{orbit}}} = (6.67 \times 10^{-11}) \frac{6 \times 10^{24}}{(6.9 \times 10^6)^2} = 8.4 \frac{\text{m}}{\text{s}^2}$$

This is still 86 percent of the value at Earth's surface, so the astronauts are clearly not weightless. But they are in free fall, just as in the situation described earlier. An astronaut who was simply raised to a height of 300 miles and released would fall straight down, just like the student jumping out a window. If the astronaut were given the right initial velocity perpendicular to the vertical, however, he would still fall but would keep missing Earth as he fell. A bathroom scale traveling with him would read 0 since it too was in free fall, moving under only the influence of gravity. Astronauts in orbit are definitely not weightless; the "weight force," the force of gravity, actually keeps them in orbit. If an astronaut were to travel far from Earth and other gravitational influences, then he or she would indeed approach weightlessness.

KEY FORMULAS

Newton's Law of Gravity

$$\vec{F}_{1on2} = -G\,\frac{m_1 m_2}{r^2}\,\hat{r}$$

Local g

$$g_p = G\,\frac{M_p}{R_p^2}$$

Circular Orbit Speed

$$v = \sqrt{\frac{GM}{R}}$$

CHAPTER 6

PRACTICE EXERCISES

SECTION I MULTIPLE CHOICE

1. Two masses separated by a distance R exert a gravitational force F on each other. To triple the force, the separation must be changed to

   (A) $3R$ (B) $\dfrac{R}{3}$ (C) $\dfrac{R}{9}$ (D) $\sqrt{3}R$ (E) $\dfrac{R}{\sqrt{3}}$

2. A student with mass 60 kg imagines she travels to a planet with twice the mass of the Earth and four times the radius of the Earth. Her weight on this planet would be closest to

   (A) 7.5 N   (B) 30 N   (C) 75 N   (D) 300 N   (E) 4,800 N

3. A satellite is currently moving in a circular orbit of radius R with orbital speed v. With the aid of onboard rockets, it moves out of this orbit and eventually establishes a new circular orbit of radius $\frac{1}{2}R$. The orbital speed will be

   (A) $\sqrt{2}v$ (B) $2v$ (C) $\dfrac{v}{2}$ (D) $\dfrac{v}{\sqrt{2}}$ (E) $4v$

4. In an elliptical orbit about the Sun, which of the following planetary properties is conserved?
   I. mechanical energy
   II. linear momentum
   III. angular momentum

   (A) I and II only   (B) I and III only   (C) II and III only   (D) I only   (E) I, II, and III

5. Astronauts float around inside the space shuttle as it orbits because

   (A) the effects of gravity are almost negligible
   (B) the net force on them is 0 because centrifugal force cancels out gravity
   (C) they are accelerating toward the Earth's center at the same rate as the shuttle and everything within it
   (D) the buoyant force of air is comparable to the force of gravity
   (E) the gravitational attraction of the astronauts to each other and the shuttle is comparable to their attraction to Earth

6. A satellite circularly orbits Earth at a radius R taking a time T to complete one orbit. What would the time for one orbit of the same radius be on a planet with twice the mass of Earth?

   (A) $\dfrac{T}{2}$ (B) $\dfrac{T}{\sqrt{2}}$ (C) T (D) $\sqrt{2}T$ (E) $2T$

PRACTICE EXERCISES

SECTION I FREE RESPONSE

1. A 100 kg satellite is placed in a low Earth circular orbit with radius 1.2×10^7 m. An identical satellite is to be placed in circular orbit with twice the orbital period.
   (a) Find the speed of the first satellite.
   (b) Find the radius of the second satellite.

2. Two satellites have mistakenly been put in identical Earth orbits of radius R. Satellite A with mass m is orbiting clockwise while satellite B with mass $2m$ is orbiting counterclockwise. The two satellites have a head-on collision and move as one after the collision. In terms of the given quantities, what orbit radius would the collided objects have to possess in order to move in a circular path?

Answers and Explanations

MULTIPLE CHOICE

1. The answer is E. Since the force gets larger, the separation gets smaller. For the original separation, you can write $F \propto \frac{1}{R^2}$. Then for E, you have

$$F' \propto \frac{1}{\left(\frac{R}{\sqrt{3}}\right)^2} = \frac{3}{R^2} = 3F$$

2. The answer is C. Doubling the mass of the planet for a fixed radius doubles the weight. Quadrupling the radius for a fixed mass decreases the weight by $\frac{1}{16}$. Then the overall factor will be $2 \cdot \frac{1}{16} = \frac{1}{8}$. Since the weight on Earth is 600 N, C is correct.

3. The answer is A. For a circular orbit, $v = \sqrt{\frac{GM}{R}}$. As R becomes $\frac{1}{2}R$, v becomes bigger by $\sqrt{2}$.

4. The answer is B. Because gravity is an external force acting on the planet, its linear momentum isn't conserved. Gravity is a conservative force exerting 0 torque about the rotation axis, however, so energy and angular momentum are conserved.

5. The answer is C. From the point of view of the astronauts, the objects are just floating because the objects, the astronauts, and the shuttle itself are all accelerating at the same rate, the local g value, toward Earth's center.

6. The answer is B. For a circular orbit $2\pi R = vT$. Since R stays the same, v and T are inversely proportional. Since $v = \sqrt{\frac{GM}{R}}$, doubling the planet mass increases v by $\sqrt{2}$, so the period T must decrease by the same factor.

FREE RESPONSE

1. (a) Gravity supplies the centripetal force.

$$G\frac{mM}{R^2} = m\frac{v^2}{R}$$

$$\Rightarrow v = \sqrt{\frac{GM}{R}} = \frac{(6.67 \times 10^{-11})(5.98 \times 10^{24})}{1.2 \times 10^7} = 5{,}765\frac{m}{s}$$

(b) The period of the first satellite satisfies

$$2\pi R = vT \quad \Rightarrow \quad T = \frac{2\pi R}{v} = \frac{2\pi(1.2 \times 10^7)}{5{,}765} = 1.31 \times 10^4 \text{ s}$$

You can relate the radius of circular orbits to their periods like this:

$$2\pi R = vT = \sqrt{\frac{GM}{R}}\,T \quad \Rightarrow \quad R = \left(\frac{GMT^2}{4\pi^2}\right)^{\frac{1}{3}}$$

$$R = \left(\frac{(6.67 \times 10^{-11})(5.98 \times 10^{24})(2.62 \times 10^4)^2}{4\pi^2}\right)^{\frac{1}{3}} = 1.91 \times 10^7 \text{ m}$$

2. Before the collision, each satellite has the same speed $v = \sqrt{\frac{GM_e}{R}}$ independent of the satellites' masses. Apply momentum conservation to the collision process, using just before the collision as the initial state and just after the collision as the final state.

$$P_0 = P_f$$

$$2mv + m(-v) = 3mv' \Rightarrow v' = \frac{1}{3}v$$

The circular orbit that corresponds to this speed satisfies

$$v' = \sqrt{\frac{GM_e}{R'}} = \frac{v}{3} = \frac{1}{3}\sqrt{\frac{GM_e}{R}} \quad \Rightarrow \quad R' = 9R$$

CHAPTER 7

Oscillations

This chapter focuses on the motion of objects that is repetitive. The prototype for this description is the spring-mass system, which you've already seen as a model to illustrate energy concepts, but there are other systems you should be familiar with too. At the B level, the study of oscillations is largely descriptive: you should understand the qualitative nature of the motion and be familiar with the period formulas explained in the chapter.

Description

Consider a mass undergoing oscillations or vibrations, such as a spring-mass system oscillating on a frictionless, horizontal surface. The object moves under the influence of a **restoring force**. This force is 0 at the **equilibrium position**, and it tends to bring the mass back to the equilibrium position when the object is displaced from that point. To describe an oscillating system, you'll usually assume the origin is at the equilibrium position. This ensures that the position of the object is the same as the displacement from the origin. In fact, often *displacement* simply refers to the displacement from the origin.

For a spring-mass system, the spring force $F = -kx$ supplies the restoring force. The **amplitude** is the maximum value of the displacement. While displacement may be positive or negative, the amplitude is a positive quantity. The **period** is the time it takes for one complete oscillation, and the **frequency** is the number of oscillations in one second. If the frequency is 10 oscillations/s, then it takes $\frac{1}{10}$ s to complete just one vibration. Generally, you can say

$$T = \frac{1}{f}$$

where T is the period and f is the frequency. The unit for frequency is Hertz (Hz), which represents 1 oscillation.

Simple Harmonic Motion

Any repetitive motion can be described as harmonic motion. But if the restoring force satisfies a particularly simple relation, then the motion is **simple harmonic motion** (SHM). For simple harmonic motion, the restoring force must be directly proportional to the displacement.

$$F_{\text{restore}} = -K \,(\text{displacement})$$

If the displacement doubles, for example, the magnitude of the force also doubles. The minus sign ensures that as the magnitude of the displacement increases, the speed decreases and vice versa.

SPRING-MASS

The spring-mass system obviously satisfies the SHM condition with $F = -kx$ where k is the spring constant and x is the displacement. When the spring-mass system hangs vertically, two things happen. First, gravity is acting, so the total force acting on the mass is now $F = -kx + mg$. This would seem to destroy the SHM condition, because the gravity force isn't proportional to the displacement. A second change occurs, however: The equilibrium position of the mass shifts downward (figure 1).

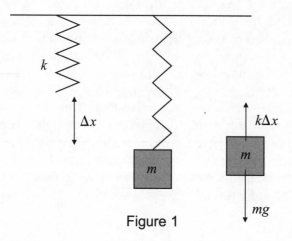

Figure 1

If you attach a mass to a vertical spring and gently allow it to come to rest, the spring force up will just equal the weight:

$$k\Delta x = mg \Rightarrow \Delta x = \frac{mg}{k}$$

Here Δx is the displacement from the unstretched length of the spring. Left on its own, the mass will just sit at this position. If it's displaced further, it will oscillate and this point will be the new center of oscillation, the new equilibrium point. To see this, let x be the displacement from the new equilibrium point (figure 2).

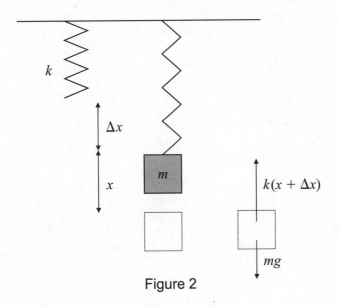

Figure 2

The force acting on the mass is

$$F = -k(x + \Delta x) + mg = -k(x + \tfrac{mg}{k}) + mg$$
$$F = -kx$$

Now if you measure displacements from the new equilibrium point, the system behaves like a spring-mass system with the same k and m, and gravity is eliminated from the problem. The moral of the story is: For vertical springs, find the new equilibrium point, measure displacements from there, and ignore the force of gravity.

SIMPLE PENDULUM

The motion of a simple pendulum is a common repetitive motion. It consists of a point mass m attached to a pivot by a light string of length L (figure 3).

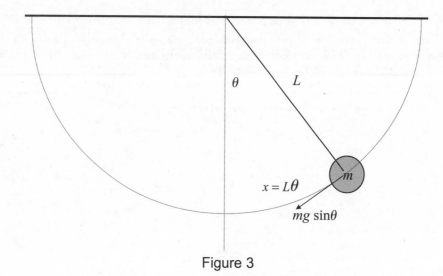

Figure 3

Does it meet the SHM criterion? Clearly the equilibrium position is the point directly below the pivot. Since the mass is constrained to move on a circular arc, the displacement is the arc length. If you use radian measure for the angle, then from the definition of radian measure you get

$$x = L\theta$$

The restoring force is supplied by the component of gravity that tends to bring the mass back along the arc to the equilibrium point. From figure 3 you can see that

$$F_{restore} = -mg \sin\theta$$

Because of $\sin\theta$, the SHM condition can't be met:

$$F_{restore} \neq -Kx$$

However, if θ doesn't get too big, then $\sin\theta \cong \theta$, which means you can replace the sine of the angle by the angle itself. If you don't believe this, try it on your calculator. Use radian mode and take the sine of 0.2 rad, about 11°. Replacing $\sin\theta$ by θ is called the small-angle approximation. In this approximation, you have

$$F_{restore} = -mg \sin\theta = -\frac{mg}{L} L\sin\theta \cong -\left(\frac{mg}{L}\right)(L\theta)$$

$$F_{restore} = -Kx \qquad K = \frac{mg}{L}$$

The end result is that a simple pendulum executes SHM in the small-angle approximation.

REFERENCE CIRCLE

For SHM, you can apply the second law to get

$$F_{\text{restore}} = -Kx = ma$$

$$a = -\frac{K}{m}x$$

For any object executing SHM, the acceleration will be directly proportional to the displacement. Consider an object moving in a vertical circle with a constant speed v_0 and radius R. What does this have to do with SHM? Just imagine a bright light shining down on the object—as the shadow moves on the floor, it's clear that this motion repeats itself (figure 4).

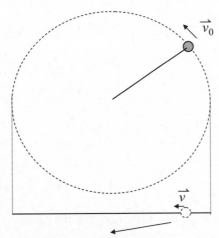

Shadow moves back and forth with properties equal to horizontal component of circularly moving object.

Figure 4

Could it be SHM? Yes, if you can show that the acceleration of the shadow is proportional to its displacement. The key idea is that only the horizontal components of the circularly moving object's properties project down and become properties of the oscillation. For example, at the extreme ends of the oscillation, the circularly moving object is moving vertically, with no horizontal velocity component. This is consistent with the velocity of the oscillator being 0 at the end points. Focusing on the positions and accelerations of the object and the shadow (figure 5), you can see that

$$a = \frac{v_0^2}{R}\cos\theta$$

$$x = R\cos\theta$$

$$a = \frac{v_0^2}{R^2}(R\cos\theta) = \frac{v_0^2}{R^2}x$$

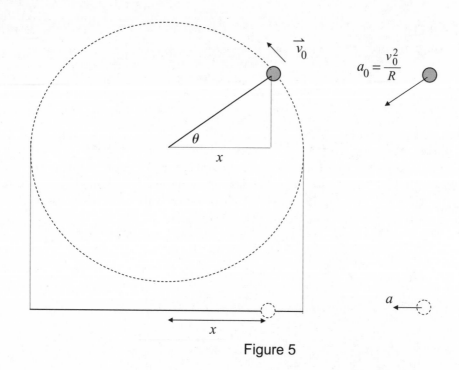

Figure 5

Since v_0 and R are constant, the acceleration of the shadow is directly proportional to its displacement, so its motion is SHM.

Now let's reverse this argument. For every real system executing SHM, you can imagine a **reference circle** whose uniform circular motion matches up with the real system. The reference circle would have to have a radius equal to the amplitude of the real system. The constant speed on the reference circle would be the maximum speed of the real system. The period of the reference circle would be the same as the real system. You can use these ideas to develop an expression for the period of an object executing SHM. Since the object moves one circumference on the reference circle in one period, you have

$$2\pi A = v_0 T \Rightarrow T = \frac{2\pi A}{v_0}$$

Here A is the amplitude and v_0 is the maximum speed of the SHM.

For a spring-mass system, energy conservation tells you that the PE at full extension equals the KE as the object passes through the equilibrium point.

$$E_i = E_f$$

$$\frac{1}{2}kA^2 = \frac{1}{2}mv_0^2 \quad \Rightarrow \frac{A}{v_0} = \sqrt{\frac{m}{k}}$$

Substituting into the equation for T, you get

$$T_{\text{spring}} = 2\pi\sqrt{\frac{m}{k}}$$

This tells you how the period of the spring-mass system depends on the system properties. You can determine the period of a simple pendulum in the small angle approximation by simply replacing k for the spring by $K = \frac{mg}{L}$. This leads to

$$T_{\text{pend}} = 2\pi\sqrt{\frac{L}{g}}$$

Notice that the period of a pendulum is independent of its mass.

EXERCISE

A spring with $k = 100$ N/m hangs vertically with a 2 kg mass at one end currently at rest. A 1 kg mass is gently added to the 2 kg mass, setting the system into oscillation. Determine the period, amplitude, and maximum speed of the oscillation.

The vertical motion doesn't affect the period. Since 3 kg is oscillating, you have

$$T_{spring} = 2\pi\sqrt{\frac{m}{k}} = 2\pi\sqrt{\frac{3}{100}} = 1.1 \text{ s}$$

The system will oscillate about an equilibrium point that's determined by how far the 1 kg mass would stretch the spring if it were allowed to reach equilibrium.

$$\Delta x = \frac{mg}{k} = \frac{(1)(10)}{100} = 0.1 \text{m}$$

Because the 1 kg mass is added gently, the system has no KE when it returns to its highest point. But that means this is also the largest displacement from the new equilibrium point as well, so $A = 0.1$ m.

To find the maximum speed, use energy conservation for a spring-mass system oscillating about the new equilibrium point.

$$E_i = E_f$$

$$\frac{1}{2}kA^2 = \frac{1}{2}mv_0^2$$

$$(100)(0.1)^2 = (3)v_0^2 \implies v_0 = 0.58\frac{m}{s}$$

KEY FORMULAS

Period-Frequency $\qquad\qquad\qquad T = \dfrac{1}{f}$

Period, Spring-Mass $\qquad\qquad T_{spring} = 2\pi\sqrt{\dfrac{m}{k}}$

Period, Simple Pendulum $\qquad T_{pend} = 2\pi\sqrt{\dfrac{L}{g}}$

PRACTICE EXERCISES

SECTION I MULTIPLE CHOICE

1. A mass is attached to a spring on a frictionless, horizontal surface. When it's set into oscillation, its period is T. An equal mass collides head-on with this mass, and the two masses stick together. The oscillation period is now

    (A) T   (B) $\sqrt{2}T$ (C) $2T$ (D) $\dfrac{T}{\sqrt{2}}$ (E) $\dfrac{T}{2}$

2. A spring-mass system with parameters m and k is oscillating vertically. A second spring-mass system with 3 times the mass is set up beside the first. If the two systems are to oscillate in unison, the spring constant of the second system must be

    (A) $3k$ (B) $\dfrac{k}{3}$ (C) $\sqrt{3}k$ (D) $\dfrac{k}{\sqrt{3}}$ (E) $9k$

3. To increase the period of a simple pendulum by a factor of two, you could
      I. double the mass
     II. double the length
    III. quadruple the length

    (A) I only   (B) II only   (C) III only   (D) I and II only   (E) I and III only

4. A given pendulum on Earth has a period T. On the Moon, where the acceleration due to gravity is $\frac{1}{6}$ that of Earth, the period will be

    (A) $\dfrac{1}{6}T$ (B) T (C) $\sqrt{6}T$ (D) $\dfrac{T}{6}$ (E) $\dfrac{T}{\sqrt{6}}$

5. A mass M is attached to a spring on a frictionless, horizontal surface and set into oscillation. A smaller mass sits on top of the first and moves with it without slipping. The static friction force exerted on the smaller mass

    (A) is equal to $\mu_s N$ throughout the motion
    (B) reaches a maximum value as the masses reach their maximum speed
    (C) reaches a maximum value as the masses reach their minimum speed
    (D) reaches a maximum value at a point where the speed is between its maximum and minimum values
    (E) remains constant but is less than $\mu_s N$

6. A mass m is attached to a spring with constant k, hung vertically, and allowed to come to rest. Supporting the mass from below so that the spring cannot stretch further, a student adds a second mass $2m$ to the first mass. The support is then removed, and the system begins to execute vertical oscillations with amplitude

    (A) $\dfrac{mg}{k}$ (B) $2\dfrac{mg}{k}$ (C) $3\dfrac{mg}{k}$ (D) $\dfrac{mg}{2k}$ (E) $\dfrac{mg}{3k}$

CHAPTER 7 PRACTICE EXERCISES

SECTION II FREE RESPONSE

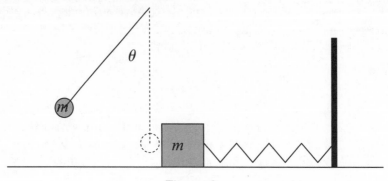

Figure 6

1. A mass m is attached to a light string of length L, making a simple pendulum. It is displaced an angle θ from the vertical and released at $t = 0$. Directly below the pivot of the pendulum is a stationary second mass m equal to the first, attached to a spring of constant k on a frictionless, horizontal surface. When the first mass collides with the stationary mass, the first mass detaches from the string and sticks to the second mass.

    (a) At what time will the spring first reach its maximum compression?

    (b) Find the amplitude of the spring oscillations.

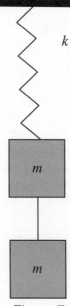

Figure 7

2. Two equal masses m connected by a light string are currently at rest. One of the masses is connected by a spring with constant k to a fixed point directly above it. At $t = 0$, the string is cut, and the mass connected to the spring begins to oscillate.
   (a) Determine the period of the oscillations.
   (b) Determine the amplitude of the oscillations.
   (c) Determine the maximum speed of the mass.
   (d) How much is the spring stretched when the mass is moving at half its maximum speed?

Answers and Explanations

Multiple Choice

1. The answer is B. Since $T \propto \sqrt{m}$, it follows that doubling m increases the period by $\sqrt{2}$.

2. The answer is A. Oscillating vertically doesn't affect the period. Since $T \propto \sqrt{\dfrac{m}{k}}$, if the mass is tripled, then k must be tripled to keep the same period—which is what's required for unison oscillations.

3. The answer is C. The period is independent of the mass and $T \propto \sqrt{L}$, so increasing L by a factor of 4 will double the period.

4. The answer is C. Since $T \propto \dfrac{1}{\sqrt{g}}$, making g smaller by a factor of $\frac{1}{6}$ will increase the period by a factor of $\sqrt{6}$.

5. The answer is C. The static friction force must behave qualitatively like the spring force on the larger mass. Otherwise, the small mass wouldn't oscillate. This force reaches a maximum when the displacement is at its largest value, and here the speed is 0.

6. The answer is B. The equilibrium point before the second mass is added has a spring stretch given by

$$kx_0 = mg \Rightarrow x_0 = \frac{mg}{k}$$

When the second mass is added and released from rest, it will oscillate about a new equilibrium point determined by

$$kx_0' = 3mg \Rightarrow x_0' = \frac{3mg}{k}$$

The difference in the two equilibrium positions is the original displacement of the system with respect to the new equilibrium point. This is the amplitude since there is no KE here.

$$A = x'_0 - x_0 = \frac{2mg}{k}$$

FREE RESPONSE

1. (a) The total time will be $t = \frac{1}{4}T_{\text{pend}} + \frac{1}{4}T_{\text{spring}}$. For the pendulum, you have

$$T_{\text{pend}} = 2\pi\sqrt{\frac{L}{g}}$$

For the spring, $2m$ is oscillating, so you have

$$T_{\text{spring}} = 2\pi\sqrt{\frac{2m}{k}}$$

This means that $t = \frac{\pi}{2}\left(\sqrt{\frac{L}{g}} + \sqrt{\frac{2m}{k}}\right)$.

(b) The maximum compression of the spring will correspond to the amplitude of the oscillations. You can use energy conservation to find the speed of the pendulum mass just before collision.

$$E_i = E_f$$

$$mg(L - L\cos\theta) = \frac{1}{2}mv^2$$

$$v = \sqrt{2gL(1 - \cos\theta)}$$

Next, apply momentum conservation to find the speed of the masses just after collision.

$$P_i = P_f$$

$$mv = 2mv$$

$$V = \frac{1}{2}v = \frac{1}{2}\sqrt{2gL(1 - \cos\theta)}$$

Finally, use energy conservation to determine the maximum compression.

$$E_i = E_f$$

$$\frac{1}{2}(2m)V^2 = \frac{1}{2}kA^2$$

$$A = \sqrt{\frac{2m}{k}}\, V = \frac{mgL(1 - \cos\theta)}{k}$$

2. (a) Gravity doesn't change the period. Since one mass is oscillating, you have

$$T = 2\pi\sqrt{\frac{m}{k}}$$

(b) Initially the two masses are at rest, so the spring force will just equal the force of gravity.

$$kx_0 = 2mg$$

$$x_0 = \frac{2mg}{k} \qquad x_0 \text{ is initial equilibrium point}$$

After the string is cut, the single mass will oscillate about a new equilibrium point determined by m alone.

$$x_0' = \frac{mg}{k} \quad x_0' \text{ is equilibrium point of single mass}$$

Since no initial speed is imparted to the mass when the string is cut, the difference in the two equilibrium positions will be the amplitude of the oscillation. When the mass returns to x_0, it will be instantaneously at rest again.

$$A = x_0 - x_0' = \frac{mg}{k}$$

(c) Use energy conservation. When you measure spring displacements from the new equilibrium point, gravity can be ignored. The initial energy is then all spring potential energy.

$$E_0 = \frac{1}{2}kA^2 = \frac{1}{2}\frac{(mg)^2}{k}$$

The maximum speed occurs when all the energy is kinetic.

$$\frac{1}{2}mv_{max}^2 = E_0 = \frac{1}{2}\frac{(mg)^2}{k} \Rightarrow v_{max} = g\sqrt{\frac{m}{k}}$$

(d) Applying energy conservation using the point where the mass has $\frac{1}{2}$ the maximum speed gives

$$E_0 = E_f$$

$$\frac{1}{2}\frac{(mg)^2}{k} = \frac{1}{2}m\left(\frac{v_{max}}{2}\right)^2 + \frac{1}{2}kx^2$$

$$\frac{(mg)^2}{k} = m\left(\frac{g\sqrt{\frac{m}{k}}}{2}\right)^2 + kx^2 \Rightarrow x = \frac{1}{\sqrt{2}}\frac{mg}{k}$$

8

Fluid Mechanics

In a solid, the molecules or atoms occupy relatively fixed positions, with some fluctuations about these positions. A **fluid** is a substance in which the constituent atoms or molecules don't have fixed positions. **Liquids**, for example, are characterized by moderate forces of attraction between the molecules, resulting in relatively small distances between molecules on the average. Under a given set of conditions, a liquid will have a well-defined volume. **Gases**, on the other hand, are characterized by very weak intermolecular forces. The molecules can move about quite freely and will fill any container in which they are placed, so a gas does not have a characteristic volume. Neither a liquid nor a gas has a shape of its own. In fact, when external forces act on a fluid, it will flow, continuously deforming and redistributing the mass consistent with the laws of mechanics. This chapter will focus on the properties of fluids in the absence of fluid flow—their hydrostatic properties—along with the most basic properties of fluids in motion.

Hydrostatic Pressure

Pressure is a measure of how much of a force is distributed over an area. It's a scalar quantity defined more precisely as

$$p = \frac{F_\perp}{A}$$

Here $F_\perp$ is the magnitude of the force component that's perpendicular to the area A. The unit of pressure is $\frac{N}{m^2}$, called a Pascal (Pa).

A simple example of pressure is a student standing on a horizontal surface. In equilibrium, the normal force supporting the student will be equal in magnitude to the student's weight, $N = mg$. The support force is distributed over the area of the student's shoes, so the pressure exerted on the bottom of the shoes is

$$p = \frac{N}{A} = \frac{mg}{A}$$

If the student stands on one foot, N stays the same because the weight is the same, but the pressure doubles because now the support is distributed over half the area.

Consider a fluid at rest—for example, the water in a still swimming pool. Imagine a small surface placed in the pool at a given depth and oriented in different directions (figure 1).

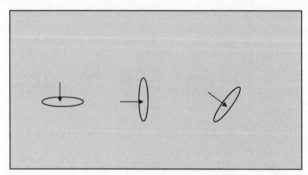

Figure 1

In each case, the force exerted by the fluid on the surface will be perpendicular to the surface. If there were a component parallel to the surface, then the surface would exert an equal and opposite reaction force on the fluid, putting it in motion and contradicting the assumption of the fluid being at rest. The pressure associated with this force is called the **hydrostatic pressure**. Near the Earth's surface, the hydrostatic pressure within a static fluid depends on depth and density. Imagine a column of fluid with density ρ, with cross section A extending from the surface to a depth h (figure 2).

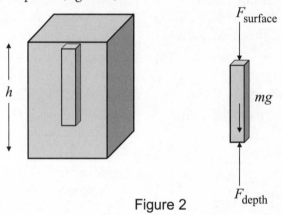

Figure 2

Since it's in equilibrium, the net force on it must be 0. Let's call the pressure at the top of the fluid p_0, and assume that the fluid density doesn't change as a result of p_0. Such fluids are said to be **incompressible**. Water is incompressible to a very good approximation. Gases, on the other hand, are highly compressible. The equilibrium condition is

$$netF = 0$$
$$F_{surface} + mg - F_{depth} = 0 \qquad \text{Define } \rho = \frac{m}{V} = \frac{m}{Ah}$$
$$p_0 A + (\rho A h)g - pA = 0 \Rightarrow p = p_0 + \rho g h$$

The hydrostatic pressure at a given depth of an incompressible static fluid, then, increases linearly from the value of the pressure at the surface.

EXAMPLE

To what depth would a diver have to descend in the ocean for the pressure to be twice the value at the surface? ($\rho = 1{,}000 \; \frac{\text{kg}}{\text{m}^3}$ for water)

At the surface, atmospheric pressure is 1.01×10^5 Pa. This leads to

$$p = p_0 + \rho g h \Rightarrow h = \frac{p - p_0}{\rho g}$$

$$h = \frac{(2.02 - 1.01) \times 10^5}{(1{,}000)(10)} \Rightarrow h = 10\text{m}$$

Notice that if p_0 changes, the fluid pressure changes by the same amount. This is known as **Pascal's principle**:

> Any change in pressure applied to an enclosed incompressible static fluid is transmitted undiminished throughout the fluid.

Hydraulic lifts and presses use Pascal's principle to produce large output forces from moderate input forces. The moderate force F is applied to a small area A of the fluid. The resulting pressure is transmitted throughout the fluid, producing a large force F' over a large area A' (figure 3).

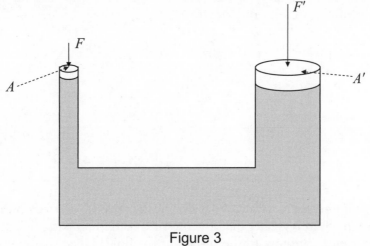

Figure 3

$$p = \frac{F}{A} = \frac{F'}{A'} \Rightarrow F' = F\frac{A'}{A}$$

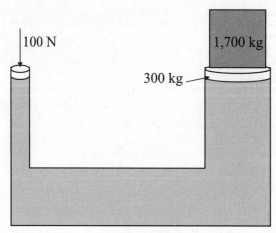

Figure 4

EXAMPLE

A hydraulic lift consists of a platform that is supported by a cylindrical piston, which resides in a tube connected to a reservoir of hydraulic fluid (figure 4). The piston and platform have a mass of 300 kg. The input force is generated at a smaller piston connected to the same reservoir. If the radius of the smaller piston is 2 cm, what must be the radius of the larger piston so that a moderate force of 100 N will lift a 1,700 kg car?

The input force must support the car, piston, and platform with total mass 2,000 kg. From the preceding formula you can write:

$$\frac{A'}{A} = \frac{F'}{F} = \frac{2,000(10)}{100} = 200$$

$$\frac{\pi r^2}{\pi (2)^2} = 200 \Rightarrow r = 28.3 \text{ cm}$$

Buoyancy

When an object is immersed in a fluid of density ρ_f, the pressure exerted on the part of the object that's deeper into the fluid is greater than the pressure exerted on parts that are not as deep. This results in a net force upward toward the surface of the fluid, called the buoyant force. Consider a cylindrically shaped object (figure 5) with height h and cross-sectional area A.

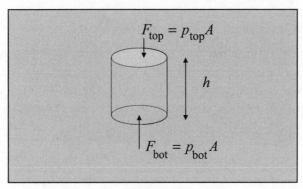

Figure 5

$$F_B = F_{\text{bot}} - F_{\text{top}} = p_{\text{bot}}A - p_{\text{top}}A = (p_{\text{bot}} - p_{\text{top}})A$$

$$F_B = \rho_f ghA = (\rho_f Ah)g = M_f g = M_{\text{displaced}}g$$

$$F_B = W_{\text{displaced}}$$

Here $M_{\text{displaced}}$ and $W_{\text{displaced}}$ refer to the mass and weight of the water displaced by the object. The **buoyant force** is just equal to the weight of the fluid displaced by the object when it's immersed. This is called **Archimedes' principle**:

For any object at equilibrium that is either completely immersed or partially immersed in a fluid, the buoyant force will be equal in magnitude to the weight of the fluid displaced by the object.

If the object is less dense than the fluid, it can't displace its entire volume, so it floats, displacing a weight of water just equal to its entire weight. If an object is denser than water, it will displace its entire volume, but this still won't supply a buoyant force large enough to keep it from sinking.

EXERCISE

Determine the initial acceleration of a 1 kg solid aluminum chunk (density $2,700 \frac{\text{kg}}{\text{m}^3}$) released from rest by a diver 10 m under the ocean.

The net force will be the difference between the weight and the buoyant force. Then, you can use the second law to find the initial acceleration. Use the density and mass of the aluminum to find the volume of the sphere.

$$F_B = W_{\text{displ}} = (\rho_{\text{water}}V)g = \rho_{\text{water}}\frac{m_{al}g}{\rho_{al}}$$

$$F_B = (1,000)\frac{(1)(9.8)}{2,700} = 3.63\text{N}$$

$$a = \frac{netF}{m_{al}} = g - \frac{F_B}{m_{al}} = 9.8 - 3.63 = 6.2\frac{\text{m}}{\text{s}^2}$$

Fluid Flow

When a fluid such as water flows, the motion can be very complex. At every point within the fluid, you can measure the local properties of the fluid—the density, pressure, and velocity of the fluid. When a flow is first established in a long pipe with many twists and turns, these quantities may change rapidly as the water reflects off the boundaries created by the pipe. But if the turns are not too sharp and the flow rate is not too high, a **steady state** can be established. This means that if you focus on an arbitrary point in the flow, the values of the density, pressure, and velocity no longer change at that point. They may vary along the length of the pipe or across the diameter of the pipe, but each point in the flow has its own values of ρ, p, and $\vec{v}$ that don't change. When a real fluid flows through a pipe, the pipe can exert drag forces on the layer of fluid next to it, and between layers of the fluid itself. These forces are called viscous forces, and such flow is called **viscous flow**. This is an energy-absorbing process. While you should be familiar with the concept, the AP test will not address viscous flow in a quantitative way. If the fluid is both incompressible and nonviscous, it is called an **ideal fluid**. The AP test will focus on the steady-state flow of an ideal fluid.

STREAMLINES

In the steady-state condition, the velocity at a given point within the fluid remains the same. You can imagine continuous lines within the fluid, with the velocity of the fluid at a given point tangent to these lines (figure 6).

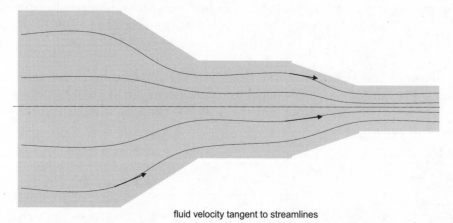

fluid velocity tangent to streamlines

Figure 6

These are called **streamlines**. They provide a visualization of the fluid flow because they represent the trajectories of the fluid particles in the steady state. Notice that streamlines never cross; if they did, a fluid particle would have two possible velocities at a given point, contrary to the assumption of steady-state flow.

CONTINUITY EQUATION

In the steady state, the rate at which fluid mass moves through a tube with a single entry point and a single exit point remains the same, even if the cross section of the tube varies. If this were not the case, you could imagine $1\frac{\text{kg}}{\text{s}}$ of fluid entering the tube and only $0.5\frac{\text{kg}}{\text{s}}$ exiting the tube, which clearly isn't possible in the steady state if there are no other exits. To keep the mass flow rate constant, the fluid must speed up or slow down when the tube cross section changes. In figure 7,

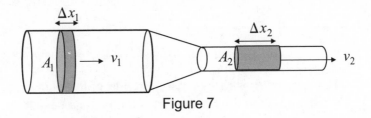

Figure 7

a mass Δm of fluid is shown in regions of a tube with different cross sections. You can calculate the mass flow rate by calculating $\frac{\Delta m}{\Delta t}$ for a fixed value of Δt. The fact that the value of $\frac{\Delta m}{\Delta t}$ remains the same in both sections of the pipe will lead to a relation between the fluid speed and the cross-sectional area. Specifically, you can write

$$\frac{\Delta m}{\Delta t} = \frac{\rho A_1 \Delta x_1}{\Delta t} = \rho A_1 v_1 \qquad\qquad \frac{\Delta m}{\Delta t} = \frac{\rho A_2 \Delta x_2}{\Delta t} = \rho A_2 v_2$$

$$\rho A_1 v_1 = \rho A_2 v_2$$

$$A_1 v_1 = A_2 v_2$$

This is called the **continuity equation**. For an incompressible fluid in the steady state, the fluid will speed up or slow down in inverse proportion to the ratio of cross-sectional areas. If the area doubles, for example, the speed becomes half as much.

EXAMPLE

Blood flows out of the heart into the aorta (inner radius of 0.009 m), where its speed is 0.33 m/s. Eventually it reaches the capillary system, where the fluid speed is 3.4×10^{-4} m/s. Find the effective cross-sectional area of the entire capillary system.

$$A_{\text{aorta}} v_{\text{aorta}} = A_{\text{cap}} v_{\text{cap}}$$

$$\pi(0.009)^2 (0.33) = A_{\text{cap}}(3.4 \times 10^{-4})$$

$$A_{\text{cap}} = 0.25\,\text{m}^2$$

BERNOULLI'S EQUATION

The continuity equation tells you that when a horizontal pipe is constricted, the fluid speeds up. This must mean that each element of the fluid is accelerated as it enters the constricted region. The force responsible for this acceleration is a result of the pressure difference in the two regions.

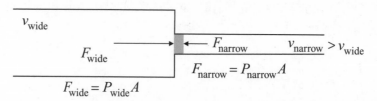

The greater pressure in the wide part of the pipe accelerates the fluid as it enters the narrow section.

Figure 8

Figure 8 focuses on an element of fluid as it enters the narrow region where the cross-sectional area is A. Applying Newton's second law, you get

$$netF = ma$$
$$P_{wide}A - P_{narrow}A = ma > 0$$
$$P_{wide} > P_{narrow}$$

In a horizontal pipe, then, a region of fast-moving fluid will have a lower pressure than a region of slow-moving fluid.

You have also seen that in the static situation, fluid pressure depends on the depth. If a fluid is motionless in a pipe that can rise or fall vertically, the lower sections of pipe will have a higher pressure (figure 9).

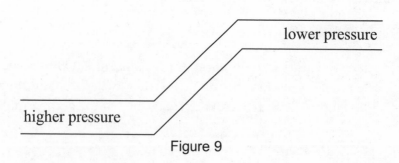

Figure 9

This will continue to be true if the fluid is moving, as long as the cross-sectional area remains constant. If you allow for the cross-sectional area to change too, then the situation gets more complicated because of the pressure changes associated with fluids moving at different speeds. The forces on an element of fluid due to pressure differences and gravity, however, can be incorporated into the work-energy theorem to produce a relationship known as **Bernoulli's equation**. In the steady-state flow of an ideal fluid of density ρ, the following equation is satisfied along a given streamline:

$$\frac{1}{2}\rho v^2 + \rho g h + p = \text{constant}$$

For certain types of fluid flow called **irrotational**, this equation is true even across streamlines. Imagine putting a little paddle wheel into the fluid. If the fluid flows so that the wheel doesn't turn, the flow is irrotational. One way for a flow to be irrotational is for the fluid speed to be uniform over a given cross section of pipe (figure 10).

Uniform fluid speed across the flow
will not cause the paddle wheel to turn.
Figure 10

Notice the similarity between Bernoulli's equation and the conservation of mechanical energy relation. Instead of mass, density appears. You can think of the first term as the KE density at a point. The second term is the gravitational PE density. Notice that the pressure p plays the role of a potential energy density. If you compare the flow at two different positions, you can write

$$\frac{1}{2}\rho v_1^2 + \rho g h_1 + p_1 = \frac{1}{2}\rho v_2^2 + \rho g h_2 + p_2$$

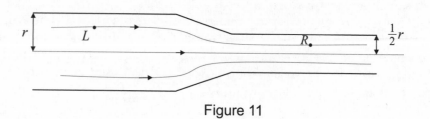

Figure 11

EXAMPLE

In figure 11, water is moving at point L, where the pipe radius is r, with a speed of 5 m/s. Point R is on the same streamline but is inside a region where the pipe radius is $\frac{1}{2}r$. What is the difference in pressure between L and R?

First, use the continuity equation to find the speed at R.

$$A_L v_L = A_R v_R$$

$$\pi r^2(5) = \pi\left(\frac{1}{2}r\right)^2 v_R \Rightarrow v_R = 20\,\frac{m}{s}$$

Next, use Bernoulli's equation, noting that there is no height difference.

$$\frac{1}{2}\rho v_1^2 + \rho g h_1 + p_1 = \frac{1}{2}\rho v_2^2 + \rho g h_2 + p_2$$

$$p_1 - p_2 = \frac{1}{2}\rho v_2^2 - \frac{1}{2}\rho v_1^2$$

$$\Delta p = \frac{1}{2}(1,000)(20^2 - 5^2) = 1.888 \times 10^5\,Pa$$

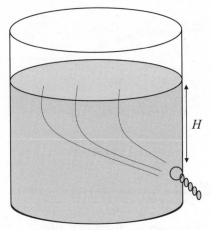

Figure 12

EXAMPLE

A cylindrical water tank filled to a height has a small hole in its side at a distance H below the water level in the tank. Find the speed of the water as it exits the hole (figure 12).

You can apply Bernoulli's equation, focusing on a point at the top of the tank (where the fluid speed is assumed to be essentially 0), and a point on the same streamline just outside the hole. You can make the reasonable assumption that the pressure at both points is just atmospheric pressure.

$$\frac{1}{2}\rho v_1^2 + \rho g h_1 + p_1 = \frac{1}{2}\rho v_2^2 + \rho g h_2 + p_2$$

$$0 + \rho g H + p_{\text{atm}} = \frac{1}{2}\rho v_2 + p_{\text{atm}}$$

$$v = \sqrt{2gH}$$

Notice that this is the same result as if the fluid element had just fallen freely through a height H.

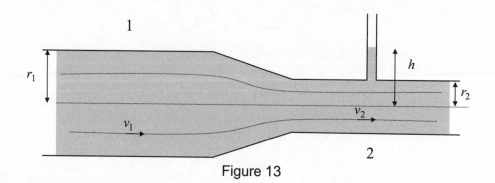

Figure 13

EXAMPLE

A cylindrical pipe has two regions labeled 1 and 2 with different radii r_1 and r_2. A narrow tube with cross section a, open to the atmosphere on top, is connected to the pipe in region 2 as shown (figure 13). If the fluid speed and pressure are v_1 and p_1, respectively, in region 1, determine the height h above the centerline of the fluid in the narrow tube in terms of the stated quantities.

First, use the continuity equation to determine v_2.

$$A_1 v_1 = A_2 v_2 \Rightarrow v_2 = v_1 \frac{r_1^2}{r_2^2}$$

Next, determine p_2, the pressure in region 2, using Bernoulli's equation.

$$\frac{1}{2}\rho v_1^2 + \rho g h_1 + p_1 = \frac{1}{2}\rho v_2^2 + \rho g h_2 + p_2$$

$$p_2 = p_1 + \frac{1}{2}\rho(v_1^2 - v_1^2) \text{ since } h_1 = h_2$$

$$p_2 = p_1 + \frac{1}{2}\rho v_1^2\left(1 - \frac{r_1^4}{r_2^4}\right)$$

Finally, notice that the pressure p_2 supports the column of water in the tube. Since this column doesn't move vertically, you can treat it statically, with net vertical force on the column equal to 0.

$$netF = (p_2 a - p_{\text{atm}} a) - m_{\text{column}}\, g = 0$$

$$(p_2 a - p_{\text{atm}} a) - (\rho h a)g = 0 \Rightarrow h = \frac{1}{\rho g}(p_2 - p_{\text{atm}})$$

Then substitute for p_2.

$$h = \frac{1}{\rho g}\left(p_1 - p_{\text{atm}} + \frac{1}{2}\rho v_1^2\left(1 - \frac{r_1^4}{r_2^4}\right)\right)$$

KEY FORMULAS

Pressure
$$p = \frac{F_\perp}{A}$$

Hydrostatic Pressure
$$p = p_0 + \rho g h$$

Pascal's Principle
$$F' = F\frac{A'}{A}$$

Archimedes' Principle
$$F_B = W_{\text{displ}}$$

Continuity Equation
$$A_1 v_1 = A_2 v_2$$

Bernoulli's Principle
$$\frac{1}{2}\rho v^2 + \rho g h + p = \text{constant}$$

CHAPTER 8 PRACTICE EXERCISES

SECTION I MULTIPLE CHOICE

1. A hydraulic lift is designed for a gain of 100, so that a 10 N force applied at the input piston will produce a force of 1,000 N at the output piston. If the radius of the input piston is 2 cm, the radius of the output piston is

    (A) 200 cm   (B) 0.02 cm   (C) 400 cm   (D) 20 cm   (E) 0.05 cm

2. A cube of side L is made of a substance that is ¼ as dense as water. When placed in a calm water bath, the cube will

    (A) float with $\frac{1}{2} L$ above the surface
    (B) sink to the bottom
    (C) float with $\frac{1}{4} L$ above the surface
    (D) float with $\frac{1}{4} L$ below the surface
    (E) float with $\sqrt[3]{\frac{1}{4}}$ below the surface

3. A cylindrical pipe has a radius of 12 cm in one region where the fluid speed is 0.2 m/s. In another region, the pipe is narrower with a radius of 4 cm. The fluid speed in this region is most nearly

    (A) $9 \frac{m}{s}$ (B) $0.6 \frac{m}{s}$ (C) $1.8 \frac{m}{s}$ (D) $0.011 \frac{m}{s}$ (E) $0.067 \frac{m}{s}$

4. A water pump is attached to the left end of a horizontal pipe that consists of a rigid section and a flexible second section that can have its cross-sectional area adjusted. A pool needs to be filled with the output of the flexible section. Which of the following will increase the rate at which the pool will fill?
    I. Increase pump pressure.
    II. Decrease the cross-sectional area of the second section.
    III. Increase the cross-sectional area of the second section.

    (A) I only   (B) II only   (C) III only   (D) I and II only   (E) I and III only

5. An ideal fluid flows through a pipe that runs up an incline and gradually rises to a height H. The cross-sectional area of the pipe is uniform. Compared with the flow at the bottom of the incline, the flow at the top is

    (A) moving slower at lower pressure
    (B) moving slower at higher pressure
    (C) moving at the same speed at lower pressure
    (D) moving at the same speed at higher pressure
    (E) moving faster at lower pressure

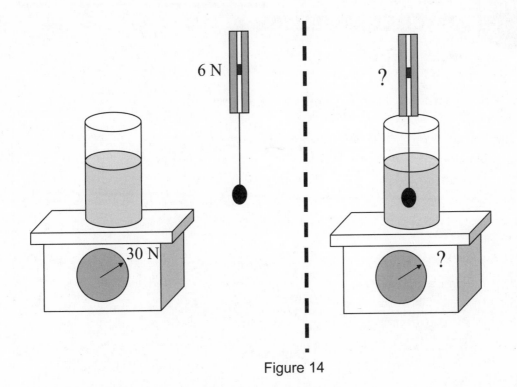

Figure 14

6. A beaker of water sits on an electronic scale with an initial reading of 30 N. A mass with 3 times the density of water hangs from a spring scale with an initial reading of 6 N. Still attached to the spring scale, the mass is completely immersed in the water. The readings on the two scales (in electronic, spring order) will be

(A) 30 N, 2 N   (B) 32 N, 6 N   (C) 36 N, 2 N   (D) 32 N, 4 N   (E) 36 N, 4 N

PRACTICE EXERCISES

SECTION II FREE RESPONSE

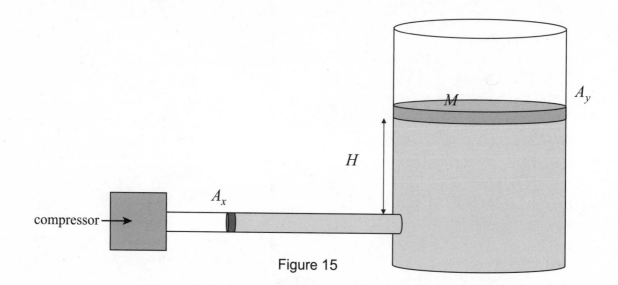

Figure 15

1. A piston of cross section A_x can move inside a long tube that's connected to a large cylindrical reservoir with cross section A_y of fluid that has a density ρ. Currently a piston of mass M is supported at the top of the cylinder at a height H above the long tube. Compressed air is pumped to the left of the small piston and maintains it in its current position.

   (a) Find the pressure of the compressed air.

   The piston needs to be raised an amount Δy.
   (b) How far must the small piston move?
   (c) How much must the air pressure be increased to lift the piston?

2. A vendor at a flea market for the rich and famous claims the crown he is selling is pure gold. On a precise spring scale, you weigh the crown and read a value of 25.14 N. Next, you immerse the crown in water while it's still hanging from the scale, this time getting a reading of 20.65 N. Since you know the ratio of gold density to water density is 19.32, what do you conclude about the vendor's claim?

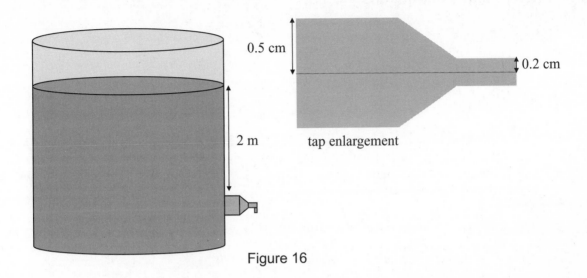

0.5 cm

0.2 cm

2 m

tap enlargement

Figure 16

3. A large storage container in a commercial wine cellar is cylindrical in shape. To test the contents (density of 1,000 $\frac{kg}{m^3}$), you can insert a tapping mechanism near the base of the cylinder. This mechanism consists of a larger cylindrical pipe of radius 0.5 cm that narrows to 0.2 cm at the spigot. Currently, the tapping device is 2 m below the wine level in the container. Assume the space above the wine in the container is maintained at atmospheric pressure and that wine is an ideal fluid. You may also assume that loss of wine through the spigot does not appreciably change the volume of wine in the container.

(a) Find the time it will take to fill a 1 L flask at the spigot.

(b) Determine the speed of the fluid as it enters the tapping device.

(c) Find the difference between atmospheric pressure and the fluid pressure just inside the tapping device.

Answers and Explanations

MULTIPLE CHOICE

1. The answer is D. $F_{out} = F_{in} \frac{A_{out}}{A_{in}} = F_{in} \frac{\pi r^2_{out}}{\pi r^2_{in}}$, so $1{,}000 = 10 \frac{r^2_{out}}{2^2} \Rightarrow r_{out} = 20$ cm

2. The answer is D. The object will float because it is less dense than water, and it will displace an amount of water just equal to its weight. Since water is 4 times as dense, it will displace only one-quarter of its volume, so that one-quarter of the "height" will lie below the surface.

3. The answer is C. The continuity equation is

$$A_1 v_1 = A_2 v_2 \Rightarrow v_2 = v_1 \frac{A_1}{A_2} = (0.2)\frac{\pi(12)^2}{\pi(4)^2} = 1.8\frac{m}{s}$$

4. The answer is A. Since the pressure at the end of the line is always one atmosphere, Bernoulli's equation tells you that increasing the pressure at the beginning will result in an increase in the fluid speed at the end of the line for any cross section. Changing the cross-sectional area will not affect the amount of water that gets into the pool; the continuity equation states that the same amount will flow.

5. The answer is C. Since the area didn't change, the continuity equation implies that the fluid speed remains the same. Bernoulli's equation then tells you that the pressure at height H must be less.

$$\tfrac{1}{2}\rho v_{bot}^2 + p_{bot} = \tfrac{1}{2}\rho v_{top}^2 + \rho g H + p_{top} \qquad v_{bot} = v_{top}$$

$$p_{top} = p_{bot} - \rho g H$$

6. The answer is D. Since the density is 3 times as great as water, the object will experience a buoyant force of one-third its weight, or 2 N. The spring scale will then read $6 - 2 = 4$ N. The reaction to the buoyant force acts on the water and eventually the electronic scale, producing an extra downward force of 2 N. The scale then reads 32 N.

FREE RESPONSE

1. (a) Without the upper piston, the pressure at the lower piston is just the fluid pressure at depth h. Adding the piston weight creates an extra pressure of $\frac{Mg}{A_y}$, which will be transmitted undiminished to all points within the fluid. The total pressure the compressed air must supply is

$$p_{air} = \rho g h + \frac{Mg}{A_y}$$

(b) The fluid volume increase in the large cylinder must equal the fluid volume change in the tube.

$$A_y \Delta y = A_x \Delta x \Rightarrow \Delta x = \Delta y \frac{A_y}{A_x}$$

(c) The increase in pressure is needed to support the extra fluid in Δy. The old pressure could already support the piston and the fluid to height H, so

$$\Delta p = \rho g \Delta y$$

2. The difference in the two scale readings is the buoyant force (the buoyancy of air isn't taken into account). Since this is the weight of the displaced water, you have

$$\Delta W = 25.14 - 20.65 = 4.49 = \rho_{water} g V_{crown} \Rightarrow V_{crown} \Rightarrow V_{crown} = \frac{4.49}{\rho_{water} g}$$

Then use the first reading to calculate the density.

$$\rho_{crown} = \frac{M_{crown}}{V_{crown}} = \frac{W_{crown}}{g V_{crown}} = \frac{25.14}{\left(\frac{4.49}{\rho_{water}}\right)} \Rightarrow \frac{\rho_{crown}}{\rho_{water}} = 5.60$$

The crown is much less dense than pure gold, and the vendor is mistaken.

3. (a) Apply Bernoulli's principle, comparing the spigot output, where the pressure is just atmospheric pressure, to the fluid at the top of the container, where the fluid is essentially at rest and where the pressure is also one atmosphere.

$$\frac{1}{2}\rho v_1^2 + \rho g h_1 + p_1 = \frac{1}{2}\rho v_2^2 + \rho g h_2 + p_2^2$$

$$0 + \rho g h + p_{atm} = \frac{1}{2}\rho v_{out}^2 + p_{atm}$$

$$v_{out} = \sqrt{2gh} = 6.32 \frac{m}{s} = 632 \frac{cm}{s}$$

Since the area of the spigot opening is $\pi(0.2)^2$, in a time T, the output volume of the spigot will be

$$V_{out} = \pi(0.2)^2(632)T$$

Since you need $1\ L = 1{,}000\ cm^3$, you have
$$1{,}000 = 79.4T \Rightarrow T = 12.6s$$

(b) You can apply the continuity equation comparing the spigot output with the input of the tapping device.

$$A_{in}v_{in} = A_{spig}v_{spig} \Rightarrow v_{in} = v_{spig}\frac{A_{spig}}{A_{in}} = \frac{6.32\pi(0.2)^2}{\pi(0.5)^2} = 1.01\frac{m}{s}$$

(c) Use Bernoulli's equation, comparing the top of the fluid with the beginning of the tap.

$$\frac{1}{2}\rho v_1^{\,2} + \rho gh_1 + p_1 = \frac{1}{2}\rho v_2^{\,2} + \rho gh_2 + p_2$$

$$0 + \rho gh + p_{atm} = \frac{1}{2}\rho v_{in}^{\,2} + p_{in}$$

$$p_{in} - p_{atm} = (1,000)(10)(2) - \frac{1}{2}(1,000)(1.01)^2$$

$$\Delta p = 1.95 \times 10^4 Pa$$

9

Thermal Physics

Thermal physics is the study of large systems that contain many particles, typically 10^{23} or more. A glass of water, a sheet of copper, and the air in a balloon are all examples of this kind of large system. Interestingly, scientists were studying the behaviors of such systems even before the development of atomic theory. Classical thermodynamics was remarkable because it could say so much about the behavior of systems without even considering what kinds of substances made up the systems. The three laws of thermodynamics formed a basis for describing and analyzing a wide range of phenomena; the only limitation was that the system had to be large enough.

With the advent of atomic and molecular theory, scientists developed a more fundamental understanding of the thermodynamic laws. They were seen as the manifestation of the properties of particles making up the system. The branch of science that explains large-scale properties of systems through analysis of the properties and interactions of constituent particles is called statistical mechanics. A modern approach to thermal physics combines the classical approach's generality with the microscopic viewpoint of statistical mechanics, and this is the approach used in the B-level Physics. In this chapter, you'll be introduced to the key concepts of temperature, internal energy, heat, and work. You'll also become acquainted with the laws of thermodynamics, with particular emphasis on their application to ideal gases.

Temperature

Back in first grade, your teacher might have had the entire class stand in a line, then rearranged the order of the line so that tall kids were at one end and short kids were at the other end. You could think of height as the ordering parameter that determined who was in front and who was at the rear. Temperature is an ordering parameter in much the same way. If you have three objects, you can order them from hottest to coldest (figure 1), but what is the nature of the properties "hot" and "cold"?

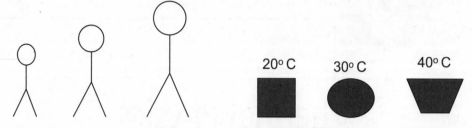

Students can be ordered by height.

Objects can be ordered by temperature. Energy will flow spontaneously from higher temperatures to lower temperatures.

Figure 1

Quite simply, object A is hotter than object B if energy flows spontaneously from A to B when the objects are placed in a position to exchange energy. **Temperature** measures the tendency for energy to leave an object spontaneously. If there's no tendency for A to give up energy to B or for B to give up energy to A, the two objects are at the same temperature, in **thermal equilibrium**.

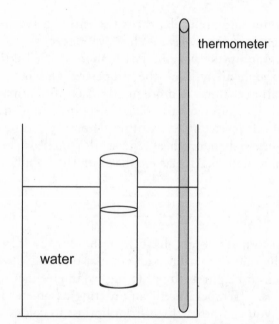

Liquid in the test tube is in thermal equilibrium with the water in the beaker.

Figure 2

Suppose you have a test tube with a liquid in it, immersed in a beaker of water (figure 2). Let's also assume that the water and liquid are in thermal equilibrium, so that there's no tendency for either to gain or lose energy to the other. If you place a thermometer into the water and wait for equilibrium to be established, the thermometer will read the temperature of the water. Now what will happen if you place the thermometer in the liquid? Nothing! The liquid and the water are in thermal equilibrium, and after the thermometer comes to equilibrium with the water, it will automatically be in equilibrium with the liquid. This is the essence of the **zeroth law of thermodynamics**:

If body A is in thermal equilibrium with body B and body B is in thermal equilibrium with body C, then body A is in thermal equilibrium with body C.

While this may seem obvious, it has been recognized as an implicit assumption to classical thermodynamics only since 1931. Because the other three laws of thermodynamics depend on this assumption, it was termed the zeroth law instead of the fourth law.

Since you know that matter is made of atoms and molecules, an obvious question is, What does temperature measure in terms of their properties and interactions? A fundamental answer that would be correct in all situations is beyond the scope of the B-level test, but for ordinary matter at reasonable temperatures, the answer is simple: Temperature is a direct measure of the average translational KE of the molecules or atoms in a material. When an object has a high temperature, the average molecular KE is high. There is rapid, random motion of the molecules, and if the object is allowed to exchange energy with another object at a lower temperature and lower average KE, some of the energy in the hot object will tend to end up in the cold one.

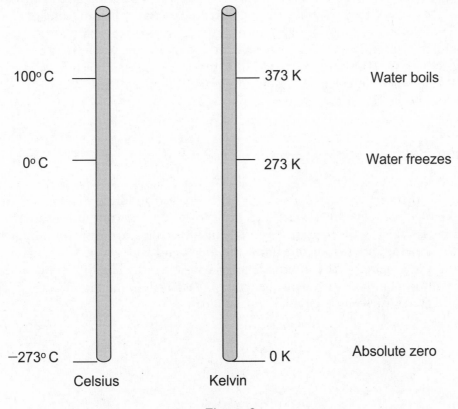

100° C	373 K Water boils
0° C	273 K Water freezes
−273° C	0 K Absolute zero
Celsius	Kelvin

Figure 3

There are two common scales (figure 3) used to measure temperature, the Celsius scale and the Kelvin scale. Only the Kelvin scale directly measures the average KE of the molecules, in the sense that doubling the average KE means doubling the temperature. The zero point of the Celsius scale is set at the freezing point of water, where there is still considerable molecular movement. The Kelvin scale is identical to the Celsius scale except that the zero point is set at $-273.15°$ C, which corresponds to the absolute minimum in molecular motion for any material. Rounding off, you can get the Kelvin scale temperature by adding 273 to the Celsius temperature.

EXERCISE

A glass of water at 22° C is heated so the temperature rises by 3° C. Find the starting temperature in Kelvin, and express the change in Kelvin.

$$T_K = T_C + 273 = 22 + 273 = 295 \text{ K}$$

Because the Kelvin and Celsius degrees are the same size, the change is 3 K.

Internal Energy

Within a substance, the molecules or atoms are constantly moving and exerting forces on each other. As a result, they have kinetic and potential energy. The sum total of all the energy associated with molecular motions and positions is called the **internal energy, U**. In a solid, for example, the vibrating molecules have KE, and as they move away from their equilibrium positions they also acquire PE, much like many masses connected by springs. In a monatomic gas where interactions among molecules are often extremely weak, the internal energy is simply the KE of the gas atoms.

Work and Heat

Imagine a system consisting of many particles—a wood block. Let's place the system into an environment where it can exchange energy with the surroundings. There are two types of energy exchange between this system and the surroundings: work and heat. If the energy exchange is associated with organized motion of molecules in the surroundings, **work** has been done. For example, if someone grabs the block and slides it over a rough surface, the block will get warmer, and the internal energy will increase. The organized motion of the hand with all of its molecules moving together is responsible for the increase in the block's internal energy, so work has been done on the block.

You could also place the block on a surface that's at a higher temperature than the block. Energy will then flow spontaneously from the surface into the block. Here there's no organized motion in the surroundings (the surface), only the random motion of the molecules in the surface. Because the average KE of the molecules in the surface is higher, there's a tendency for some of the energy in this random motion to be transferred to the block. This type of energy transfer, a result of random motions in the surroundings, is called **heat**. Heat can be transferred only between systems that are at different temperatures.

First Law of Thermodynamics

Work and heat both refer to energy transfers. They differ in terms of what takes place in the surroundings, but their effects are the same for the system: The internal energy changes by the amount of the transfer. This is the **first law of thermodynamics**:

$$\Delta U = Q + W$$

Here Q refers to the heat transferred to the system, and W refers to work done on the system. The total change in the internal energy is the sum of the two types of transfers, so the first law is a statement of energy conservation. After a transfer has occurred, the work or heat becomes part of the internal energy. You don't say that a system contains heat or work: It contains internal energy that can be changed through transfers of heat or work. When heat flows *into* a system, Q is positive. W is positive when the work done *on* the system results in an increase in the system's energy.

Heat Transfer Mechanisms

Heat transfer between two systems can occur only if the systems are at different temperatures. There are three common mechanisms for this transfer.

Conduction is a process where the molecular collisions between the warmer substance and the cooler substance result in heat transfer to the cooler substance. When a metal pot is placed on a hot plate, the molecules in the hot plate are vibrating very rapidly. At the molecular level, they have many collisions with the molecules at the bottom of the pot and transfer energy to them. These molecules in turn will collide with neighboring molecules, and eventually the heat will conduct through the entire pot. Notice that in conduction, the energy is transferred, but the molecules remain more or less where they were. On the B-level test, you won't be asked to calculate conduction rates, but you should have a qualitative grasp of the parameters that affect these rates.

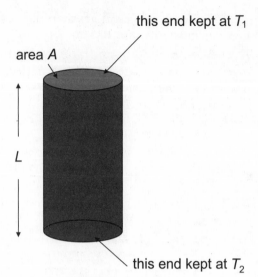

area A

this end kept at T_1

L

this end kept at T_2

Conduction depends on length, area, and
temperature difference.

Figure 4

Let's look at a concrete example: If a metal bar of length L and cross-sectional area A has its
ends held at two different temperatures (figure 4), the rate at which heat flows between the
ends will increase if you

(a) increase the temperature difference ΔT between the ends

(b) increase the area A

(c) decrease the length L

There will also be a factor that depends on the material; for example, metals conduct better
than wood.

Convection is a process that occurs in fluids, involving transport of the more energetic
molecules themselves. If there is water in your pot on the hot plate, as the bottom of the pot
gets hot, the water molecules at the bottom will gain energy, and the volume they occupy
will increase. Since their mass remains the same, the density of the water near the bottom
decreases. Cooler, denser water from above sinks to the bottom as the warmer, less dense
water rises. A region of fluid circulation called a convection cell is set up, with the hot
molecules physically moving from the bottom to the top of the pot. Unlike conduction and
convection, **thermal radiation** is a heat transfer mechanism that doesn't need a material
medium between the two systems exchanging heat. At any temperature above absolute 0,
thermal motion of atoms and molecules can cause electrons in the material to move to
excited energy levels. They won't remain in these levels long, and as they jump to a lower
level, the released energy is carried away in the form of electromagnetic radiation (see
Chapters 14 and 18). Electromagnetic radiation can be created in a variety of ways. When
it's the result of the random excitations associated with thermal activity, it's called thermal
radiation. When you sit in front of a fireplace and feel the warmth on your face, it's primarily

thermal radiation that you're absorbing. Of course, you also emit radiation, but since you are cooler than the fire, there will be a net transfer to you.

Ideal Gas

An **ideal gas** is an idealization, an approximation of the behavior of real gases. Specifically, you can make these assumptions about the gas:

1. On average, the space between molecules is much larger than the actual size of the molecules. Within their container, the molecules themselves occupy a negligible volume.
2. Molecules collide elastically with the container walls and each other.
3. While molecules exert forces on each other during a collision, there are no long-range forces between them, so there is no internal potential energy in an ideal gas.

At pressures and densities that aren't too high, most gases will behave close to the ideal model. Important atmospheric gases like oxygen and nitrogen, however, form diatomic molecules. They still exhibit ideal behavior, but because they're shaped like small dumbbells, they can rotate as well as translate. This adds a level of complexity to their description that isn't covered at the B level. Instead, you can focus on understanding the behavior of monatomic ideal gases.

IDEAL GAS LAW

At the macroscopic level, the gas properties to measure are the volume (V), pressure (p), temperature (T), and amount of substance. You can express the latter in many ways; the number of moles (n) and the number of molecules (N) are the most common. In recent years, the B-level test questions involving gases have been written in terms of the **mole**. The quantities p, V, n, and T aren't independent but are related by an equation of state. You can perform various experiments where two of these quantities are held fixed and a relation between the other two is determined. These "mini-laws" have names like Boyle's law and Charles's law (figure 5).

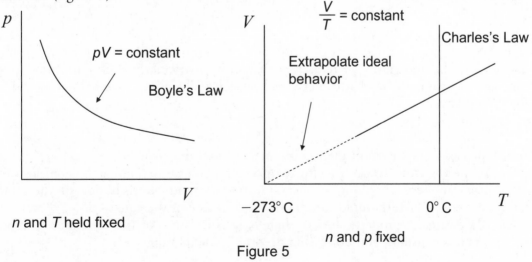

Figure 5

Notice that Charles's law is a linear relation between volume and temperature. In the ideal limit, as the temperature is decreased to absolute 0, the volume of the gas goes to 0. Of course, real gases will deviate from this, but if you use the Kelvin scale, you'll have not only a linear relation but direct proportion between V and T as well. You'll find a similar result when you look at pressure vs. temperature (law of Gay-Lussac). The results of all the various two-variable laws are consistent with one general law, the **ideal gas law**:

$$\frac{pV}{nT} = R$$

Here R is the so-called ideal gas constant with a value of 8.31 $\frac{J}{Kmol}$. The value of R will change if different units for pressure, volume, or amount of substance are used, but the gas law is valid only if the temperature unit is kelvins. The law tells you that however you attempt to adjust the parameters of the gas, when equilibrium is established, the ratio of $\frac{pV}{nT}$ will keep the same value.

EXERCISE

Find the volume occupied by 1 mole of ideal gas maintained at 1 atm pressure and 0° C, standard temperature and pressure (STP).

Using 1 atm = 1.01×10^5 Pa and 0° C = 273 K, you have

$$V = \frac{nRT}{p} = \frac{1(8.31)(273)}{1.01 \times 10^5}$$

$$V = 0.0224 m^3 = 22.4 L$$

The fact that the ratio $\frac{pV}{nT}$ remains constant is particularly useful in comparing the properties of a gas before and after a change has occurred. Calling "before" state 1 and "after" state 2, you have

$$\frac{p_1 V_1}{n_1 T_1} = \frac{p_2 V_2}{n_2 T_2}$$

Two properties of this form of the gas law make it useful:
1. While you must use kelvins for temperature, you can use any consistent unit for the other properties as long as the same unit is used on each side of the equation; conversion factors would cancel out on each side of the equation.
2. If a particular property doesn't change, it cancels out of the equation. As long as it remains constant, you don't even need to know its value.

EXERCISE

Two moles of gas are in a container whose volume can be adjusted with a moveable piston. When the volume is 3.2 L, the temperature is 25° C. With a constant pressure maintained, heat is added to the gas and the piston is allowed to move until the volume is 5.1 L. Find the final temperature.

Here both n and p remain the same, so the equation becomes

$$\frac{V_1}{T_1} = \frac{V_2}{T_2} \Rightarrow T_2 = T_1 \frac{V_2}{V_1}$$

$$T_2 = (298)\frac{5.1}{3.2} = 475 \text{ K} = 202° \text{ C}$$

KINETIC MOLECULAR THEORY

Kinetic molecular theory attempts to understand the large-scale behavior of gases by analyzing the behavior of the molecules themselves. By applying Newton's laws of mechanics to the collisions of the molecules within the container and making reasonable assumptions about the effects of many molecules in the gas, you can arrive at equations that relate temperature and pressure to molecular properties. Consider a cube of side L aligned with the xyz axes, containing N molecules with average speed v (figure 6).

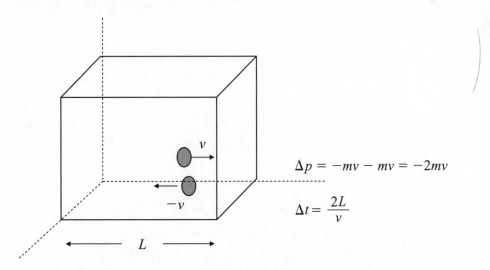

$$\Delta p = -mv - mv = -2mv$$

$$\Delta t = \frac{2L}{v}$$

A molecule of mass m collides elastically with one wall.

Figure 6

If you focus on 1 molecule of mass m bouncing back and forth parallel to the x-axis, you can see that with each collision with the right face, the molecule changes momentum by $-2mv$. This momentum change is effectively spread out over the time $\Delta t = \frac{2L}{v}$, since that's how long it takes to make another collision with the same wall. The average force exerted on the molecule by this wall is

$$f_{av} = \frac{\Delta p}{\Delta t} = \frac{-2mv}{\frac{2L}{v}} = -\frac{mv^2}{L}$$

Newton's third law tells you that the force on the wall is equal and opposite to this. The pressure due to this force will be $p = \frac{f_{av}}{\text{area}} = \frac{f_{av}}{L^2}$. If you assume that on the average, $\frac{1}{3}$ (three space dimensions) of all the molecules are moving in this back-and-forth manner, you can find for the total pressure on the wall:

$$p = \frac{1}{3}N\frac{mv^2}{L^3} = \frac{1}{3}N\frac{mv^2}{V}$$

$$pV = \frac{1}{3}Nmv^2 = \frac{2}{3}N(\frac{1}{2}mv^2) = \frac{2}{3}V(KE_{av})$$

Here KE_{av} is the average kinetic energy of a molecule. If you now invoke the ideal gas law:

$$pV = nRT = NkT$$

$$k = \frac{R}{6.02 \times 10^{23}} = 1.38 \times 10^{-23} \frac{J}{K} \quad (k \text{ is called Boltzmann's constant})$$

You can equate terms to derive

$$KE_{av} = \frac{3}{2}kT$$

This confirms the interpretation of temperature: It's directly proportional to the average translational KE of the molecules. Since the internal energy of an ideal gas is just the total KE of all the molecules, you have

$$U = \frac{3}{2}NkT = \frac{3}{2}nRT$$

Notice that the internal energy depends only on the temperature.

Work and *pV* Diagrams

Consider a fixed amount of ideal gas in a container whose volume can vary by means of a moveable piston (figure 7).

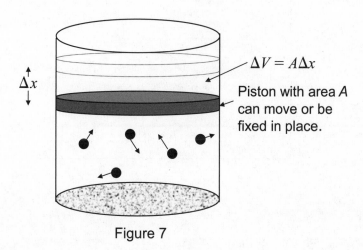

Figure 7

Gas molecules are constantly colliding with the piston, exerting a force F on it, and if the piston is allowed to move an amount Δx, work will be done. If the piston were to move rapidly, then the gas properties wouldn't be uniform throughout the volume, and the pressure would be difficult to define. But if you require that the piston move slowly, then at any instant you're always close enough to equilibrium so that the ideal gas law will be valid and the pressure will be well defined. You can assure that the piston will move slowly if you're always close to mechanical equilibrium, where the external pressure and the gas pressure are nearly equal.

In the following examples, assume this is the case. That will assure that the work done by the gas on the surroundings is the negative of the work done by the surroundings on the gas. Let's suppose the pressure remains constant as the gas expands an amount $\Delta V = A\Delta x$. The work done by the gas in the expansion will be

$$W_{by} = F\Delta x = (pA)\Delta x$$

$$W_{by} = p\Delta V$$

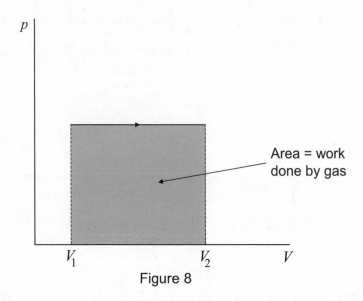

Figure 8

It's easy to interpret this work on a pV diagram (figure 8): It's just the area under the graph. Even if the pressure doesn't remain constant, the area under the pV graph will always be the area under the graph. If ΔV corresponds to an increase in volume, then the area is positive. When a process is depicted on a pV diagram, directional arrows are used on the graph. In a process that moves to the right, the gas will do positive work on the surroundings; in a process that moves to the left, the gas will do negative work on the surroundings (in other words, the surroundings do work on the gas).

When you're describing a process that involves a gas expanding or compressing, you'll need to use specific nomenclature. A process is called **isobaric** if the pressure remains constant throughout; it is called **isothermal** if the temperature remains constant; and if no heat energy enters or leaves the gas, it is called **adiabatic**. The corresponding graphs are called isobars, isotherms, and adiabats (figure 9).

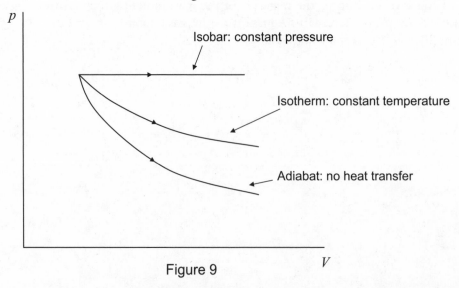

Figure 9

Finally, let's connect the gas/piston system with the first law of thermodynamics:

$$\Delta U = Q + W$$

In this relation, W is positive for work done on a gas, so when the gas does work on the surroundings, W will be negative. Try to become comfortable with thinking about the work done in expansion either as work done on the gas by the surroundings (W) or as work done by the gas on the surroundings ($-W$).

Recall that the internal energy of an ideal gas is

$$U = \frac{3}{2}nRT$$

If heat energy flows into this system while a constant volume is maintained, no work is done by the gas. You can write

$$\Delta U = \frac{3}{2}nR\Delta T = Q$$

For 1 mole to increase in temperature $1°$ C, an amount of energy $\frac{3}{2}R$ must be added.

Now let's add heat energy to the gas while maintaining a constant pressure. The temperature of the gas will increase, but some of the heat energy will be used in moving the piston out to maintain a constant pressure:

$$\Delta U = Q + W$$

$$\frac{3}{2}nR\Delta T = Q - p\Delta V$$

From the gas law, you know that $p\Delta V = nR\Delta T$. Substituting above, you get

$$Q = \frac{5}{2}nR\Delta T$$

To raise 1 mole of gas $1°$ C while maintaining a constant pressure, you must add $\frac{5}{2}R$ of heat energy.

Second Law of Thermodynamics

The **second law of thermodynamics** can be stated in several different ways, some more fundamental than others. Let's look at three of these ways.

1. The spontaneous flow of energy between two systems is always from the warmer system to the colder system.

You've already encountered this idea in defining temperature. Notice that energy conservation (the first law) wouldn't be violated if energy flowed spontaneously from the cold object to the hot one, as long as every Joule was accounted for. The fact that this never happens indicates that some other principle is at work, which you can identify with the second law. Energy can be made to move from a cold body to a hot body, but it never happens spontaneously.

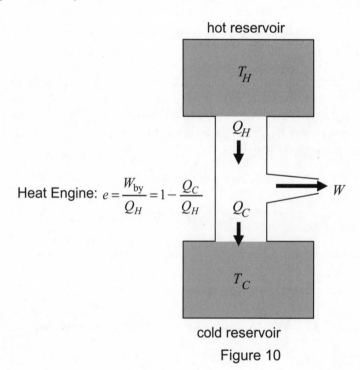

Figure 10

To understand the next form of the second law, you'll need to understand the concept of a heat engine. A **heat engine** (figure 10) is a device that extracts heat energy Q_H from a hot reservoir maintained at temperature T_H, converts some of it to useful work W, and finally expels unused "waste heat" Q_C into a cold reservoir maintained at T_C. **Reservoirs** are systems so large that they can give up heat energy without changing their temperature significantly. The **efficiency** of any engine would be most naturally defined as the ratio of useful work to initial energy available: $e = \dfrac{W_{by}}{Q_H}$. The first law also tells you that $Q_H = Q_C + W_{by}$. Now you can also write the efficiency as

$$e = 1 - \frac{Q_c}{Q_H}$$

To get better or even ideal efficiency, it looks as if you'd only have to design a device so that Q_C was as small as possible. Unfortunately, as was shown by Carnot, the maximum efficiency is determined not by any clever engineering but by the temperatures of the two reservoirs:

$$e = 1 - \frac{T_c}{T_H}$$

This is called the **Carnot efficiency**. While energy conservation would allow for $Q_C = 0$ and $e = 1$, another principle prevents this from occurring. This other principle is the next way of stating the second law:

2. The maximum efficiency that can be achieved by a heat engine operating between reservoirs held at T_H and T_C is $e = 1 - \frac{T_c}{T_H}$.

One type of heat engine uses the expansion of an ideal gas to generate useful work output. The behavior of the engine can be displayed on a pV diagram. Because the engine always returns to its initial state after a number of processes, the diagram and overall process is called a cycle (figure 11).

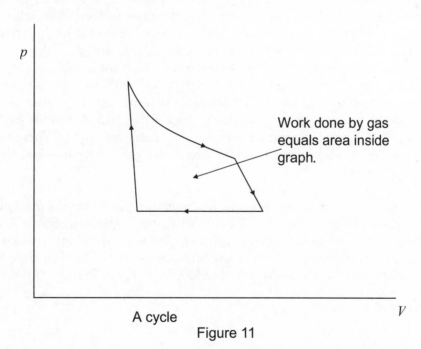

A cycle

Figure 11

For any cycle, the net work done by the gas is the area contained inside the graph, and the overall change in internal energy is 0, since you end up back in the same state you began.

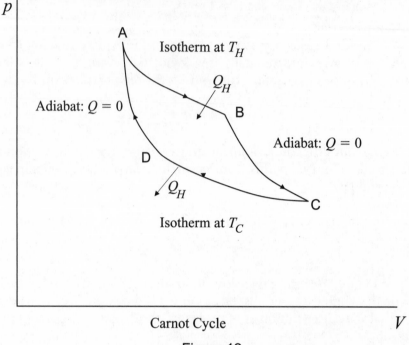

Carnot Cycle

Figure 12

An important cycle to understand is the **Carnot cycle**. In a Carnot cycle (figure 12), you have an ideal gas confined in a container with a moveable piston, as in figure 7. The bottom of the container will allow heat transfer and can be placed on a hot reservoir (T_H), a cold reservoir (T_C), or an insulator. The cycle proceeds in four steps, all done slowly so the gas can always be considered very close to equilibrium, with the work done by the gas on the surroundings being just the negative of the work done by the surroundings on the gas.

1. With the gas initially on the hot reservoir at some initial pressure and volume (A on the graph), heat energy Q_H will flow into the gas, and it expands isothermally at T_H to point B. Since temperature remains the same, the internal energy doesn't change. The gas does work, however—the area under the isotherm—and the first law says $0 = Q_H + W_1$.

2. The container is removed from the hot reservoir, placed on the insulator, and allowed to expand further to point C. This is adiabatic expansion because no heat enters or leaves the gas while it's on the insulator. The work done in expansion comes at the price of internal energy, and the gas cools. At point C, the temperature is the same as the cold reservoir T_C, so $\Delta U_2 = \frac{3}{2}nR(T_C - T_H) = W_2$, since $Q_2 = 0$.

3. The container is placed on the cold reservoir and compressed isothermally at T_C to point D. Heat energy Q_C flows out of the gas into the cold reservoir. Once again, as in step 1, the internal energy doesn't change, but work is done on the gas by the surroundings, the area under this isotherm. Notice that this area is less than the area under the T_H isotherm because you're compressing at temperature T_C, where the pressure is lower. For this process, $0 = Q_C + W_3$.

4. The container is placed on the insulator and compressed adiabatically. Work is done on the gas, its temperature increases, and you continue until A is reached. For this process, $\Delta U_4 = \frac{3}{2}nR(T_H - T_C) = W_4$, since $Q_4 = 0$.

Notice that the cycle consists of two isotherms connected by two adiabats. Along each isotherm, $\Delta U = 0$. For each adiabat, you have $W = \Delta U$. Notice also that $W_2 = -W_4$, since each adiabat connects the same two isotherms, but process 2 is an expansion while process 4 is a compression. Table 1 summarizes the various changes for each step.

	ΔT	ΔU	Q	W
A → B isothermal expansion	0	0	$Q_H > 0$	$-Q_H$
B → C adiabatic expansion	$T_C - T_H$	W_2	0	$W_2 = \frac{3}{2}nR(T_C - T_H)$
C → D isothermal compression	0	0	$Q_C < 0$	$-Q_C$
D → A adiabatic compression	$T_H - T_C$	W_4	0	$W_4 = \frac{3}{2}nR(T_H - T_C)$

Table 1

EXERCISE

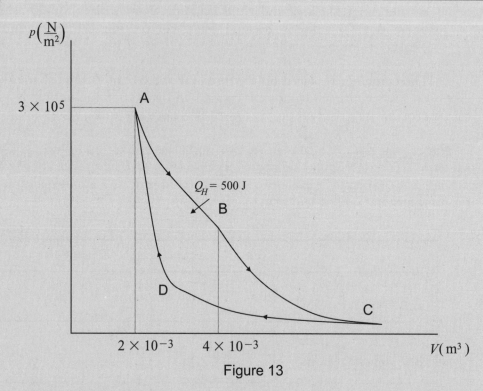

Figure 13

A Carnot engine using a monatomic ideal gas as a working substance operates between two reservoirs held at 300 K and 200 K, respectively. Starting at point A with pressure and volume as indicated on the graph (figure 13), the gas expands isothermally to point B, where the volume is 4×10^{-3} m^3. 500 J of heat energy is absorbed by the gas in this process.

(a) How many moles of gas are present?
(b) Find the work done on the gas during the $A \to B$ process.
(c) Find the work done on the gas during the process $B \to C$, adiabatic expansion.
(d) How much heat is expelled in the process $C \to D$?
(e) Find the change in internal energy in the process $D \to A$.

Solution:
(a) Using the gas law and the given pressure, volume, and temperature, you have

$$n = \frac{PV}{RT} = \frac{(3 \times 10^5)(2 \times 10^{-3})}{(8.31)(300)} = 0.24 \text{ moles}$$

(b) Along the $A \to B$ isotherm, there's no change in internal energy, so the first law gives you $\Delta U = 0 = Q + W$. But Q is given as 500 J, so $W = -500$ J.

(c) Since $B \to C$ is adiabatic ($Q = 0$), the first law tells you that $\Delta U = W$. The adiabat connects two isotherms where you know the temperature, and since an ideal gas internal energy depends on only temperature, you have

$$\Delta U = \tfrac{3}{2}nR\Delta T = \tfrac{3}{2}(0.24)(8.31)(200 - 300) = -299 \text{ J}$$

Then, $W = -299$ J.

(d) For the Carnot cycle, $e = 1 - \frac{T_C}{T_H} = 1 - \frac{200}{300} = 0.33$. For a any engine, you can also write the efficiency as $e = 1 - \frac{Q_C}{Q_H}$. You can combine these to find Q_C, since Q_H is known.

$$0.33 = 1 - \frac{Q_c}{500} \Rightarrow Q_C = 333 \text{ J}$$

(e) For $D \to A$, once again you're connecting two isotherms. Since internal energy depends on only temperature, you have

$$\Delta U = \tfrac{3}{2}nR\Delta T = \tfrac{3}{2}(0.24)(8.31)(300 - 200) = 299 \text{ J},$$
$$\text{the opposite of } B \to C$$

Entropy

To understand the second law in its most fundamental form, you need to understand the concept of entropy. You won't have to perform any calculations involving entropy on the AP test, but you should have a basic grasp of the concept. The **entropy** of a system, which depends on the system's energy and volume, tells you the number of ways that the molecules in the system can have their individual properties changed while the large-scale properties, such as pressure and temperature, stay the same. It's a property of the system as a whole, just like energy or pressure.

Let's look at an example with identical coins. If you have 5 identical coins, there are 6 possible outcomes of heads and tails when the coins are thrown, as long as you don't care which particular coin is a head or a tail. These outcomes are called **macrostates**, and in this case they are

$$5H \quad 4H1T \quad 3H2T \quad 2H3T \quad 1H4T \quad 5T$$

If you look at the 5H macrostate, you can see there's only 1 way this macrostate can be achieved: All the coins must be heads. There are 5 ways to achieve the 4H1T macrostate, however, depending on which of the 5 coins is a head. You can say that this macrostate has 5 **microstates**, and it has a higher entropy than the 5H macrostate. The 3H2T and 2H3T macrostates each have 10 ways that they can be achieved; these macrostates each have 10 microstates, so they have a higher entropy than the 5H state or the 4H1T state. When you throw the coins, each of the total of $32 = 2^5$ microstates is equally likely, and the macrostate with the greatest number of microstates, the macrostate with the highest entropy, will be the most probable.

That last sentence is really the essence of the second law. When you look at large systems like the ideal gas with 10^{23} particles, the most likely macrostate—described by p, V, and T and obeying the ideal gas law—has so many microstates associated with it that it's the only one you have any chance of observing. When you allow two systems at different temperatures to exchange energy with each other, the final macrostate of the system as a whole will be the one with the most number of microstates, maximizing the entropy. Now you can say why heat spontaneously flows from hot to cold: It's overwhelmingly more likely than the alternative. In terms of entropy, the second law is:

3. A closed system, or a system that won't transfer energy to or from its surroundings, will always develop to maximize the entropy of the system. The entropy will never decrease.

KEY FORMULAS

First Law of Thermodynamics	$\Delta U = Q + W$
Ideal Gas Law	$\dfrac{pV}{nT} = R \qquad \dfrac{p_1 V_1}{n_1 T_1} = \dfrac{p_2 V_2}{n_2 T_2}$
Average KE of Gas Molecule	$KE_{av} = \dfrac{3}{2} kT$
Internal Energy of Ideal Gas	$U = \dfrac{3}{2} nRT$
Expansion Work	$\Delta W_{by} = p\Delta V$
Heat Engine Efficiency	$e = 1 - \dfrac{Q_C}{Q_H}$
Carnot Efficiency	$e = 1 - \dfrac{T_C}{T_H}$

CHAPTER 9

PRACTICE EXERCISES

SECTION 1 MULTIPLE CHOICE

Questions 1 and 2

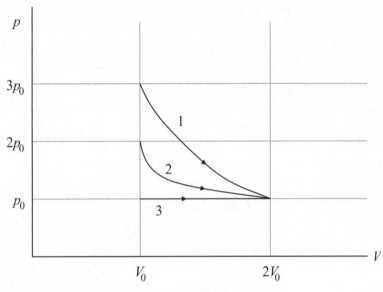

Figure 14

1. 1 mole of ideal gas is brought to a final state F by one of three processes that have
    different initial states as shown in the figure. What is true for the temperature change
    between initial and final states?

    (A) It's the same for all processes.
    (B) It's smallest for process 1.
    (C) It's smallest for process 2.
    (D) It's smallest for process 3.
    (E) It's the same for processes 1 and 2.

2. What is true for the work done by the gas?

    (A) It's positive for processes 1 and 2, but negative for process 3.
    (B) It's smallest for process 1.
    (C) It's smallest for process 2.
    (D) It's smallest for process 3.
    (E) Zero work is done along process 3.

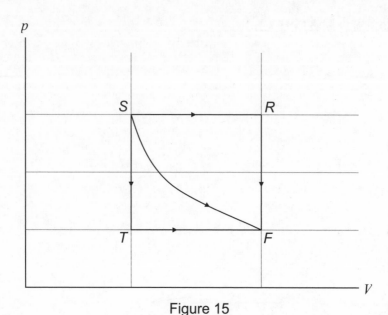

Figure 15

3. An ideal gas is brought from $S \rightarrow F$ by three different paths: SRF, SF, STF. The temperature at S is the same as the temperature at F. Which of the following is true?

(A) Process SRF occurs at constant temperature.
(B) The work done by the gas along SRF is the same as the work done by the gas along STF.
(C) Net heat into the gas along STF is greater than the work done by the gas along this path.
(D) The change in the internal energy is the same for all three paths.
(E) Work done by the gas along STF is greater than the work done by the gas along SF.

Questions 4 and 5

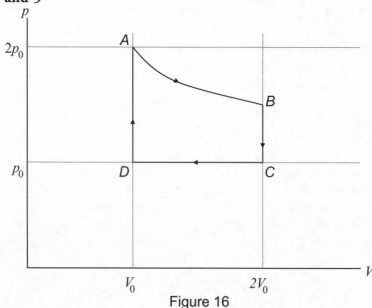

Figure 16

4. What is true for the process $D \to A$?

 (A) $\Delta U = 0$ $Q > 0$
 (B) $\Delta U = 0$ $Q < 0$
 (C) $W = 0$ $\Delta U > 0$
 (D) $W = 0$ $\Delta U < 0$
 (E) $W = 0$ $Q = 0$

5. What is true for the two-step process $A \to B \to C$?

 (A) $\Delta U = 0$ $Q = 0$
 (B) $\Delta U = 0$ $Q > 0$
 (C) $W = 0$ $Q > 0$
 (D) $W = 0$ $Q < 0$
 (E) $W > 0$ $Q < 0$

6. 200 J enters a Carnot engine from the hot reservoir, held at 400 K. During the entire cycle, 50 J of useful work is performed by the engine. What is the temperature of the cold reservoir?

 (A) 100 K
 (B) 200 K
 (C) 300 K
 (D) 250 K
 (E) 150 K

7. For an ideal gas in a container with fixed volume and constant temperature, which of the following is true?
 I. Pressure results from molecular collisions with the walls.
 II. The molecules all have the same speed.
 III. The average kinetic energy is directly proportional to the temperature.

 (A) I, II, and III
 (B) I and II only
 (C) II and III only
 (D) II only
 (E) I and III only

8. 1 mole of ideal gas is in a container of volume V, temperature T, and pressure p. If the volume is halved and the temperature is doubled, the pressure will be

 (A) p
 (B) $2p$
 (C) $4p$
 (D) $\frac{1}{2}p$
 (E) $\frac{1}{4}p$

9. Two identical containers contain 1 mole each of two different monatomic ideal gases, gas A and gas B, with the mass of gas B 4 times the mass of gas A. Both gases are at the same temperature. 10 J of heat is added to gas A, resulting in a temperature change ΔT. How much heat must be added to gas B to cause the same ΔT?

(A) 10 J
(B) 100 J
(C) 40 J
(D) 2.5 J
(E) 1,600 J

10. The entropy of a closed macroscopic system will never decrease because

(A) energy wouldn't be conserved if entropy decreased
(B) for large systems, the probability of such a decrease is negligible
(C) mechanical equilibrium couldn't be sustained with a decrease in entropy
(D) heat can never be made to flow from a cold object to a hot object
(E) molecular motions reach their minimum only at absolute 0

11. During a certain process, 600 J of heat is added to a system. While this occurs, the system performs 200 J of work on the surroundings. The change in internal energy of the system is

(A) 200 J
(B) 800 J
(C) 400 J
(D) −400 J
(E) impossible to determine without knowing the temperature

12. Which of the following is *not* true about thermal radiation?

(A) It's a mechanism of energy exchange between systems at different temperatures.
(B) It involves atomic excitations.
(C) Ice at 0° C will emit thermal radiation.
(D) It requires some material substance to travel through.
(E) It's a byproduct of the food we eat.

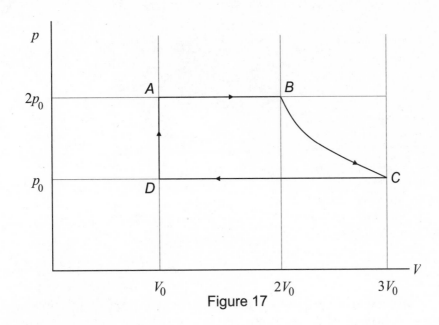

Figure 17

1. 1 mole of monatomic ideal gas is brought through a cycle $A \to B \to C \to D \to A$ as depicted above. All processes are performed slowly. Respond to the following in terms of p_0, V_0, and R.
   (a) Find the temperature at each vertex.
   (b) Find the heat added to the gas for the process $A \to B$.
   (c) Find the work done on the gas for the process $C \to D$.
   (d) Find the heat added to the gas for the process $D \to A$.
   (e) Find the change in internal energy for
       (i) process $B \to C$
       (ii) the entire cycle

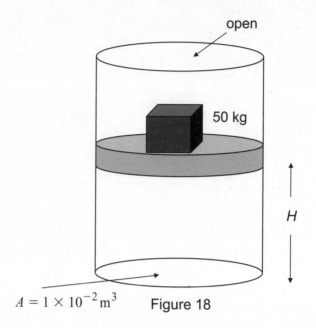

open

50 kg

H

$A = 1 \times 10^{-2}\,\text{m}^3$ Figure 18

2. 2 moles of ideal gas are in a cylindrical container with cross-sectional area 1×10^{-2} m³. The cylinder is fitted with a light, movable piston that's open to the atmosphere, where the pressure is 1×10^5 Pa. A 50 kg mass placed on the piston keeps it in mechanical equilibrium when the temperature is 300 K.
    (a) Find the pressure of the gas.
    (b) Find the height H of the piston.
    (c) The temperature is now reduced to 250 K.
        (i) Find the pressure.
        (ii) Find the new height H of the piston.
    (d) After the temperature change, what was the change in the internal energy of the gas?

Answers and Explanations

Multiple Choice

1. The answer is C. The temperature for the gas at any point will be $T = \frac{pV}{R}$. Since all three processes end at the same temperature, $\frac{p(2V_0)}{R}$, the smallest change will be for the one that starts closest to this value. Process 2 actually begins at this temperature, so its change is 0.

2. The answer is D. The work done by the gas is equal to the area under the pV curve. This is different for all three processes and smallest for process 3.

3. The answer is D. The internal energy of an ideal gas depends only on temperature. If final and initial temperatures are the same, there's no change in internal energy. Since $\Delta U = 0$ for all three paths, $W = -Q$ for each process, which eliminates C. Area considerations eliminate B and E, and the fact that the temperature at R is greater than that at S (gas law) eliminates A.

4. The answer is C. There is no work since the volume doesn't change and the temperature increases (gas law), so the internal energy also increases.

5. The answer is B. The gas law gives you the same temperature at A and C, so $\Delta U = 0$. The work done on the gas is negative (the gas does positive work in expanding), so the first law says $Q > 0$.

6. The answer is C. $e = \dfrac{W_{by}}{Q_H} = \dfrac{50}{200} = 0.25$ from the definition of efficiency. Since this is a Carnot engine, $0.25 = 1 - \dfrac{T_C}{400} \Rightarrow T_C = 300$ K.

7. The answer is E. There is a distribution of speeds among the molecules, leading to an average value, but the molecules certainly do not all have the same speed.

8. The answer is C. The gas law gives you $\dfrac{pV}{T} = \dfrac{p'V'}{T'} \Rightarrow p' = p\dfrac{V}{V'}\dfrac{T'}{T} = 4p$.

9. The answer is A. $\Delta U = \frac{3}{2}nR\Delta T$. For the same number of moles, ΔT depends only on the energy added, not the masses of the gas molecules.

10. The answer is B. A macroscopic closed system will never decrease in entropy because the probability of such a macrostate occurring is essentially 0.

11. The answer is C. Be careful of the signs. In the first law statement, $\Delta U = Q + W$, both Q and W are positive for work done *on* the system. In this problem, $Q = +600$ J but $W = -200$ J, because it is the work done *by* the system.

12. The answer is D. Electromagnetic radiation doesn't need a material medium for transit. In E, we eat to maintain body temperature, and we emit a lot of energy as thermal radiation, derived from our food energy intake. In C, ice is cold by human standards of sensation, but it still radiates.

FREE RESPONSE

1. (a) The gas law gives you at any point: $T = \dfrac{pV}{R}$. This means that $T_A = \dfrac{2p_0V_0}{R}$,

$T_B = \dfrac{4p_0V_0}{R}$, $T_C = \dfrac{3p_0V_0}{R}$, $T_D = \dfrac{p_0V_0}{R}$.

(b) $A \rightarrow B$ occurs at constant pressure. We can use the first law to find Q since we can calculate ΔU from the temperature differences and we can get the work done on the gas from the area under the graph for that part of the cycle.

$$\Delta U = Q + W \Rightarrow Q = \Delta U - W = \frac{3}{2}nR\Delta T - W = \frac{3}{2}nR(T_B - T_A) - W$$

$$Q = \frac{3}{2}R\left(\frac{4p_0 V_0}{R} - \frac{2p_0 V_0}{R}\right) + 2p_0 V_0 = 5p_0 V_0$$

(c) The area under the $D \rightarrow C$ graph is $2p_0 V_0$. The decrease in volume corresponds to positive work done on the gas.

(d) $D \rightarrow A$ is a constant volume process, so no work is done. Use the first law to find Q.

$$\Delta U = Q = \frac{3}{2}nR\Delta T = \frac{3}{2}R\left(\frac{p_0 V_0}{R}\right) = \frac{3}{2}p_0 V_0.$$

(e) i) For $B \rightarrow C$, $\Delta U = \frac{3}{2}nR\Delta T = \frac{3}{2}R\left(-\frac{p_0 V_0}{R}\right) = -\frac{3}{2}p_0 V_0.$

ii) For the entire cycle, you end up back in the same state, so $\Delta U = 0$.

2. (a) The gas pressure will be the sum of the atmospheric pressure and the pressure exerted by the weight sitting on the piston:

$$p = 1 \times 10^5 + \frac{50(10)}{1 \times 10^{-2}} = 1.5 \times 10^5 \text{ Pa}$$

(b) The gas law gives you $V = \frac{nRT}{p} = \frac{2(8.31)(300)}{1.5 \times 10^5} = (1 \times 10^{-2})H \Rightarrow H = 3.3 \text{ m}$

(c) i) The condition for mechanical equilibrium doesn't depend on temperature, so the pressure stays the same.

ii) The number of moles, pressure, and cross sections stays the same, so the gas law gives you

$$\frac{H}{T} = \frac{H'}{T'} \Rightarrow 3.3 \frac{250}{300} = 2.75 \text{ m}$$

(d) $\Delta U = \frac{3}{2}nR\Delta T = \frac{3}{2}(2)(8.31)(250 - 300) = -1,247 \text{ J}$

Electric Force and Electric Field

As its name implies, **electrostatics** is the study of electric charges at rest. In this chapter, you'll look at how these charges exert forces on each other, and you'll explore the field concept. You'll also learn how to calculate the electric field for some simple configurations.

Electric Charge

Electric charge is a fundamental property of many of the basic constituents of matter. There are two types of charge—positive and negative. Charge is a **quantized** entity, which means it has a fundamental unit that cannot be subdivided. The electron carries a negative charge equal to this basic unit, while the proton carries a positive charge equal to this unit. The value of this basic unit is

$$e = 1.6 \times 10^{-19} \text{ C}$$

Here C is short for **Coulomb**, the SI unit of charge. Any macroscopic amount of charge must be an integral multiple of the basic unit.

Coulomb's Law

Electric charges exert forces on each other. Like charges ($++$ or $--$) will repel each other, and unlike charges ($+-$) will attract. For two point charges q_1 and q_2, this force acts along the line connecting the two charges, is directly proportional to the product of the two charges and is inversely proportional to the square of the distance between the two. In symbols (figure 1), the force exerted on q_2 by q_1 is

$$\vec{F}_{1 \to 2} = k \frac{q_1 q_2}{R^2} \hat{R} \qquad\qquad k = 9 \times 10^9 \frac{\text{N} \cdot \text{m}^2}{\text{C}^2}$$

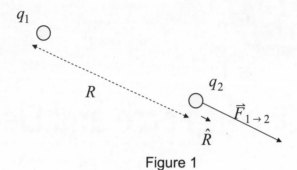

Figure 1

Here $\hat{R}$ is a unit vector directed along the line connecting the two point charges. The force law, known as **Coulomb's law**, also describes the force between two spherical charges where R is the distance between the centers of the two charges.

EXERCISE

Three charges are arranged along the x-axis: $+3 \, \mu C$ at the origin, $-2 \, \mu C$ at $x = -2$ m, and $-4 \, \mu C$ at $x = +3$ m. Find the net force on the charge at the origin (figure 2).

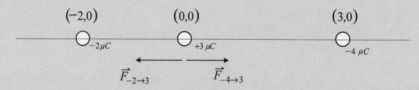

Figure 2

The $+3 \, \mu C$ charge will experience a force in the $-x$ direction due to the $-2 \, \mu C$. The magnitude of this force is

$$F_{-2 \to 3} = 9 \times 10^9 \frac{(3 \times 10^{-6})(2 \times 10^{-6})}{2^2} = 1.37 \times 10^{-2} \, \text{N}$$

The $+3 \, \mu C$ charge will experience a force in the $+x$ direction due to the $-4 \, \mu C$. The magnitude of this force is

$$F_{-4 \to 3} = 9 \times 10^9 \frac{(3 \times 10^{-6})(4 \times 10^{-6})}{3^2} = 1.20 \times 10^{-2} \, \text{N}$$

The net force will point in the $-x$ direction and have a magnitude equal to the difference of the two contributions.

$$netF = 1.5 \times 10^{-3} \, \text{N}$$

Because both charges and vector components can carry a minus sign, it's easy to make sign errors in calculating electric forces. To guard against that, use the process from the example. First, find the magnitude of the force contribution, which is always positive, and then use your diagram to combine the different contributions with the correct signs.

Electric Field

How is it that two charges separated by a distance can exert forces on each other? How does one charge know about the presence of the other? The answer lies in the field concept. Each charge creates an **electric field** in the space surrounding it. Another charge placed at some point will experience the field created by the first charge at that point. But the field at that point exists whether a charge is there to experience it or not. The electric field created by a distribution of charges is defined in terms of the force that a test charge would experience if it were placed at some point. A **test charge** is defined as a positive charge that's so small that its presence doesn't change the original charge distribution. Specifically, that is

$$\vec{E} = \frac{\vec{F}}{q_t}$$

The SI units for electric field are $\frac{N}{C}$. When an electric field is created solely by charges at rest, it's called an **electrostatic field**. In principle, you can measure the field at any point in space by placing a small positive charge at that point and measuring the force exerted on it.

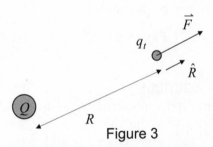

Figure 3

You can use the definition of the field to determine the field created by various distributions of charge. The simplest and most important is the field created by a single point charge. Imagine a positive charge Q (figure 3). By symmetry, the magnitude of the field will depend only on the distance from the charge, and the direction will be radially outward. If you bring a test charge to some point a distance R away, you have for $\vec{E}$:

$$\vec{E} = \frac{(k\frac{Qq_t}{R^2}\hat{R})}{q_t} = k\frac{Q}{R^2}\hat{R}$$

This is the formula for the field created by any point charge. It's also valid for the field created by a spherical charge for points outside of the charge. As mentioned earlier, the direction of the field is radially outward for a positive charge. If Q is negative, the field will be radially inward. The concept of **electric field lines** will help you visualize the field. These are continuous lines that begin on positive charges, end on negative charges, and satisfy two criteria:

1. The electric field at a given point is tangent to the field line that passes through that point.
2. The density of field lines at a point is proportional to the strength of the electric field at that point.

You'll find some examples in figure 4.

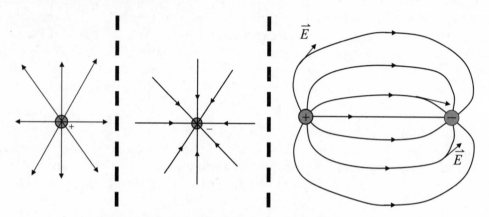

Field lines start on + charges and end on − charges.
The electric field is tangent to field lines.

Figure 4

FIELD DUE TO POINT CHARGE DISTRIBUTIONS

If several point charges are present, you can calculate the total field using the **principle of superposition**. This principle states that the total field at a point can be determined by finding the contribution that each individual charge would make if it were the only charge present, then vector-adding all the contributions. For the principle of superposition to apply to a theory, certain conditions must be met by the laws that underlie the theory. Without going into the mathematical detail of the conditions, let's simply say that this principle can be applied to both electricity and magnetism.

EXAMPLE

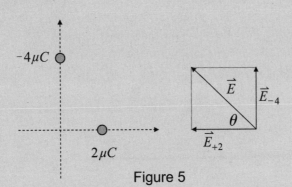

Figure 5

A $-4 \, \mu C$ charge is located at the point (0, 3), and a $+2 \, \mu C$ is located at the point (2, 0). Find the total electric field, magnitude, and direction at the origin (figure 5).

You can find the field created by each charge separately, and then combine them using vector addition.

$$E_{-4} = 9 \times 10^9 \, \frac{(4 \times 10^{-6})}{3^2} = 4 \times 10^3 \, \frac{N}{C} \, (+y \text{ direction})$$

$$E_{+2} = 9 \times 10^9 \, \frac{(2 \times 10^{-6})}{2^2} = 4.5 \times 10^3 \, \frac{N}{C} \, (-x \text{ direction})$$

You can use basic trigonometry to find the magnitude and direction.

$$E = \sqrt{E_{-4}^2 + E_{+2}^2} = 6.02 \times 10^3 \, \frac{N}{C} \qquad \tan\theta = \frac{E_{-4}}{E_{+2}} = \frac{4}{4.5}$$

$$\theta = 41.6°$$

MOTION OF A CHARGE IN AN ELECTRIC FIELD

If you happen to know the field at a given point, you can use the definition of an electric field to find the force on a charge that's placed at the point, assuming the introduction of the charge doesn't change the local charge distribution and the field.

$$\vec{F} = q\vec{E}$$

This equation gives you the force on a charge q placed at a point where the field is $\vec{E}$.

EXAMPLE

Find the acceleration of an electron placed at the origin in the previous example.

You can find the force from the electric field, and then use Newton's second law.

$$F = qE = (1.6 \times 10^{-19})(6.02 \times 10^3) = 9.63 \times 10^{-16} \text{ N}$$

$$F = ma$$

$$9.63 \times 10^{-16} = 9 \times 10^{-31} \, a$$

$$a = 1.1 \times 10^{15} \, \frac{\text{m}}{\text{s2}}$$

KEY FORMULAS

Coulomb's Law $\qquad\qquad \vec{F} = k \frac{q_1 q_2}{R^2} \hat{R}$

Electric Field $\qquad\qquad \vec{E} = \frac{\vec{F}}{q}$

Field of Point Charge $\qquad \vec{E} = k \frac{Q}{R^2} \hat{R}$

PRACTICE EXERCISES

SECTION I MULTIPLE CHOICE

Questions 1 and 2. Two charges are arranged on the corners of a square as pictured.

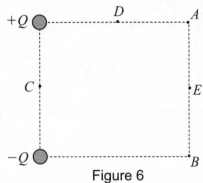

Figure 6

1. The direction of the net electric field at the center of the square is

   (A) ↑ (B) → (C) ↓ (D) ↙ (E) ↗

2. The magnitude of the field will be strongest at

   (A) *A* (B) *B* (C) *C* (D) *D* (E) *E*

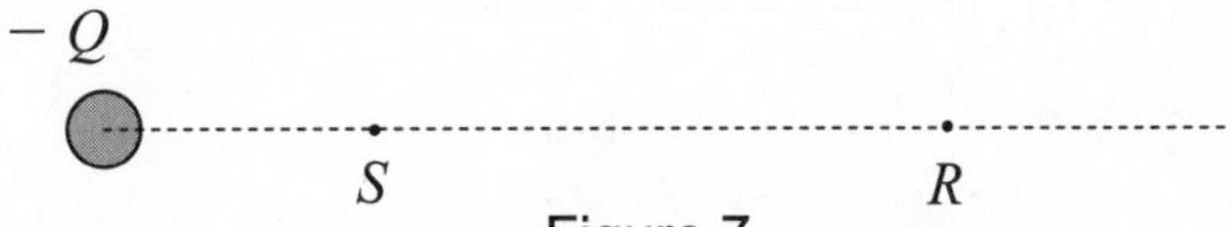

Figure 7

3. The figure shows an isolated negative charge fixed in position. Point *R* is 3 times as far away as point *S*. The ratio of the field strength at *S* to the field strength at *R* is

   (A) 9 to 1 (B) 3 to 1 (C) 1 to 9 (D) 1 to 3 (E) 1 to 1

4. A 2 μC charge with mass 0.1 kg accelerates at 2 m/s^2 in a uniform electric field. The magnitude of the field is most nearly

   (A) $10^5 \frac{N}{C}$ (B) $10^{-5} \frac{N}{C}$ (C) $2 \frac{N}{C}$ (D) $0.2 \frac{N}{C}$ (E) $0.1 \frac{N}{C}$

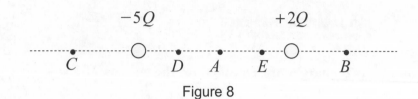

Figure 8

5. Charges $+2Q$ and $-5Q$ are situated as shown. At what point could the electric field be equal to 0?

(A) A (B) B (C) C (D) D (E) E

6. Starting from rest a charge moves a distance d along uniform field lines after which it has a speed v. If an identical charge moves from rest through a distance $2d$ along the same field lines it will have a speed of

(A) $\frac{1}{2}v$ (B) $\frac{1}{4}v$ (C) $\sqrt{2}v$ (D) $2v$ (E) $4v$

7. Charge q with mass m is a distance R from a second charge $2q$ with mass $2m$. If F and a are the force and acceleration of the first charge, the force and acceleration of the second charge are

(A) F and $2a$ (B) $2F$ and a (C) $2F$ and $\frac{1}{2}a$ (D) $2F$ and $2a$ (E) F and $\frac{1}{2}a$

CHAPTER 10

PRACTICE EXERCISES

SECTION II FREE RESPONSE

1. Two charges are located along the x-axis, $-3\ \mu C$ at the origin and $+6\ \mu C$ at the point $(2, 0)$.
   (a) Determine the electric field at the point $(-1, 0)$.
   (b) Find the magnitude and direction of the force on an electron placed at $(-1, 0)$.
   (c) Determine the point on the x-axis where the electric field is 0.

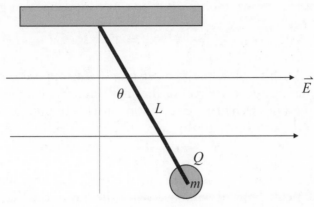

Figure 9

2. A nonconducting sphere of charge $+Q$ and mass m is attached to a string of length L and hangs from a ceiling. When a uniform electric field directed horizontally is introduced, equilibrium is eventually established with the mass hanging at an angle θ with respect to the vertical. In terms of g and the given quantities, find the strength of the electric field and the tension in the string.

3. A positive charge q is initially at the origin and moving with velocity $v_0 > 0$ opposite to a uniform electric field E directed in the negative x direction. The effects of gravity are negligible.
   (a) Determine the maximum coordinate x the charge attains.
   (b) Determine the time it takes for the charge to return to its starting point.
   (c) Determine the speed of the charge when it has the coordinate $-x$.

Answers and Explanations

MULTIPLE CHOICE

1. The answer is C. At the center, the field created by the top left charge is directed along the diagonal away from that charge, while the field created by the bottom left charge is directed toward it along the other diagonal. Since the two fields have the same strength, the horizontal components cancel out.

2. The answer is C. This point is closest to both charges, and the two separate fields created by each charge are in the same direction—down—so there is no cancellation.

3. The answer is A. The field at S is $3^2 = 9$ times bigger since R is 3 times further away.

4. The answer is A. *netF = ma* implies *qE = ma*. Substituting, you get

$$E = \frac{(0.1)(2)}{2 \times 10^{-6}} = 10^5 \, \frac{\text{N}}{\text{C}}$$

5. The answer is B. At this point, the two separate fields oppose each other. Because *B* is closer to the smaller charge, the effect of the smaller charge can be large enough to offset the field due to the bigger charge. At *C*, the two fields oppose each other but can never cancel out due to the proximity to the larger charge. At *A*, *D*, and *E*, the fields reinforce each other.

6. The answer is C. Since *F = qE* is constant, the second charge has twice as much work done on it by the field. Thus, it will have twice the KE as the first charge.

$$\tfrac{1}{2}mv'^2 = 2(\tfrac{1}{2}mv^2) \Rightarrow v' = \sqrt{2}v$$

7. The answer is E. Each charge exerts an equal but opposite force on the other. Since the force on the second is the same, it will have $\frac{1}{2}$ the acceleration since it has twice the inertia.

FREE RESPONSE

1. (a) The field due to the $-3 \, \mu$C charge points in the $+x$ direction and has magnitude

$$E^{-3} = 9 \times 10^9 \, \frac{(3 \times 10^{-6})}{1^2} = 2.7 \times 10^4 \, \frac{\text{N}}{\text{C}}$$

The field due to the other charge points in the $-x$ direction with magnitude

$$E^{+6} = 9 \times 10^9 \, \frac{(6 \times 10^{-6})}{3^2} = 0.6 \times 10^4 \, \frac{\text{N}}{\text{C}}$$

The overall field points in the $+x$ direction with magnitude

$$E = (2.7 - 0.6) \times 10^4 = 2.1 \times 10^4 \, \frac{\text{N}}{\text{C}}$$

(b) An electron placed at this point will feel a force in the opposite direction to the field, the $-x$ direction. The magnitude will be

$$F = qE = (1.6 \times 10^{-19})(2.1 \times 10^4) = 3.4 \times 10^{-15} \, \text{N}$$

(c) Between the two charges on the *x*-axis, the two fields will reinforce each other. To the left of the origin, closer to the smaller charge, the fields tend to cancel out, and if the point is chosen properly, the two contributions will cancel out. This will occur at some point $x < 0$.

$$k \frac{3 \times 10^{-6}}{x^2} = k \frac{6 \times 10^{-6}}{(2-x)^2}$$

$$\frac{(2-x)^2}{x^2} = 2 \Rightarrow \frac{2-x}{x} = \pm\sqrt{2} \quad \Rightarrow x = \frac{2}{1-\sqrt{2}} = -4.83 \text{ m}$$

Only the $-$root gives a negative x-value.

2. This is an equilibrium problem. You can find the net force components in each direction and set them equal 0 to get the two unknowns.
From the freebody diagram (figure 10), you have

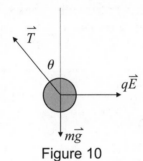

Figure 10

$$netF_x = 0 \qquad\qquad netF_y = 0$$
$$T \sin\theta - qE = 0 \qquad T \cos\theta - mg = 0$$
$$T \sin\theta = qE \qquad\quad T \cos\theta = mg$$

Dividing the two equations gives you

$$E = \frac{mg}{q} \tan\theta$$

The tension is given directly from the y-components:

$$T = \frac{mg}{\cos\theta}$$

3. (a) The acceleration of the charge follows from Newton's second law.

$$netF = ma = qE \Rightarrow a = \frac{qE}{m} \quad \text{(in } -x \text{ direction)}$$

The fourth motion equation can be used to determine the maximum x-coordinate.

$$v^2 = v_0^2 + 2a\Delta x$$

$$0 = v_0^2 - 2\frac{qE}{m}x \Rightarrow x = \frac{mv_0^2}{2qE}$$

(b) Since the static electric force is conservative, the charge will return to the origin with the same speed but in the opposite direction. The first motion equation will then give the time.

$$v = v_0 + at$$

$$-v_0 = v_0 - \frac{qE}{m}t \Rightarrow t = \frac{2mv_0}{qE}$$

(c) Use the fourth motion equation.

$$v^2 = v_0^2 + 2a\Delta x$$

$$v^2 = v_0^2 - 2\frac{qE}{m}(-x) = v_0^2 - 2\frac{qE}{m}\left(-\frac{mv_0^2}{2qE}\right)$$

$$v = \sqrt{2}v_0$$

CHAPTER **11**

Electric Potential and Electric Potential Energy

When you're studying mechanics, you can often simplify problems by introducing the energy concept. Because it's a scalar, energy is easier to work with than vector quantities, such as force and acceleration. In this chapter, you'll learn how electrostatics lends itself to a scalar description as well. The concept of electric potential gives you a tool to describe the energy of any charge placed in a region where an electric field is present. As you develop the concept of electric potential, you'll also learn about important properties of conductors.

Electric Potential

Suppose that several point charges are distributed through a given region (figure 1). At every point in space, an electric field $\vec{E}$ is present. To move a charge slowly from A to B will take work because the agent moving the charge will have to provide a force just equal to the electric force $\vec{F} = q\vec{E}$.

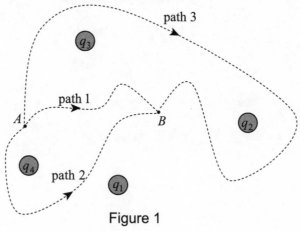

Figure 1

For an electrostatic field, this force is conservative—the work done in slowly moving the charge between A and B is independent of the path taken. This means that the work done along the three different paths in the figure is the same for each path. But the work will depend on the magnitude of the charge moved, since the force is directly proportional to this charge. If you moved a + 2 μC charge, for example, it would take twice the work as a + 1 μC charge. It's useful to define a quantity that's closely related to this work but which doesn't depend on the charge moved. The **electric potential difference** between A and B is defined as

$$\Delta V_{A \to B} = \frac{W_{A \to B}^{\text{agent}}}{q}$$

Here $W_{A \to B}^{\text{agent}}$ is the work an agent must do to move the charge q slowly from A to B. Since this is done slowly, the work done by the agent is just the opposite of the work done by the field.

$$W_{A \to B}^{\text{agent}} = -W_{A \to B}^{\text{field}}$$

For the potential difference, you can write

$$\Delta V_{A \to B} = -\frac{W_{A \to B}^{\text{agent}}}{q}$$

By dividing by q, you make the value of ΔV independent of the charge moved. It will depend only on the two points chosen and, of course, the distribution of charge creating the field in the first place. The units of electric potential difference are $\frac{\text{J}}{\text{C}}$, called a **volt** (V).

EXAMPLE

It takes $+5\ \mu\text{J}$ of work for an agent to move a $+ 2\ \mu\text{C}$ charge from A to B. Determine the potential difference between A and B and the amount of work that would be required to move a $- 3\ \mu\text{C}$ charge between A and B.

From the definition of potential difference, you have

$$\Delta V_{A \to B} = \frac{W_{A \to B}^{\text{agent}}}{q} = \frac{5 \times 10^{-6}}{2 \times 10^{-6}} = 2.5\text{V}$$

To move a $- 3\ \mu\text{C}$ charge through the same potential difference, you have

$$2.5 = \frac{W}{-3 \times 10^{-6}} \Rightarrow W = -7.5\ \mu\text{J}$$

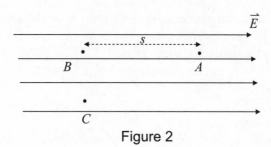

Figure 2

Suppose you have a region of uniform electric field $\vec{E}$ (figure 2). The potential difference between two points can be explicitly written in terms of the field. In moving from A to B along a field line, an agent does positive work or the field does negative work on a small positive charge. You can write

$$\Delta V_{A \to B} = -\frac{W_{A \to B}^{\text{field}}}{q} = -\frac{(-qE)s}{q}$$

$$\Delta V_{A \to B} = Es$$

Note that ΔV is positive as you proceed against the field lines. Only the change in electric potential has physical significance. You can choose the zero point anywhere that's convenient. If you choose A as the zero point, then you can refer to the potential at B and write it as

$$V_B = Es$$

Whenever you refer to the potential at some point, what you're really talking about is the potential difference between that point and the zero point.

You'll need to be careful in using the $\Delta V = Es$ formula. It's exact only if the magnitude of the field is constant along the field line. If the field isn't uniform, this relation will be true if E is interpreted as the average field strength along the field line followed. The s in the formula refers to the distance along the field lines. This means that point C in the figure is at the same potential as B even though it is a greater physical distance from A.

POTENTIAL DUE TO POINT-CHARGE DISTRIBUTIONS

The simplest charge distribution is a single point charge. For example, you could ask what the electric potential is at a distance R from the charge Q. Let's arbitrarily define the 0 of potential to be at infinity, far away from the charge. Then what you really need to know is how much work the field does on a test charge q as it's brought from infinity to the final position (figure 3).

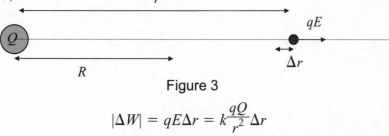

Figure 3

$$|\Delta W| = qE\Delta r = k\frac{qQ}{r^2}\Delta r$$

Mathematically, this isn't that simple because the strength of the field is changing as the test charge gets closer to Q. This means that the magnitude of the little bit of work done by the field as the charge moves the small distance Δr is

$$|\Delta W| = k\frac{qQ}{r^2}\Delta r$$

which depends on r, the current position.

To find the total work, you'll need to sum up all of these. With calculus, the answer is

$$W_{\text{field}} = -k\frac{qQ}{R}$$

Then, relative to infinity, the potential at R is

$$V = k\frac{Q}{R}$$

This is the electric potential a distance R from a point charge Q. It will also be valid for a spherical charge with R measured from the center.

When several point charges are present, the potential at a point can be determined using the superposition principle. You can find the potential due to each charge individually as if none of the others are present and then add the individual values. Symbolically, you can write

$$V = k\frac{q_1}{r_1} + k\frac{q_2}{r_2} + \dots$$

Because the potential is a scalar, this is an easy operation. Unlike using superposition with the electric field, there are no directions to worry about.

EXAMPLE

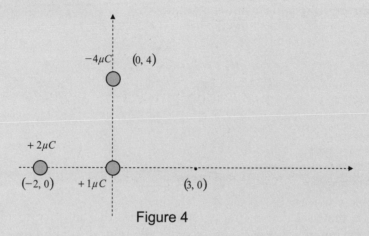

Figure 4

Three charges are distributed as shown in figure 4. Determine the electric potential at the point (3, 0).

To get the total, just add the individual potentials contributed by each charge. Be sure to include the proper sign with each charge as you calculate.

$$V = V_{+2} + V_{+1} + V_{-4}$$

$$V = (9 \times 10^9) \left\{ \frac{2 \times 10^{-6}}{5} + \frac{1 \times 10^{-6}}{3} + \frac{-4 \times 10^{-6}}{5} \right\}$$

$$V = -600 \text{ V}$$

Equipotential Surfaces and Conductors

Looking back at figure 2, you can see that it will take no work to move a charge from B to C. That's because the field and the force are always at right angles to the displacement along such a path. It follows that there will be no potential difference between B and C either. In fact, any planar surface that's perpendicular to the field lines in figure 2 will be have the property that any two points on the surface have no potential difference between them because moving along such a surface will always involve moving at right angles to the field. A connected surface where all points have 0 potential difference between them is called an **equipotential surface**. Each surface can be labeled by a unique voltage value with respect to the zero point, and the electric field will always be perpendicular to the equipotential surfaces. For a point charge or spherical distribution, the equipotential surfaces are concentric spheres centered on the charge (figure 5). For more complicated distributions, the surfaces can contort quite a bit.

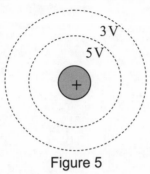

Figure 5

A **conductor** is a material that contains many charges that are free to move. For example, many of the electrons in a metal are not specifically bound to any one atom and can move freely throughout the material. Should they experience an electric field, these mobile electrons will move and redistribute themselves. If the electric field applied is static, not changing in time, then the condition of **electrostatic equilibrium** will be achieved quite quickly. In this state, charges no longer move, and this can only mean that the net electric field inside the conductor is 0. The redistributed charges lie along the surface of the conductor and create their own field that exactly cancels out the original field within the conductor. At the surface of the conductor, the electric field lines enter or leave at right angles to the surface, since any parallel component would cause charges on the surface to move.

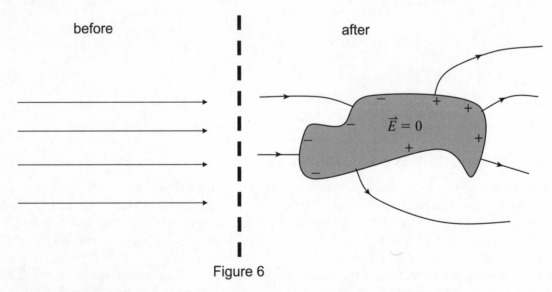

Figure 6

Figure 6 depicts what happens when a conducting shape is placed in a uniform static field. Notice the distortion of the field outside of the conductor. This is a result of the superposition of the original uniform field and the field due to the charges on the conductor that moved to the surface in response to it.

If a test charge is moved along the surface of the conductor, the electric field will do no work on it because the field is at right angles to the displacement of the charge. This means that the surface is an equipotential surface. In fact, it takes no work to move a charge anywhere within the material since the field is 0 inside, so the entire conductor is characterized by a single value of electric potential.

EXERCISE

Two identical spherical conductors labeled A and B with radius R are separated by a distance d that's very large compared with R. Conductor A has a charge Q on it, while B is neutral. The two conductors are brought together so that they touch, and then they are moved back to their original positions. Find the potential at a point just outside the surface of A
  (a) before they are brought together
  (b) after they are touched and returned to their positions

(a) Initially, A behaves as a point charge just outside its radius. Since it carries a charge Q, the potential is

$$V_{before} = \frac{Q}{4\pi\epsilon_0 R}$$

(b) When they touch, the charge will distribute itself equally over both spheres as the combined surface of the two conductors becomes one large equipotential surface. Each sphere will then carry $\frac{1}{2} Q$. When they are returned to their initial positions, you can find the potential at the surface of A using superposition.

$$V_{after} = \frac{\frac{1}{2}Q}{4\pi\epsilon_0 R} + \frac{\frac{1}{2}Q}{4\pi\epsilon_0 d}$$

Electric Potential Energy

As you've already learned, electric potential at a given point was originally defined as the negative of the work done by the field in slowly moving a charge from the zero point to the chosen point. The electric force associated with static fields is conservative (the work is independent of path), so you can identify the negative work with the change in the **electric potential energy**. In symbols, you have

$$\Delta V = -\frac{W_{field}}{q} = \frac{\Delta U}{q} \Rightarrow \Delta U = q\Delta V$$

For a positive charge to decrease in potential energy, $\Delta U < 0$, the charge must move downhill from higher to lower electric potential. But for a negative charge to decrease in potential energy, it must move from lower to higher electric potential, or uphill. If this seems confusing, remember that electric potential is a property of the point in space, independent of any charge placed there; electric potential energy is a specific property of a charge. You can look at this behavior concretely in figure 7.

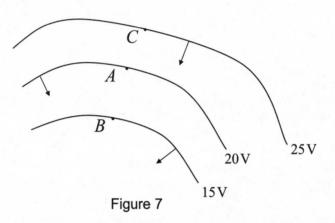

Figure 7

Here, you can see three equipotential surfaces, labeled with their voltage levels. The electric field is perpendicular to the surfaces and points toward lower electric potential. A positive charge placed at A would be forced by the field toward B, where the electric potential is lower and where the charge will have less potential energy. A negative charge placed at A would be forced toward C, where the electric potential is higher but where the charge will have lower potential energy.

EXAMPLE

A $-2\,\mu C$ charge with mass 5×10^{-8} kg is released from rest at point A in figure 7. How fast will it be moving if it eventually passes through C?

The charge will decrease in PE and gain KE, $\Delta K = -\Delta U$.

$$\tfrac{1}{2}mv^2 = -q\Delta V = -(-2 \times 10^{-6})(25-20) = +10 \times 10^{-6}$$

$$v = \sqrt{\frac{20 \times 10^{-6}}{5 \times 10^{-8}}} = 20\frac{m}{s}$$

When several point charges are present in a given region, each charge has potential energy. Since you can easily calculate the electric potential due to a configuration of point charges, you can just as easily calculate the PE of a charge placed in the region.

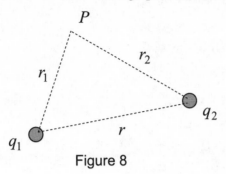

Figure 8

For example, in figure 8, the two charges q_1 and q_2 create an electric potential at P (0 at infinity) given by

$$V_P = k \frac{q_1}{r_1} + k \frac{q_2}{r_2}$$

If a third charge q_3 is placed at P, it will have potential energy, measured with respect to 0 at infinity, given by

$$U = q_3 V_P = k \frac{q_3 q_1}{r_1} + k \frac{q_3 q_2}{r_2}$$

EXAMPLE

What is the total potential energy of the system of three charges after q_3 has been placed at P?

The answer isn't just the previous result, because there's potential energy in the system of q_1 and q_2 even before q_3 is introduced. To sort this out, imagine constructing the system from scratch with all the charges out at infinity. The PE of the system will be the PE gained by everything as the charges are placed in position. Let's say you bring in q_1 first. This takes no work because there are no charges present yet to move against. Next, you bring in q_2. Since q_1 creates a potential at the position of q_2, it gains an amount of PE written as

$$U_{12} = q_2 V_1 = k \frac{q_2 q_1}{r}$$

Finally, q_3 is placed so that the total gain in PE is

$$U_{\text{total}} = k \frac{q_2 q_1}{r} + k \frac{q_3 q_1}{r_1} + k \frac{q_3 q_2}{r_2}$$

Sometimes this total PE is called the **energy of assembly,** for obvious reasons.

Electric Potential and Electric Potential Energy   217

KEY FORMULAS

Definition of Electric Potential $\Delta V = -\dfrac{W_{\text{field}}}{q}$

Potential Difference in Uniform Field $\Delta V = Es$

Potential Due to a Point Charge $V = k\dfrac{Q}{R}$

Potential Due to Several Point Charges $V = k\dfrac{q_1}{r_1} + k\dfrac{q_2}{r_2} + \ldots$

Electric Potential Energy $\Delta U = q\Delta V$

Electric PE of Two Point Charges $U = k\dfrac{q_1 q_2}{R}$

PRACTICE EXERCISES

SECTION I MULTIPLE CHOICE

Questions 1–3

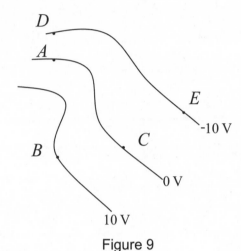

Figure 9

1. The direction of the electric field at *A* is

   (A) →   (B) ↑   (C) ↓   (D) ↗   (E) ↙

2. An electron placed at *C* and released would most likely pass closest to

   (A) *A*   (B) *B*   (C) *C*   (D) *D*   (E) *E*

3. The distance between *D* and *A* is 10^{-2} m. The strength of the electric field at *A* is most nearly

   (A) $10\frac{V}{m}$ (B) $10^{2}\frac{V}{m}$ (C) $10^{-1}\frac{V}{m}$ (D) $10^{3}\frac{V}{m}$ (E) $10^{-2}\frac{V}{m}$

4. A positive charge *Q* is a distance *R* from a point *P*. The electric potential at *P* could be doubled by
   I.   placing an identical charge *Q* at another point a distance *R* from *P*
   II. placing charge 2*Q* at a distance 2*R* from *P*
   III. placing charge 4*Q* at a distance 2*R* from *P*

   (A) I only (B) II only   (C) III only   (D) I and II only   (E) I and III only

Questions 5 and 6

Two equal positive charges are fixed on the *x*-axis equal distances from the origin.

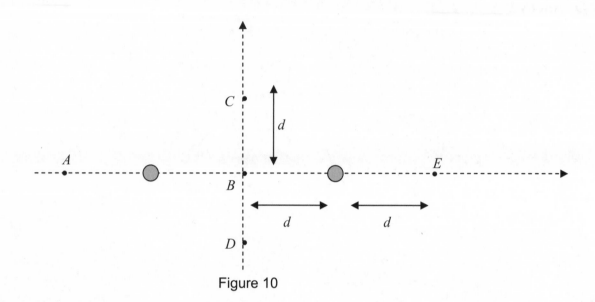

Figure 10

5. The electric potential is a maximum at

    (A) *A* (B) *B* (C) *C* (D) *D* (E) *E*

6. It would take 0 work to move a charge from

    (A) *A* to *B* (B) *C* to *B* (C) *B* to *D* (D) *A* to *E* (E) *C* to *E*

7. An isolated conductor has a charge *Q* placed on it. When equilibrium is established,

    (A) excess charge will reside on the surface, and the electric field will be 0 outside the conductor
    (B) the charge will spread throughout the conducting material, making the electric field 0 inside the conductor
    (C) all points of the conductor will be at the same potential, with electric field lines tangential to the surface
    (D) the excess charge will move to the surface, and all points of the conductor will be at the same potential
    (E) the excess charge will move to the surface, making the electric field inside the conductor equal to the field just outside the conductor

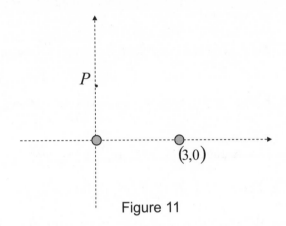

P

$(3,0)$

Figure 11

1. Two identical $+6\ \mu C$ charges with mass 10^{-6} kg are placed as shown in figure 11.

   (a) Determine the electric potential at P, with position $(0, 3)$.
   (b) An identical third charge is brought slowly from far away to P. How much work did this take?
   (c) The third charge is then released. Calculate the maximum speed it will retain.

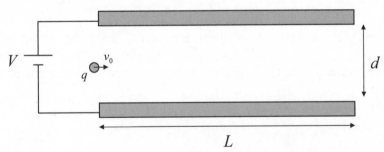

V

v_0

q

d

L

Figure 12

2. Two identical square conducting plates of side L are separated by a distance d. They are connected to a battery that maintains a potential difference V between the plates. A charge q, with mass m, moving parallel to the plates (figure 12), enters the region midway between the plates with speed v_0 and is deflected so that it just misses the top plate as it leaves the region. Express your answers to the following in terms of d, V, q, m, and v_0.

   (a) Determine the magnitude and direction of the nearly uniform electric field in the region between the plates.
   (b) What is the sign of the charge q?
   (c) Determine the speed of the charge as it exits the region between the plates.
   (d) Determine the length L of the plates.

Answers and Explanations

MULTIPLE CHOICE

1. The answer is B. The electric field is perpendicular to the equipotentials, pointing toward lower potential.

2. The answer is B. Electrons are negative and will move toward higher potential, which would take the electron from 0 V toward the $+10$ V surface.

3. The answer is D. The average field in the region between A and D is $E = \frac{\Delta V}{s} = \frac{10}{10^{-2}}$

4. The answer is D. For several point charges, just add the contribution of each. The contribution from I is $k\frac{Q}{R}$, the same as the original, so the potential is doubled. The contribution from II is also the same. Number III, however, gives $k\frac{4Q}{2R}$, which is twice the original.

5. The answer is B. At any point, the two charges contribute $V = k\left(\frac{q}{r_1} + \frac{q}{r_2}\right)$. By making r_1 and r_2 as small as possible, simultaneously you get the biggest value of V. This occurs at B.

6. The answer is D. A and E are both at the potential $V = k\left(\frac{q}{R} + \frac{q}{3R}\right)$, so there's no potential difference between the two points. This means it takes no net work to move a charge between the points. Notice that C and D are also at the same potential, but they weren't a choice.

7. The answer is D. In electrostatic equilibrium, excess charge on a conductor lies on the surface. Since the field is 0 inside and enters at right angles at the surface, it takes no work to move a charge anywhere on or in the conductor, so the entire object is at the same potential.

FREE RESPONSE

1. (a) Superpositions allows you to add the potentials of each charge as if the other weren't present.

    $$V_P = 9 \times 10^9 \left(\frac{6 \times 10^{-6}}{3} + \frac{6 \times 10^{-6}}{3\sqrt{2}}\right) = 3.1 \times 10^4 \text{V}$$

    (b) The work follows from the definition of electric potential.

    $$W = qV_P = (6 \times 10^{-6})(3.1 \times 10^4) = 0.19 \text{ J}$$

(c) When the third charge is brought in to point P, it has increased in PE by an amount equal to the work done in bringing it in, 0.19 J. When it is released, the maximum speed attained will occur when this PE is lost and converted into KE.

$$0.19 = \frac{1}{2}mv^2 = \frac{1}{2}(10^{-6})v^2$$

$$v = 616\frac{m}{s}$$

2. (a) From the battery orientation, the top plate is at higher potential, so the field points down between the plates. The magnitude of the uniform field is $E = \frac{V}{d}$.

(b) Since the charge was attracted to the top plate where the potential was higher, it must be negative.

(c) Use the work-energy theorem. The electric force did positive work.
$$W_{electric} = \Delta K$$

$$|q|(\tfrac{V}{2}) = \tfrac{1}{2}mv^2 - \tfrac{1}{2}mv_0^2 \ c \ v = \sqrt{v_0^2 + \frac{|q|V}{m}}$$

(d) Since $v = \sqrt{v_0^2 + v_y^2}$, it follows from (c) that $v_y = \sqrt{\frac{|q|V}{m}}$.

The acceleration of the charge has only a y-component and is determined from Newton's Second Law.

$$a_y = \frac{qE}{m} = \frac{qv}{md}$$

The first motion equation will give you the time between the plates.

$$v_y = v_{y0} + at = 0 + \frac{qV}{md}t$$

$$\sqrt{\frac{|q|V}{m}} = \frac{|q|V}{md} \ c t = d\sqrt{\frac{m}{|q|V}}$$

Finally the horizontal distance traveled depends only on the initial horizontal speed v_0.

$$L = v_0 t = v_0 d \sqrt{\frac{m}{|q|V}}$$

Electric Circuits

Electrostatics deals with electrical effects when all charges have stopped moving. In this chapter, you'll look at the effects of organized motion of charges. Charges can be agents for energy transfer, and electric circuits can facilitate energy transfer to various elements of the circuit. You'll also study resistors and capacitors in detail as examples of circuit elements.

Conductors and Electric Current

A conductor contains many charges, usually electrons, that aren't tightly bound to any one atom. A lump of metal sitting on a table contains many trillions of electrons undergoing random motion due to the thermal energy the material possesses. The speeds associated with these thermal motions are quite large, on the order of $10^6 \frac{m}{s}$, but the motion is random. And with many collisions occurring every second, there will always be equal numbers of electrons moving in opposite directions, so there's never a net movement of electrons in any one direction.

An **electric current** is a flow of electric charge. To get an electric current in a conductor, you need to get the electrons, which carry electric charge, to move in an organized manner. You can do this by introducing an electric field into the conductor. The mobile electrons will continue to execute their rapid thermal motion, but they'll have a tendency to drift up the field lines because there's a net force on the electrons opposite the field direction (figure 1).

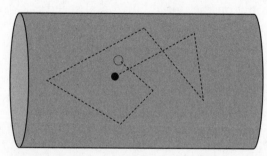

Thermal motion: electrons move rapidly but randomly.

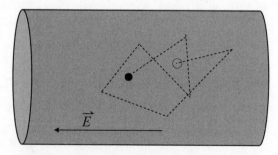

Electric field causes electrons to drift slowly opposite the field lines.

Figure 1

The rate at which electrons move along the field lines is called the **drift speed**, typically about $10^{-4} \frac{m}{s}$, which is quite small. But so many electrons are moving in a typical conductor that the currents can be quite large. Electric current is defined quantitatively as the amount of charge crossing an area in a given time divided by the time.

$$i = \frac{\Delta q}{\Delta t}$$

The unit for electric current is $\frac{C}{s}$, called an Ampere (A). If the current is changing over time, this definition gives the average current over the time interval. If you choose a very small time interval, then you can call it instantaneous current.

EXERCISE

Find the electric current established when 10^{20} electrons move through a cross section of a copper wire in 30 seconds.

Since each electron carries 1.6×10^{-19} C, you have

$$i = \frac{1.6 \times 10^{-19}(10^{20})}{30} = 0.53 \text{ A}$$

While the negative electrons actually move through the wires in common circuits, circuits are usually described in terms of the motion of positive charges moving in the opposite direction. Only precise measurements on a wire can show the difference between negative charges moving to the left and positive charges moving to the right. Electric current defined in terms of the flow of positive charge opposite the electrons is called **conventional current**, but unless it's otherwise stated, you should assume that current means conventional current (figure 2). This way, the current will always be in the same direction as the local electric field.

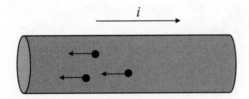

Conventional current: electron drift to the left
is equivalent to positive charge drift to the right.

Figure 2

Batteries

When a conductor is placed in an external electric field, the charges will move in response to the field. The presence of the electric field creates a potential difference between points on the conductor, and positive charge tends to move to lower potential. If the conductor is just sitting in an external field, the charges will quickly redistribute and eliminate any potential differences, as you saw in the discussion about equipotential surfaces.

But if you connect to the conductor a device that will maintain a potential difference between points on the conductor, equilibrium won't be established, and charges will continue to move from higher to lower potential. For this process to continue, the charges that have moved to lower potential must be raised back to higher potential again. Otherwise, the redistributed charges will change the potential difference impressed upon the conductor by the device. This means that the device must be able to add energy to charges and raise them to higher electric potential.

A battery is one example of such a device. The nature of the chemical reaction within the battery determines the potential difference between the terminals. In essence, the battery maintains a charge separation between the terminals (figure 3).

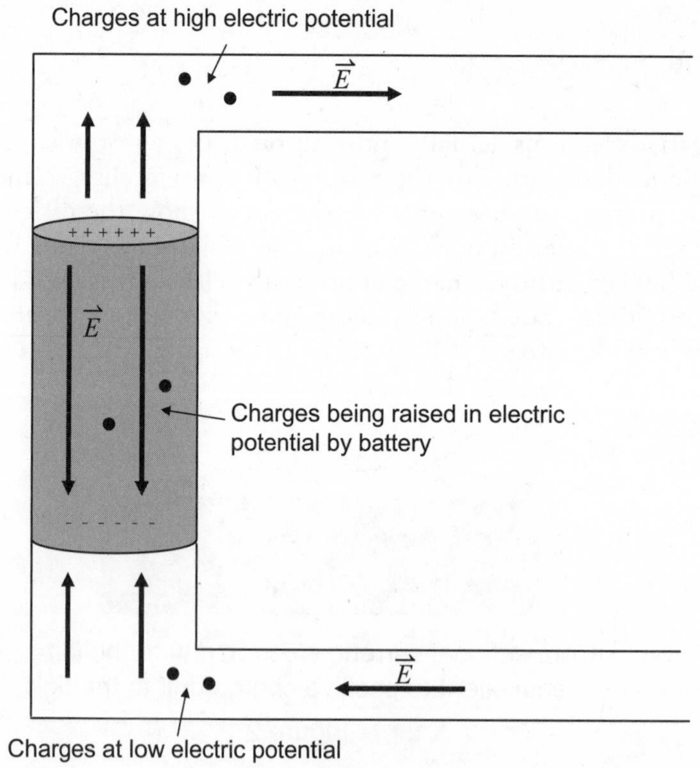

Charges at high electric potential

$\vec{E}$

$+ + + + + +$

$\vec{E}$

Charges being raised in electric potential by battery

$\vec{E}$

Charges at low electric potential

Figure 3

When the terminals are connected to a conductor, an electric field is set up in the wire very quickly, and mobile charges begin to move immediately. After a (usually) brief period of time, a **steady state** is established; the current flowing at any point in the circuit doesn't change. As the charges move around the circuit, they transfer the potential energy they gained from the battery to the circuit elements through which they pass. When they enter the battery at the negative terminal, positive charges are faced with an electric field that opposes their movement to the positive terminal. The energy required to move these charges through so that they can re-enter the circuit at the positive terminal is supplied by the chemical energy derived from the reacting chemicals. The symbol for a battery is displayed in figure 4; the positive terminal is the longer line.

Figure 4

Electrical Resistance and Ohm's Law

When a potential difference is applied across a conductor, the current established is directly proportional to the impressed voltage difference. This empirical fact is known as **Ohm's law**.

$$\Delta V \propto I$$

A plot of ΔV vs. I will be a straight line, and its slope is called the **electrical resistance** of the conductor. The name *resistance* is justified. Consider figure 5 depicting the graphs for two different conductors. You can see that the steeper slope has less current established for the same applied potential difference; this conductor resists current flow more than the conductor with smaller slope.

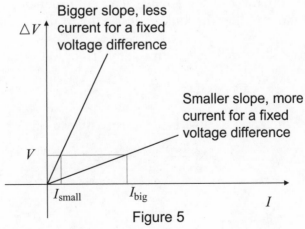

Figure 5

If you call the resistance R, Ohm's law is written as

$$\Delta V = IR$$

The SI units of resistance are $\frac{V}{A}$, called **ohms** (Ω). The resistance of a conductor will depend on a number of factors. For example, let's consider a cylindrical length L of conductor with cross-sectional area A and a fixed potential difference ΔV between the ends (figure 6).

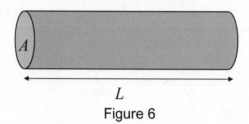

L

Figure 6

As the charges move through the material, collisions will slow them down. More collisions mean less current and greater resistance. So you might expect that a long, narrow conductor would have more resistance than a short, wide one. You might also suspect that different materials would have an effect as well. These ideas can be summed up in the relation

$$R = \rho \frac{L}{A}$$

The dependence on geometry comes from the $\frac{L}{A}$ factor. The dependence on material is contained in ρ, called the resistivity of the material.

EXERCISE

A 0.3 m length of wire with uniform cross-sectional area 8×10^{-5} m^2 has a potential difference of 5 V applied across it, producing a current of 2 A. Find the resistance of the wire and the resistivity of the material.

You can find the resistance immediately from Ohm's law.

$$R = \frac{\Delta V}{I} = \frac{5}{2} = 2.5 \ \Omega$$

Now use the given data with the resistivity relation.

$$\rho = \frac{RA}{L} = \frac{(2.5)(8 \times 10^{-5})}{0.3} = 6.7 \times 10^{-4} \ \Omega \cdot \text{m}$$

A **resistor** is a type of circuit element with a fixed resistance. Resistors are introduced into circuits to set up specific potential drops between points in the circuit or to protect delicate elements from large currents, among other things. The symbol for a resistor is shown in figure 7.

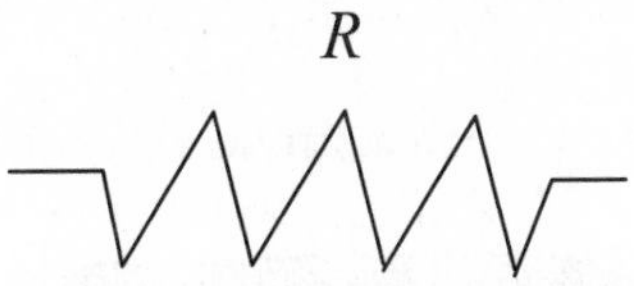

$$R$$

Figure 7

When writing the voltage drop across a resistor, you can usually drop the "Δ" and write simply: $V = I R$. While you can always define the resistance of a device for a given voltage drop and current as the ratio $\frac{V}{I}$, this ratio isn't a constant for every type of device. Something as basic as a light bulb will display a variable resistance. This subtlety is not a point of emphasis on the AP test, however, and light bulbs are treated as if they have constant resistance.

Electric Power

Consider a circuit element with a single path for current to flow through it and a potential difference V across it (figure 8). Since charge is a conserved quantity, and since there's only one path in and one path out of the element, the current i is the same coming into and out of the device.

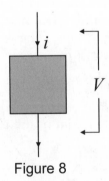

Figure 8

As a little bit of charge Δq moves through the device, it loses electrical potential energy, $\Delta U = \Delta q V$, and the device gains this energy. If you divide by the time over which this occurs, you get the rate at which energy is transferred to the device, the power consumed by the device:

$$P = \frac{\Delta U}{\Delta t} = \frac{\Delta q}{\Delta t} V = iV$$

This relation will be true for any device with a single current flowing through it. If the device also obeys Ohm's law with resistance R, you can write

$$P = i(iR) = i^2 R = \frac{V^2}{R}$$

EXAMPLE

A 1000 W hair dryer is designed to work properly with a 120 V potential difference applied. Find the resistance of the hair dryer and the current established in the connection circuit.

You can use the power relation $P = \dfrac{V^2}{R} \Rightarrow R = \dfrac{(120)^2}{1000} = 14.4\ \Omega$

Then apply Ohm's law to get the current: $i = \dfrac{V}{R} = \dfrac{120}{14.4} = 8.3\ \text{A}$

Kirchhoff's Laws

When an assembly of circuit devices is connected to one or more batteries, the current and voltage drops throughout the circuit can be determined theoretically by applying two basic laws called **Kirchhoff's laws** to the circuit. The laws themselves are statements about conservation of charge and the conservative nature of the electric force, phrased in the language of circuits.

    I. **Junction Law** (Kirchhoff's first law)—At a junction in a circuit, the sum of the current entering the junction will equal the sum of the current leaving the circuit.

$$\sum_{\text{in}} i = \sum_{\text{out}} i$$

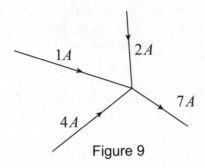

Figure 9

Consider the junction of four wires shown in figure 9. Every second, the three wires leading into the junction carry $2 + 1 + 4 = 7$ C of charge. Since charge is conserved, 7 C must leave the junction every second.

II. **Loop Law** (Kirchhoff's second law)—The sum of the potential drops around any closed loop must add to 0.

$$\sum_{\text{loop}} \Delta V = 0$$

Imagine an arbitrary point in a circuit. The potential difference between this point and itself is obviously 0. Since the electric force is conservative, the work done on a test charge must be 0 for any path that begins and ends at this point. And because the potential difference is just the work per charge, the loop law follows.

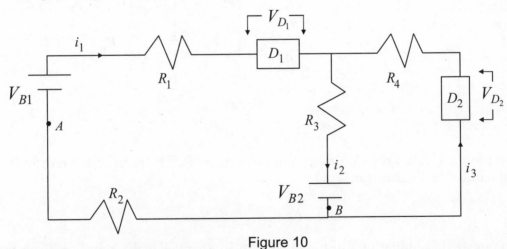

Figure 10

Consider the two-loop circuit in figure 10, consisting of two batteries, four resistors, and two other energy-consuming devices. Imagine traversing the left-hand loop clockwise, beginning at point A. First, you go up in potential as the battery is traversed from the negative to the positive terminal. The next three elements, R_1, D_1, and R_3, all have current flowing though them in the same direction that you're following. Since current flows from higher to lower potential, each element will have a negative potential difference across it—that is, you go down in potential as you move through it in this direction. Next, you traverse the second battery from the positive to the negative terminal, implying a negative potential drop. Finally, you traverse R_2 traveling with the current, so once again you have a negative drop. Applying the loop law, you have

$$+V_{B1} - i_1R_1 - V_{D_1} - i_2R_3 - V_{B2} - i_1R_2 = 0$$

If you had traversed in the opposite direction, all the signs would have reversed, giving you the same result. If you traverse the right-hand loop clockwise, starting at B, the loop law gives you

$$+V_{B2} + i_2R_3 + i_3R_4 + V_{D_2} = 0$$

Resistors in Series and Parallel

Two circuit elements are in **series** if the two elements will always have equal currents within them, regardless of other changes in the circuit. When several resistors are connected in series, you could replace them with a single resistor so that the overall current drawn from the batteries wouldn't change (figure 11).

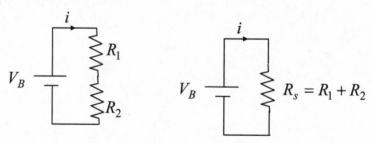

Figure 11

This resistor is called the equivalent series resistance, R_s. The value of the resistor is the sum of the individual resistors in series:

$$R_S = R_1 + R_2 + \dots$$

You can see that adding a resistor in series with another will make it more difficult for charge to move and will decrease the current if the same potential difference is applied. Then the resistance increases. In simple terms, if you think of $R = \rho\frac{L}{A}$, adding resistors in series is like increasing L, which clearly increases R.

Two circuit elements are said to be in **parallel** if the two elements will always have the same potential difference across them, regardless of other changes in the circuit. When several resistors are in parallel, more paths are available for charge to move through the circuit than when just one resistor is present. This makes it easier for charges to move. The equivalent parallel resistance—the value of the single resistor with which you could replace all the parallel resistors and maintain the same battery currents—will be less than any of the individual resistors (figure 12).

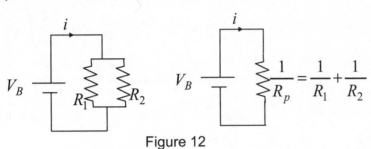

Figure 12

The value of this resistor is $\dfrac{1}{R_p} = \dfrac{1}{R_1} + \dfrac{1}{R_2} + \ldots$

Notice that for N identical resistors in parallel, the equivalent parallel resistance is $\dfrac{R}{N}$. In simple terms, if you think of $R = \rho \dfrac{L}{A}$, adding resistors in parallel is like increasing the cross-sectional area, which decreases the resistance.

EXAMPLE

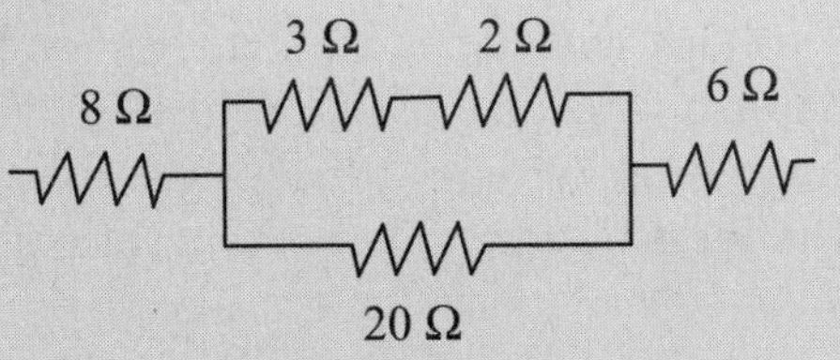

3 Ω   2 Ω

8 Ω   6 Ω

20 Ω

Figure 13

Find the equivalent resistance of the resistor combination in figure 13.

Just as you remove parentheses from the inside out in an algebraic expression, you proceed from the inside out in a resistor network. The 2 Ω and the 3 Ω are in series, giving an equivalent value of 5 Ω. This 5 Ω is in parallel with the 20 Ω. Applying the parallel formula, you have

$$\frac{1}{R_p} = \frac{1}{20} + \frac{1}{5} = \frac{1}{4} \Rightarrow R_p = 4\ \Omega$$

Finally, the 4 Ω, the 8 Ω, and the 6 Ω are all in series, making a total of 18 Ω as the equivalent resistance of the network.

Terminal Voltage

As charges are raised in electric potential within a battery, inevitably losses will occur due to collisions, and some of the theoretical potential energy gain of the charges will be lost to the random thermal motion of the battery molecules. You can model this behavior by thinking of a battery as an ideal voltage source connected in series with a resistor, the so-called **internal resistance** of the battery (figure 14).

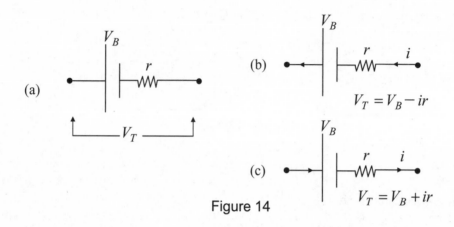

Figure 14

Of course, the "resistor" isn't a distinct element that can ever be removed. It's just a way of accounting for the electrical effects of the energy losses within the battery. The **terminal voltage** V_T of the battery is the potential difference between the terminals of the battery, and it will be different from the ideal voltage V_B, determined by the chemistry of the battery. The actual value of the terminal voltage will depend on the direction of the current through the battery. In the normal mode of operation, depicted in b, as you proceed from the right to left terminal, there is a voltage drop of $-ir$ through the internal resistance, followed by a voltage rise of V_B through the ideal battery. Then the terminal voltage will be

$$V_T = V_B - ir$$

If the battery is being recharged, the current will flow as in c. Then as you move from right to left, the potential goes up as you pass through the resistor and as you move through the ideal battery. For a recharging battery, you have

$$V_T = V_B + ir$$

Current Division

When electric current enters a junction, Kirchhoff's first law tells you that the sum of the currents entering must equal the sum of the currents leaving. But the specific values of the current entering and leaving a junction are determined by the batteries and resistances in the circuit. Consider the situation shown in figure 15a:

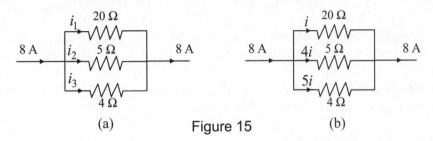

(a)   Figure 15   (b)

A current of 8 A enters the junction and divides. (Notice that the resistor values are in simple ratios.) The 20 Ω resistor will get the least current because it has the most resistance. The 5 Ω will get 4 times as much since it has $\frac{1}{4}$ the resistance, and the 4 Ω will get 5 times as much since it has $\frac{1}{5}$ the resistance. Calling the current in the largest resistor i, figure 15b and the junction law give you

$$8 = i + 4i + 5i \Rightarrow i = 0.8 \text{ A}$$

This is the fastest way to determine how currents split at a junction when resistance ratios are simple. An alternative approach uses the equivalent parallel resistance and the fact that parallel resistors all have the same potential drop across them. The equivalent resistance of the three resistors is

$$\frac{1}{R_p} = \frac{1}{20} + \frac{1}{5} + \frac{1}{4} = \frac{1}{2} \Rightarrow R_p = 2 \text{ Ω}$$

Since the 8 A effectively flows through this resistance, the voltage drop across the network is

$$V = iR_p = 8 \cdot 2 = 16 \text{ V}$$

But this must be the voltage across each resistor, because they are all in parallel. That leads to

$$16 = i_1(20) \Rightarrow i_1 = 0.8 \text{ A}$$
$$16 = i_2(5) \Rightarrow i_2 = 3.2 \text{ A}$$
$$16 = i_3(4) \Rightarrow i_3 = 4 \text{ A}$$

This might be your best approach if the ratios aren't simple.

Simple Circuits

A **simple circuit** is a connection of batteries and resistors that meets two criteria:
1. All batteries are in series.
2. The equivalent resistance of the entire circuit can be obtained by the repeated use of just the series and parallel equivalent resistance formulas.

When batteries are in series, the equivalent battery voltage will be the algebraic sum of the individual voltages of each battery. These criteria imply that a simple circuit can be reduced to a single equivalent voltage source by addition and subtraction, and a single equivalent resistance using the series and parallel formulas. While a so-called simple circuit need not look simple, the circuits that appear on the AP tests are not overly complex. You'll need to be able to determine the currents established in the circuit, potential drops across elements, terminal voltages, and energy consumption or supply by the elements.

EXAMPLE

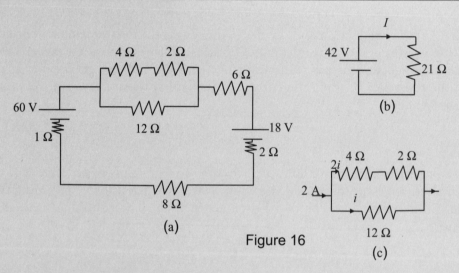

Figure 16

Figure 16a is a simple circuit. The two batteries with internal resistances of 1 Ω and 2 Ω are in series. Since the batteries are connected to oppose each other, the equivalent battery voltage for the circuit is

$$V_B = 60 - 18 = 42 \text{ V}$$

Notice that the 18 V battery is recharging. The resistors in the network, including the internal resistance, can all be reduced to a single equivalent resistance using the series and parallel rules. The 4 Ω and 2 Ω in series combine to give 6 Ω. This is then in parallel with the 12 Ω, giving you

$$\frac{1}{R_p} = \frac{1}{12} + \frac{1}{6} = \frac{1}{4} \Rightarrow R_p = 4 \text{ Ω}$$

Finally, you can add this to the 8 Ω, the 6 Ω, and the internal resistances. The total equivalent resistance of the circuit is

$$R_{equiv} = 4 + 8 + 6 + 3 = 21 \ \Omega$$

Now you've effectively reduced the circuit to what is shown in figure 16b. You can determine the current I in this make-believe circuit from the loop law:

$$41 - I(21) = 0 \Rightarrow I = 2 \ \text{A}$$

In the real circuit, this will be the current in the batteries and everything in series with them. Each battery carries 2 A, so you can find the terminal voltages:

$$V_T^{60} = 60 - 2 \cdot 1 = 58 \ \text{V}$$

$$V_T^{18} = 18 + 2 \cdot 2 = 22 \ \text{V}$$

The 2 A will divide at the junction with the 12 Ω and the 4 Ω resistor. Notice that the top path through this network has a resistance of 6 Ω, so there will be twice as much current along this path as through the 12 Ω resistor. From figure 16c and the junction law, you have

$$2 = i + 2i \Rightarrow 0.67 \ \text{A}$$

Capacitance and Capacitors

Consider two separated conductors, like two parallel plates, with external leads to attach to other circuit elements (figure 17). Such a device is called a **capacitor.**

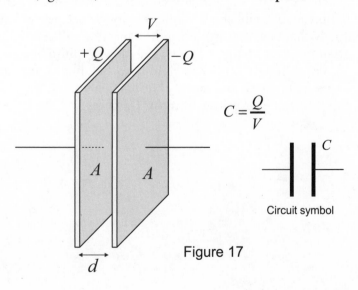

$$C = \frac{Q}{V}$$

Circuit symbol

Figure 17

When the leads are connected to a battery, charge will flow off of one conductor and onto the other until the potential drop between the conductors is equal to that across the battery. The ratio of the charge separated to the potential drop between the conductors is called the **capacitance**:

$$C = \frac{\text{charge separated}}{\text{potential difference}} = \frac{Q}{V}$$

The units of capacitance are $\frac{C}{V}$, called a **farad** (F). If you were to double the potential difference between the conductors, say by doubling the strength of the battery, twice as much charge would be separated, so the ratio would stay the same. In fact, the capacitance of two conductors depends only on the geometry of the conductors and not on the particular voltage impressed.

Think of capacitance as charge stored on each plate per volt. A large capacitance means the ability to store a large amount of charge for each volt of potential difference. For a parallel plate capacitor of area A and separation d as shown in figure 17, you might expect it to be easier to store charge if the area is bigger, making the plates roomier. Similarly, if the separation is small, the oppositely charged plate will help hold the charge of each plate in place. These observations are consistent with the formula

$$C_{\text{plate}} \propto \frac{A}{d}$$

At the B level, you won't have to calculate capacitance from first principles, but you'll need to understand the factors in determining the capacitance of a parallel plate capacitor. Increasing area increases the value, while increasing d lowers the value. The circuit symbol for a capacitor is shown in figure 17 as well.

Capacitors in Circuits

As just described, when a capacitor is initially connected to a battery, charge will flow for some time until equilibrium is established. While the flow is occurring, you have a **transient** situation, but eventually the flow of charge onto the capacitor will cease. The B-level test will only address the situation after charge has stopped flowing onto the capacitor. Transient situations will not have to be analyzed. You'll need to be able to answer questions about charge stored, voltages difference, and energy stored when one or more capacitors are connected in a circuit once the charges have stopped moving.

CAPACITORS IN SERIES AND PARALLEL

The parallel connection of two capacitors is shown in figure 18a.

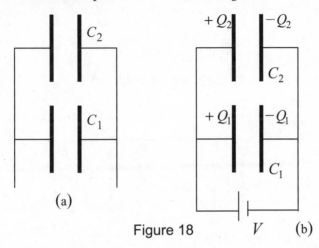

Figure 18

When connected to a battery, each capacitor will store a different amount of charge, but each will have the same potential drop across it, since each forms a separate loop with the battery. This connection effectively increases the plate area, and since capacitance is proportional to plate area, it should be no surprise that the capacitance has increased. The equivalent parallel capacitance of several capacitors connected in parallel is just the sum of the individual values.

$$C_p = C_1 + C_2 + \ldots$$

When two or more capacitors are connected in series, the equivalent capacitance is less than the smallest value of any of those connected, and the overall capacitance decreases. A battery connected to the free leads in figure 19a will separate charge on the extreme left and right

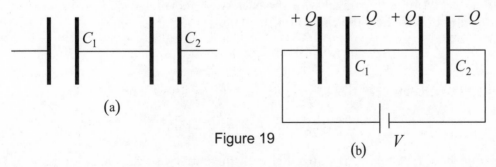

Figure 19

plates shown. The middle two plates are directly connected to each other and will end as an equipotential surface with $+Q$ and $-Q$ drawn to outer plates as shown; there will be no potential drop across the middle region. The potential drop created by the battery is now effectively distributed across the separation of both capacitors, and d has gotten bigger, making for a smaller capacitance. The equivalent capacitance of several capacitors connected in series is determined by

$$\frac{1}{C_s} = \frac{1}{C_1} + \frac{1}{C_2} + \dots$$

Notice that the charge on each series capacitor will be the same, but in general, the voltage drops will be different.

EXAMPLE

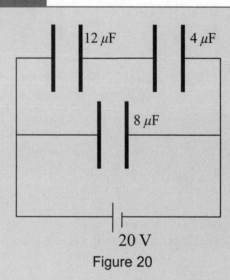

20 V

Figure 20

Three capacitors are connected to a 20 V battery as shown in figure 20. Determine the charge stored on each and the potential drop across each capacitor.

The 8 μF capacitor is in parallel with the battery, so its voltage is 20 V. From the definition of capacitance, the charge on its plates is

$$Q = CV = (8 \times 10^{-6})(20) = 160 \ \mu\text{C}$$

The series combination of the 12 μF and the 4 μF yields an equivalent capacitance:

$$\frac{1}{C_s} = \frac{1}{12} + \frac{1}{4} = \frac{1}{3} \Rightarrow C_s = 3 \ \mu\text{F}$$

This equivalent capacitance is in parallel with the battery, so the charge it stores is

$$Q = CV = (3 \times 10^{-6})(20) = 60 \ \mu\text{C}$$

This will be the charge on each of the two capacitors in series. Then you can use the definition of capacitance to get voltage drops across the two series capacitors.

$$V_{12} = \frac{Q}{C} = \frac{60}{12} = 5 \text{ V}$$

$$V_4 = \frac{Q}{C} = \frac{60}{4} = 15 \text{ V}$$

Notice that the two voltage drops add up to 20 V, as the loop law for the outer loop would require.

ENERGY AND CAPACITORS

Work must be done by the battery when it separates the charge on two conductors. Imagine the battery with voltage V moving a total charge Q from one plate to another in a parallel plate capacitor. You might suspect that the work this takes could be determined from the relation defining electric potential, $W = QV$. In this case, that assumption isn't quite right because while the capacitor is charging, the full battery voltage doesn't appear across the capacitor; it's only when charge has ceased moving that the capacitor voltage equals the battery voltage. How do you handle this? Because the capacitor voltage starts at 0 and ends at V and is a linear function of Q since $V = \frac{Q}{C}$, the average voltage on the capacitor during the charging process is just $\frac{1}{2} V$. Then, the work it takes to charge the capacitor is

$$W = \frac{1}{2} QV$$

This work can be recovered, because you can allow the capacitor to discharge and let the charges move through electrical devices to recover the energy. You can think of energy being stored in the position of the charges on the plates, a form of electrical potential energy. Using this discussion and the definition of capacitance, you can write

$$U_{cap} = \frac{1}{2} QV = \frac{1}{2} CV^2 = \frac{1}{2} \frac{Q^2}{C}$$

EXAMPLE

Find the total energy stored in the capacitors of figure 20.

You've already computed the charges and voltages of each capacitor, so you could use any of the forms given for U_{cap}. Let's use the voltage squared relation.

$$U_{total} = U_8 + U_{12} + U_4$$

$$U_{total} = \frac{1}{2}(8 \times 10^{-6})(20)^2 + \frac{1}{2}(12 \times 10^{-6})(5)^2 + \frac{1}{2}(4 \times 10^{-6})(15)^2$$

$$U_{total} = 2.2 \text{ mJ}$$

KEY FORMULAS

Electric Current	$i = \dfrac{\Delta q}{\Delta t}$
Resistor Voltage Drop	$V = iR$
Resistivity	$R = \rho \dfrac{L}{A}$
Electric Power	$P = iV$
Resistance Power	$P = i^2 R = \dfrac{V^2}{R}$
Junction Law	$\displaystyle\sum_{in} i = \sum_{out} i$
Loop Law	$\displaystyle\sum_{loop} \Delta V = 0$
Series Resistors	$R_s = R_1 + R_2 + \ldots$
Parallel Resistors	$\dfrac{1}{R_p} = \dfrac{1}{R_1} + \dfrac{1}{R_2} + \ldots$
Terminal Voltage	$V_T = V_B \pm ir$
Capacitance	$C = \dfrac{Q}{V}$
Parallel Plate Capacitor	$C \propto \dfrac{A}{d}$
Capacitors in Series	$\dfrac{1}{C_s} = \dfrac{1}{C_1} + \dfrac{1}{C_2} + \ldots$
Capacitors in Parallel	$C_p = C_1 + C_2 + \ldots$
Energy in Capacitor	$U = \dfrac{1}{2}\dfrac{Q^2}{C} = \dfrac{1}{2}CV^2 = \dfrac{1}{2}QV$

CHAPTER 12

PRACTICE EXERCISES

1. A current of 3.2 A flows in a segment of copper wire. The number of electrons crossing the cross-sectional area of the wire every second is most nearly

   (A) 3.2   (B) 2×10^{19} (C) 2×10^{-19} (D) 3.2×10^{19} (E) 3.2×10^{-19}

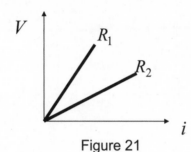

Figure 21

2. Resistors R_1 and R_2 have voltage vs. current graphs as shown in figure 21. The graph that best represents the voltage vs. current graphs for the equivalent series and parallel resistances R_s and R_p of the two is

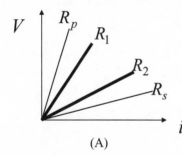

(A)

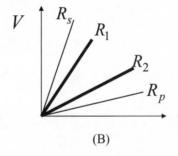

(B)

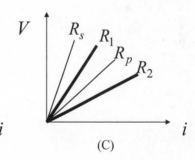

(C)

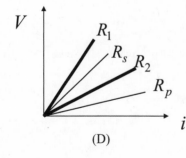

(D)

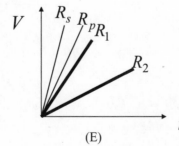

(E)

Figure 22

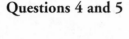

3. A cylindrical length L of conducting material with cross-sectional area A has a resistivity ρ. Another material with twice the resistivity is to be drawn to a length $2L$ to form a resistor with the same resistance as the original. Its cross-sectional area must be

(A) A (B) $2A$ (C) $3A$ (D) $4A$ (E) $\frac{1}{4}A$

Questions 4 and 5

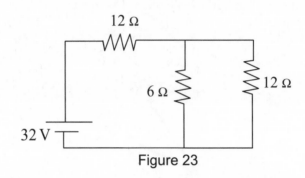

Figure 23

4. The voltage drop across the 6 Ω resistor is most nearly

(A) 16 V   (B) 10.7 V   (C) 8 V   (D) 32 V   (E) 24 V

5. The electrical energy converted to thermal energy in the resistors in 10 seconds is

(A) 240 J   (B) 24 J   (C) 64 J   (D) 1,000 J   (E) 640 J

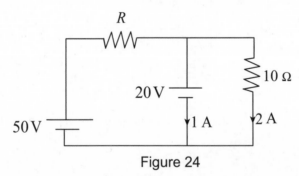

Figure 24

6. The circuit shown in the figure carries 1 A and 2 A in two branches as shown. The value of R is most nearly

(A) 10 Ω (B) 20 Ω (C) 30 Ω (D) 40 Ω (E) 50 Ω

7. Which of the following statements is true?
   I. The terminal voltage of a battery depends on the resistance connected to the terminals.
   II. The terminal voltage of a battery is always less than the ideal voltage of the battery.
   III. The terminal voltage of a battery is always greater than the ideal voltage of the battery.

   (A) none of the above   (B) I only   (C) II only   (D) III only   (E) I and II only

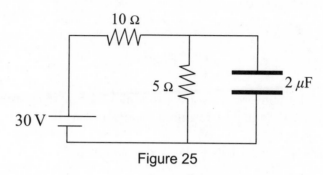

Figure 25

8. The circuit shown in the figure has been connected for a long time. The charge on one of the capacitor plates is

   (A) 60 μC   (B) 20 μC   (C) 2 μC   (D) 40 μC   (E) 30 μC

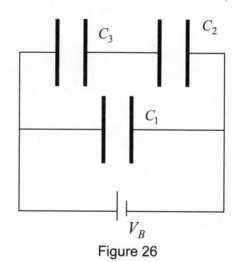

Figure 26

9. Which of the following is true for the connection shown in the figure?
   I. The magnitude of the charge on one plate of C_2 is the same as that on one plate of C_3.
   II. The potential drop across C_1 will equal the battery voltage.
   III. The magnitudes of the potential drops across C_2 and C_3 will add up to the drop across C_1.

   (A) I only   (B) II only   (C) III only   (D) I and III only   (E) I, II, and III

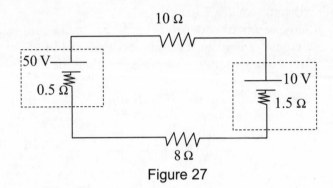

Figure 27

10. The batteries in the above circuit are contained within the dotted lines with internal resistances explicitly shown. The terminal voltage of the 10 V battery is

(A) 40 V   (B) 60 V   (C) 13 V   (D) 7 V   (E) 10 V

PRACTICE EXERCISES

SECTION II FREE RESPONSE

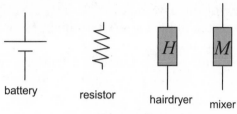

Figure 28

1. You are given a 120 V battery; a hairdryer designed to work properly at 120 V, where it's rated at 1,200 W; and a mixer designed to work properly at 60 V, where it's rated at 120 W. You also happen to have a large supply of 60 Ω resistors.

   (a) Determine the resistance of the hairdryer and the mixer at their rated voltages.

   (b) What current is established in the mixer when it's working properly?

   (c) Using the symbols shown in the figure, draw the connections needed to make both devices work simultaneously.

   (d) What power must the battery supply to run your circuit?

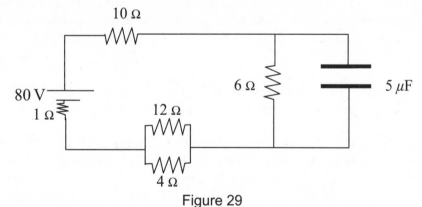

Figure 29

2. The circuit in the figure has been connected for a long time. The battery has an internal resistance of 1Ω.

   (a) Determine the terminal voltage of the battery.

   (b) Determine the current in the 4 Ω resistor.

   (c) What is the charge stored on one of the capacitor plates?

   (d) How long will it take for the 10 Ω resistor to consume as much energy from the circuit as is stored in the capacitor?

3. You are given a 9 V battery and three bulbs rated at respectively (9 V, 5 W), (9 V, 2 W), and (12 V, 6 W). Assume that the battery has negligible internal resistance and that the three bulbs obey Ohm's law and convert energy to light with equal efficiency.
   (a) When the 5 W bulb is connected to the battery terminals, what current will be established in the bulb?
   (b) What is the resistance of the 6 W bulb?
   (c) The 6 W bulb is connected to the battery terminals. How does its brightness compare to the 5 W bulb (a)? Explain.
   (d) The 5 W and the 2 W bulb are connected in series with the battery. Which bulb will be brighter? Explain.

Answers and Explanations

MULTIPLE CHOICE

1. The answer is B. Each electron carries a charge of 1.6×10^{-19} C. The definition of current equation gives

$$i = \frac{\Delta q}{\Delta t} \Rightarrow 3.2 = \frac{N(1.6 \times 10^{-19})}{1} \quad \text{So } N = 2 \times 10^{19}$$

2. The answer is B. The series resistance is the sum of the two resistors, so the slope of V vs. I must be greater than either individual graph. The parallel resistance is less than the smallest resistance, in this case R_2, so the V vs. I graph must have a slope smaller than either individual graph.

3. The answer is D. The original resistance is $\rho \frac{L}{A}$. The second resistance will be $\rho' \frac{L'}{A'} = (2\rho)\frac{2L}{A'}$. Since the two resistances must be equal, $A' = 4 A$.

4. The answer is C. The equivalent resistance of the circuit is 16 Ω since the two parallel resistors give 4 Ω, so 2 A is drawn from the battery. All of this goes through the 12 Ω resistor, so using the loop law for the left loop gives you

$$+ 32 - (2)(12) - V_{6\Omega} = 0 \Rightarrow V_{6\Omega} = 8 \text{ V}$$

5. The answer is E. The energy supplied by the battery will equal the energy consumed by the resistors. Since the battery has 2 A established in it, the power supplied by the battery is

$$P = iV_B = (2)(32) = 64 \text{ W. In 10 s, 640 J is supplied.}$$

6. The answer is A. The junction law tells you that 3 A is present in R. Applying the loop law to the left loop, you have $50 - 3R - 20 = 0$, so $R = 10 \ \Omega$.

7. The answer is B. $V_T = V_B \pm ir$, so the terminal voltage can be either greater than or less than the ideal voltage, depending on whether the battery is being recharged or is supplying energy to the circuit. This eliminates II and III. Since the current i depends on what is connected to the terminals, I is true.

8. The answer is B. After a long time, there will be no current in the capacitor branch, so the left loop has a single current established in it. Applying the loop law here gives you $30 - 10i - 5i = 0$, so $i = 2$ A. The capacitor is in parallel with the 5 Ω resistor, so its potential difference is $V_{cap} = V_{5\Omega} = (2)(5) = 10$ V. From the definition of capacitance, you have $Q = CV_{cap} = (2 \times 10^{-6})(10) = 20 \ \mu C$.

9. The answer is E. Number I is true because series connected capacitors will have the same magnitude of charge on each plate; you can think of the battery as separating the charge of the extreme left and right plates. The inner plates will redistribute charge to create inner equipotential surfaces, which involves separating the same magnitude of charge here as well. The loop law tells you that II and III are true.

10. The answer is C. The overall resistance of the circuit is 20 Ω. Since the two batteries oppose each other, the effective battery voltage is 40 V. The current established in the circuit will be $i = \frac{40}{20} = 2$ A. Since the 10 V battery is recharging, the terminal voltage will be $V_T = 10 + (2)(1.5) = 13$V.

FREE RESPONSE

1. (a) You can use the power equation $P = \dfrac{V^2}{R}$ for each device, so

$$1,200 = \frac{(120)^2}{R_H} \qquad R_H = 12 \ \Omega \qquad 120 = \frac{(60)^2}{R_M} \qquad R_M = 30 \ \Omega$$

(b) Use Ohm's law for the mixer.

$V = iR$

$60 = i(30) \Rightarrow i = 2$ A

(c)

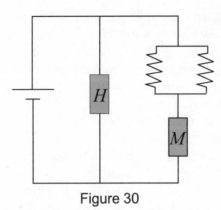

Figure 30

The hairdryer will be connected in parallel with the battery to get the needed 120 V potential difference. Since the mixer requires only 60 V, you must insert a resistor in series with it to lower the voltage drop. The resistor must have a voltage drop of 60 V as well so that the two add up to 120 V by the loop law. Since the current in the mixer is 2 A, Ohm's law says that the resistor must have a value $R = \frac{60}{2} = 30\ \Omega$. Two parallel 60 Ω resistors will do the job.

(d) The current in the hairdryer will be $i' = \frac{120}{12} = 10$ A. The junction law tells you that the total current established in the battery will then be 12 A, because there is 2 A in the mixer branch. The power supplied by the battery is

$$P = IV = (12)(120) = 1{,}440\ \text{W}$$

2. (a) After a long time, the capacitor will be fully charged. It could then be removed without changing anything in the battery-resistance part of the circuit, so you can analyze the latter as if the capacitor weren't present. The equivalent resistance of the circuit is 20 Ω since the two parallel resistors add to 3 Ω and the rest, including the internal resistance, are in series. The current established in the battery will be $i = \frac{80}{20} = 4$ A. The terminal voltage will be $V_T = V_B - ir = 80 - (4)(1) = 76$ V.

(b) The 4 A will divide at the junction of the 12 Ω and the 4 Ω resistors. If you assume a current x is established in the 12 Ω, then $3x$ will be in the 4 Ω. The junction law then says $x + 3x = 4$. Then $x = 1$ A, and the 4 Ω resistor will carry 3 A.

(c) The capacitor is in parallel with the 6 Ω resistor, so it will have the same potential difference across it. $V_{cap} = V_{6\Omega} = (4)(6) = 24$ V. From the definition of capacitance, you have $Q = CV_{cap} = (5 \times 10^{-6})(24) = 120\ \mu\text{C}$.

(d) The energy stored in the capacitor is

$$U = \tfrac{1}{2}CV_{cap}^2 = \tfrac{1}{2}(5 \times 10^{-6})(24)^2 = 1{,}440 \ \mu J$$

The power dissipated in the 10 Ω resistor is

$$P = i^2R = 4^2(10) = 160 \ W$$

Since watts are $\dfrac{J}{s}$, the time Δt must satisfy

$$P\Delta t = U$$

$$\Delta t = \frac{1{,}440 \times 10^{-6}}{160} = 9 \ \mu s$$

3. A bulb will consume energy at its rated value only when the rated voltage is applied across it. At other applied voltages you will need to know the resistance of each bulb to determine the power consumed.

(a) The 5 W bulb will consume 5 W when connected to the 9 V battery.

$$P = iV \Rightarrow i = \frac{5}{9} = 0.56 \ A$$

(b) $P = iV = \dfrac{V^2}{R} \Rightarrow R_{bulb} = \dfrac{V^2}{P_{bulb}}$

$$R_{6W} = \frac{12^2}{6} = 24 \ \Omega$$

(c) When connected to the 9 V battery, you can determine the power consumption from

$$P = \frac{V^2}{R} = \frac{9^2}{24} = 3.38 \ W$$

This is less than 5 W, so the 6 W bulb will be dimmer than the 5 W bulb when connected directly to the 9 V battery.

(d) You can get the resistance of the 5 W and 2 W bulbs just as you did in (c).

$$R_{5W} = \frac{9^2}{5} = 16.2 \ \Omega \qquad R_{2W} = \frac{9^2}{2} = 40.5 \ \Omega$$

When connected in series with the 9 V battery, the current established in each bulb will be the same.

$$i = \frac{9}{16.2 + 40.5} = 0.16 \ A$$

Since $P = i^2R$, the bulb with the greater resistance will be brighter. Thus the 2 W bulb will be brighter in this situation.

CHAPTER 13

Magnetostatics

Magnetic effects are associated with moving charges, so statics and magnetism may not seem like a natural pair. Magnetostatics, however, deals with situations where the magnetic field present doesn't change in time. In particular, this chapter will look at the effects of a magnetic field on moving charges and the creation of the magnetic field by electric currents. The next chapter will discuss magnetic fields that change over time.

Magnetic Field and Force

A **magnetic field** $\vec{B}$ can be created in a region of space in a number of ways, which you'll investigate in a later section. For now, let's assume that a field is present. Just as with an electric field, a magnetic field can be described by **magnetic field lines**. These lines give a concrete though qualitative picture of the field in a region. The magnetic field at a point will be tangential to the local field line (figure 1).

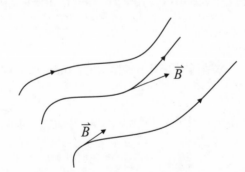

Magnetic field is tangential to the field lines.

Figure 1

The field will be strongest where the field lines are most dense. These effects of the field on an object are summarized in the force law:

$$\vec{F} = q\vec{v} \times \vec{B}$$

Here q is the charge of the object, $\vec{v}$ is the object's velocity, and $\vec{B}$ is the local magnetic field (figure 2).

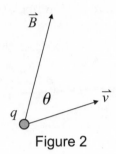

Figure 2

The SI units for magnetic field are $\dfrac{N}{C \cdot \frac{m}{s}}$, called a **tesla** (T).

Let's discuss the implications of the force law:

1. To experience a magnetic force, an object must carry electric charge and the object must be moving.
2. For a fixed speed, the magnitude of the force, $F = qvB\sin\theta$, depends on the direction of the particle's velocity vector with respect to the field. If the object moves along a field line, the force is 0. The maximum force for a fixed speed occurs when the charge moves perpendicular to the field. Conceptually, the force exerted on the charge depends on the efficiency with which it cuts across the field lines.
3. The force, velocity, and field are related through a vector cross-product. This means that the force will always be perpendicular to both the velocity and the field. There are two directions that satisfy this condition, and the right-hand rule tells you which of these is correct.
4. The instantaneous power delivered to an object by a force is $P_F = \vec{F} \cdot \vec{v}$. Since the magnetic force is always perpendicular to the velocity, $\vec{F} \cdot \vec{v} = 0$, it cannot change its energy. The magnetic force cannot do work on a moving charged particle.

Motion in a Uniform Field

When a charge enters a region where the magnetic field is uniform spatially, three basic types of motion paths are possible, depending on the relative directions of $\vec{v}$ and $\vec{B}$.

1. $\sin\theta = 0$: The particle is moving parallel or antiparallel to the field. This means the force is 0, so there's no acceleration, and the motion path will be a straight line followed with a constant speed.

2. $\sin\theta = 1$: The particle is moving perpendicular to the field. The force will be its maximum value for a given speed, $F = qvB$. You can see from figure 3 that the force keeps changing direction because the velocity changes direction.

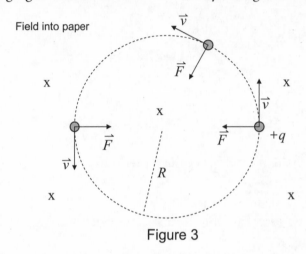

Figure 3

There's no force component to move the charge out of the plane it's in, and since the magnetic force does no work, the charge will maintain the same speed. The resulting motion path is uniform circular motion, with the field lines cutting directly through the plane of the circle. Since the magnetic force is supplying the centripetal force, you have

$$qvB = m\frac{v^2}{R} \Rightarrow R = \frac{mv}{qB}$$

3. $\sin\theta \neq 0,1$: The particle is moving neither parallel nor perpendicular to the field. To see how this works, let's break the velocity vector into components parallel to the field and perpendicular to the field: $v_\perp$, v_{11}(figure 4).

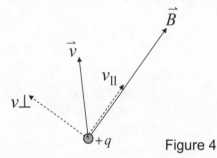

Object will circle into and out of the paper around $\vec{B}$ as it drifts along the direction of $\vec{B}$.

Figure 4

If only v_{11} were present, you would have case 1, with the particle drifting uniformly down the field lines. If only $v_\perp$ were present, you would have case 2, with the particle circling around the field lines. With both present, you have the superposition of these two motions: The motion path is a helix with its axis determined by the direction of the field.

EXAMPLE

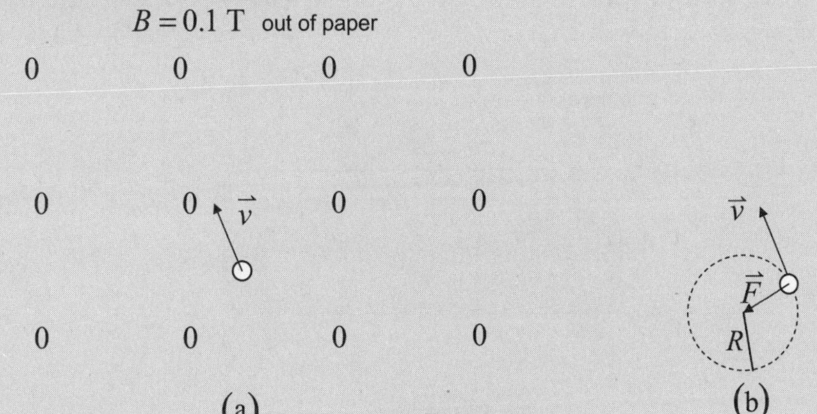

Figure 5

An electron is moving as shown in figure 5a with a speed of 2×10^5 m/s in a uniform field of 0.1 T.
   (a) Find the magnitude of the magnetic force exerted on the electron.
   (b) Sketch the circular motion path and find its radius.
   (c) How long will it take for the electron to complete one revolution?

(a) The magnitude of the force follows from the basic force law with $\sin\theta = 1$:

$$F = qvB = (1.6 \times 10^{-19})(2 \times 10^5)(0.1) = 3.2 \times 10^{-15}\text{N}$$

(b) The right-hand rule for $\vec{v} \times \vec{B}$ results in a direction to the right and up slightly in the plane of the paper, but since the electron is negative, the force is opposite this. The electron circles in a counterclockwise manner, as shown in figure 5b.

The radius is

$$R = \frac{mv}{qB} = \frac{(9 \times 10^{-31})(2 \times 10^5)}{(1.6 \times 10^{-19})(0.1)} = 1.13 \times 10^{-5}\text{m}$$

(c) In general, such a circulating charge will travel one circumference at the same speed, so

$$2\pi R = vT$$
$$2\pi \frac{mv}{qB} = vT \qquad \Rightarrow T = \frac{2\pi m}{qB}$$

This means that the period is independent of the speed of the charge; fast one move in big circles and slow ones in small circles, but they all take the same time to circulate once. For your case:

$$T = \frac{2\pi(9 \times 10^{-31})}{(1.6 \times 10^{-19})(0.1)} = 3.53 \times 10^{-10}\text{ s}$$

Magnetic Force on a Current-Carrying Wire

When a wire carrying current is placed in a magnetic field, each of the moving charges will feel a force. Since the thermal motion is random, it's only the drift speed that leads to an overall net force on the wire. While these speeds are very small, the large numbers of charges moving can lead to significant forces. Consider a straight wire segment (figure 6) of length Δl containing N charges, each with charge q.

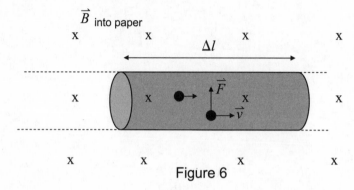

Figure 6

Let's assume the charges are moving at right angles to a field $\vec{B}$ with a speed v. The total force on the wire segment will be

$$F = N(qvB)$$

Since all N charges move through the segment in the time $\Delta t = \frac{\Delta l}{v}$ that it takes to traverse the segment, the current can be written as

$$i = \frac{\Delta q}{\Delta t} = \frac{Nq}{\frac{\Delta l}{v}} = \frac{Nqv}{\Delta l}$$

Substituting into the force equation gives you $F = i\Delta lB$.
Should the direction of current by angled with respect to the field, you'll have

$$F = i\Delta lB \sin\theta$$

where θ is the angle between the current direction and the field. You can determine the direction of the force by applying the right-hand rule to the moving charges, which are assumed to be positive since you are assuming conventional current. In vector notation, you can write the force on a current segment in a uniform field as

$$\vec{F} = i\Delta \vec{l} \times \vec{B}$$

EXAMPLE

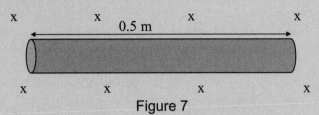

Figure 7

A straight segment of wire 50 cm long with a mass of 30 g is positioned horizontally in a uniform magnetic field of 0.025 T so that the current moves perpendicular to the field, depicted into the paper in figure 7. What current magnitude and direction must be established in the wire so that the magnetic force just counterbalances the weight of the wire?

Since the weight acts down, the magnetic force must act up. The right-hand rule tells you that the current is directed to the right. Since $\sin\theta = 1$, you have for equilibrium:

$$i\Delta lB = mg \Rightarrow i = \frac{mg}{\Delta lB} = \frac{(0.030)(10)}{(0.5)(0.025)} = 24 \text{ A}$$

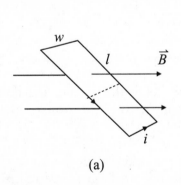

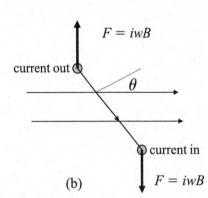

(a)   Figure 8   (b)

Consider a rectangular loop of wire of dimensions l and w, carrying current i as shown in figure 8a. The side view in b shows that the two widths experience equal but opposite forces that tend to cause the loop to rotate. This effect is the basis of the electric motor. The net torque about the central axis of the loop, shown as the dotted line in a, will be

$$net\ \tau = 2(iwB \sin\ \theta)\frac{1}{2} = iAB \sin\ \theta \qquad A = \text{area of loop}$$

Magnetic Field Due to a Long Wire

Electric fields are created by charges, and charges placed in an electric field will experience a force. An analogous statement is true for magnetic fields: Moving charges can experience a magnetic force, and moving charges create magnetic fields. A common case of moving charges is an electric current in a long straight wire. At the B level, this is the only type of current distribution for which you will have to find the field. Consider the wire in figure 9a, shown from a side view carrying current into the paper in b.

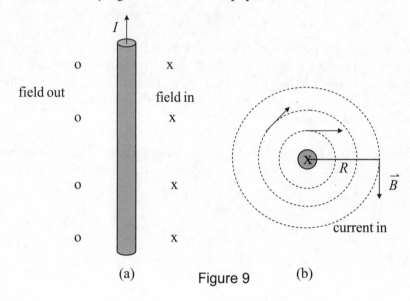

Figure 9

The field lines created by such a current form concentric circles centered on the wire. Another right-hand rule, the long wire rule, will tell you which way the field points.

Long wire rule: Place the thumb of your right hand along the wire in the direction of the current. Your fingers will wrap around the wire in the direction of the field line circulation.

Of course, the field itself is tangential to the field lines. You should try out the rule on figure 9, where the correct field directions are shown. The magnitude of the field created by such a current at a point outside the wire is given by

$$B = k'\frac{I}{R}$$

Here I is the current in the wire, and R is the distance from a point outside the wire to the center of the wire. The constant $k' = 2 \times 10^{-7} \frac{T \cdot m}{A}$.

EXAMPLE

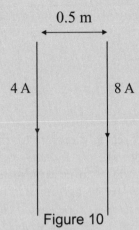

Figure 10

The two wires in figure 10, separated by 0.5 m, carry 8 A and 4 A as shown. Find the magnitude and direction of the magnetic field between the wires, 0.1m from the 4 A current.

Using the long wire rule, you can see that between the wires, the 4 A current creates a field out of the paper, while the 8 A current creates a field into the paper. The net field magnitude will then be the difference of the two individual magnitudes. You can use the formula to find the magnitudes of each:

$$B_4 = 2 \times 10^{-7} \frac{4}{0.1} = 8 \ \mu T \qquad\qquad B_8 = 2 \times 10^{-7} \frac{8}{0.4} = 4 \ \mu T$$

Since the 4 A field is larger, the net field is out of the paper, and the magnitude is $8 \ \mu T - 4 \ \mu T = 4 \ \mu T$.

Force between Long Current-Carrying Wires

Consider figure 11, depicting two parallel wires separated by a distance d, carrying currents I_1 and I_2 in the same direction.

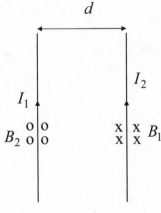

Figure 11

Each current creates a field around it, and this field will affect the other current. In the diagram, B_1, created by I_1, will affect the wire carrying I_2. A similar statement can be made for the field B_2 created by I_2. A segment of length Δl of the wire carrying I_1 will experience a force

$$F = I_1 \Delta l B_2 = I_1 \Delta l \left(k' \frac{I_2}{d} \right)$$

$$F = \Delta l \left(\frac{k' I_1 I_2}{d} \right)$$

The right-hand rule tells you this force is directed to the left: Parallel currents attract. You would have seen a similar result if you had looked at the force exerted on a segment of the wire carrying I_2; the same magnitude of force would be present but acting to the right. Of course, this is consistent with the law of action-reaction. Convince yourself using the right-hand rules that antiparallel currents repel each other. Notice that the force is proportional to the product of the currents and inversely proportional to the distance between them.

KEY FORMULAS

Magnetic Force on a Charge	$\vec{F} = q\vec{v} \times \vec{B}$
Radius of Circular Orbit	$R = \dfrac{mv}{qB}$
Magnetic Force on a Current	$F = i\Delta l B \sin\theta$
Torque on a Current Loop	$net\ \tau = iAB \sin\theta$
Field outside a Long Wire	$B = k'\dfrac{I}{R}$
Force between Parallel Currents	$F = k'\dfrac{I_1 I_2}{d}\Delta l$

PRACTICE EXERCISES

SECTION I MULTIPLE CHOICE

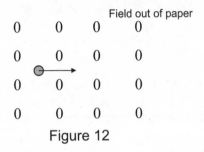

Figure 12

1. An electron is moving to the right in a region where a uniform magnetic field is directed out of the paper. The direction of the force on the electron will be

    (A) up   (B) down   (C) left   (D) right   (E) into paper

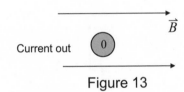

Figure 13

2. A wire carries electric current out of the paper as shown in the figure. With a magnetic field directed to the right, the force on the wire will be directed

    (A) up   (B) down   (C) left   (D) right   (E) into paper

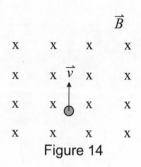

Figure 14

3. A positive charge q is moving with velocity $\vec{v}$ perpendicular to a magnetic field $\vec{B}$ shown into the paper in the figure. The magnitude and direction of the electric field that will allow the charge to pass undeflected are

	Magnitude	Direction
(A)	qvB	left
(B)	$\dfrac{B}{v}$	left
(C)	Bv	right
(D)	Bv	left
(E)	Bv	out of paper

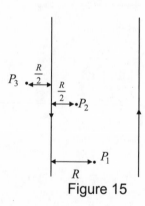

Figure 15

4. Two long parallel wires carry equal currents in opposite directions. A proton moving at a speed of 2×10^5 m/s would experience the maximum force

(A) at P_1 moving left   (B) at P_2 moving left   (C) at P_3 moving left
(D) at P_2 moving into paper   (E) at P_1 moving into paper

5. An electron moving with a speed of 2×10^6 m/s perpendicular to a uniform magnetic field of 10^{-3} T will execute one revolution of a circular path in a time most nearly

(A) 1 s   (B) 10^{-6} s   (C) 10^{-8} s   (D) 10^{-10} s   (E) 10^{-15} s

6. Two long parallel wires separated by a distance D carry currents I_1 and I_2. To increase the force exerted by each wire on the other by a factor of 2, you could
    I. double each current and double the separation
    II. double one current only and keep the separation the same
    III. keep the currents the same and halve the separation

    (A) I and II only   (B) I and III only   (C) II and III only
    (D) I, II, and III   (E) II only

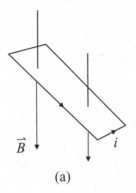
(a)

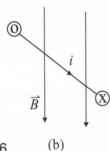
(b)

Figure 16

7. A rectangular loop carrying current i is positioned in a uniform magnetic field as shown in the figure. Referring to b where the loop is shown from the side, the loop will

    (A) move down as a unit   (B) move up as a unit (C) remain stationary
    (D) rotate clockwise   (E) rotate counterclockwise

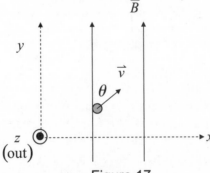

Figure 17

8. A positive charge currently has a velocity in the x-y plane, making an angle θ with respect to a uniform magnetic field directed along the $+y$-axis. The subsequent motion of the charge could best be described as

    (A) circular motion in the x-y plane
    (B) uniform motion
    (C) circular motion in the x-z plane
    (D) helical motion with axis parallel to the z-axis
    (E) helical motion with axis parallel to the y-axis

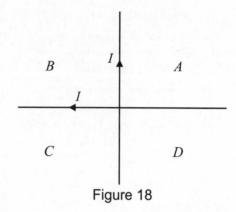

Figure 18

9. Two wires carrying equal currents are perpendicular to each other as shown in the figure. The largest magnitude of magnetic field pointing out of the paper is in region

(A) A   (B) B   (C) C   (D) D   (E) field does not point out in any of these regions

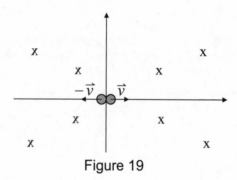

Figure 19

10. An elementary particle process creates two equal but oppositely charged (q), equal mass m particles at the origin in a region where a uniform magnetic field $\vec{B}$ is directed into the paper. At the instant they are created they have equal but opposite velocities. The two particles will collide after a time

(A) $\dfrac{2\pi m}{qB}$ (B) $\dfrac{\pi m}{qB}$ (C) $\dfrac{\pi m}{2qB}$ (D) $\dfrac{3\pi m}{2qB}$ (E) They do not collide.

PRACTICE EXERCISES

SECTION II FREE RESPONSE

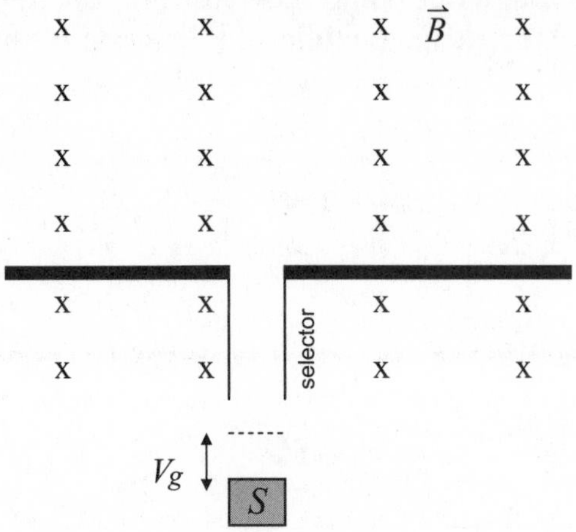

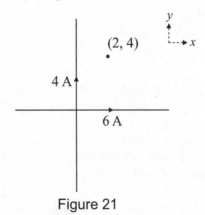

Figure 20

1. A mass spectrometer design has the following components: Positive ions of charge q and mass m are formed at a source S and accelerated through a potential difference V_g. The ions pass through a grid and into a velocity selector where there exists a magnetic field $\vec{B}$, as shown in the figure, and an electric field. When the charges leave the selector, they enter a region where the same magnetic field is present, but there is no electric field. Respond to the following in terms of q, m, V_g, and B.

   (a) Determine the speed v_0 of the charges as they pass through the grid if they were initially at rest as they left the source.
   (b) Sketch the path of the charges after they leave the selector.
   (c) Determine the radius of the path.
   (d) Charges leaving the source may have nonzero speeds. What electric field, magnitude, and direction must exist in the selector to ensure that only the charges with v_0 leaving the grid will pass undeflected through the selector?

Figure 21

2. Two wires, carrying currents of 4 A and 6 A respectively, are oriented perpendicular to each other and cross without electrical connection at the origin.

(a) Determine the magnetic field magnitude and direction at the point (2, 4).
(b) An electron passes through this point, moving with a speed of $3 \times 10^5 \frac{m}{s}$ toward the 4 A wire ($-x$ direction). Find the magnitude and direction of the force on the electron.

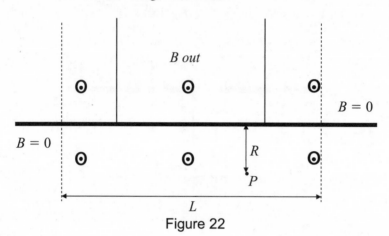

Figure 22

3. A long wire of mass m carrying current is suspended by two support cables above the floor in a laboratory. The two support cables are placed equally to the left and right of the wire center of mass. A magnetic field $\vec{B}$ of constant magnitude directed out of the paper exists in a region of length L as shown in the figure.

(a) Find the magnitude and direction of the current that will ensure that the tension in the support cables is 0.
(b) If the current is reversed, what will the tension in the cables be?
(c) With the current as in (b), a positive charge q enters the region moving to the right with speed v through point P a distance R from the wire. Find the magnitude and direction of the force exerted on the charge.

ANSWERS AND EXPLANATIONS

1. The answer is A. The right-hand rule for $\vec{v} \times \vec{B}$ gives a direction down, but since the electron is negative, the force is up.

2. The answer is A. The drift velocity of the charges is out of the page, so $\vec{v} \times \vec{B}$ is up. Since current is assumed to be the flow of positive charge, this is the answer.

3. The answer is C. The magnetic force is qvB directed to the left, so the electric force must equal this and point to the right. Since the charge is positive, this is the field direction as well. For the magnitude, you have

$$qvB = qE \Rightarrow E = Bv$$

4. The answer is B. The field created by either wire is directed into or out of the paper at any of the points, so D and E would yield 0 force. The fields created by each current are directed out of the paper for regions between the wires, so they reinforce each other in this region. At P_3, the two contributions oppose each other, and the point is also farther away from the right-hand current. This means that only A or B could be correct. The stronger total field occurs at P_2, as you can see:

$$B_2 = \frac{\mu_0 i}{2\pi}\left(\frac{1}{\frac{R}{2}} + \frac{1}{\frac{3R}{2}}\right) = \frac{\mu_0 i}{2\pi}\frac{8}{3R}$$

$$B_1 = \frac{\mu_0 i}{2\pi}\left(\frac{1}{R} + \frac{1}{R}\right) = \frac{\mu_0 i}{2\pi}\frac{2}{R}$$

5. The answer is C. The equation is $T = \frac{2\pi m}{qB} \cong \frac{2\pi(10^{-30})}{(10^{-19})(10^{-3})} \cong 10^{-8}$ s. The exact answer is 3.5×10^{-8} s.

6. The answer is D. The force on either wire is given by

$$F = k'\frac{I_1 I_2}{d}L$$

where L is the length of a wire. Doubling each current and doubling the separation causes F to change by a factor $\frac{(2)(2)}{2} = 2$, so the force doubles. Similar reasoning for the other choices shows that all three will double the force.

7. The answer is D. Referring to figure 16b, the right-hand rule tells you that the force on the segment carrying current out of the page is to the right, while the force on the segment carrying current into the page will be to the left. These two forces produce a torque that tends to cause clockwise rotation.

8. The answer is E. Since the velocity has components both parallel and perpendicular to the field, it will drift down the field lines as it circles them. This is a helix with axis along the field, the y-axis.

9. The answer is C. Using the long wire right-hand rule, you find that both wires create a field that points out of the paper in this region. Thus, every point in the region has a field magnitude that is the sum of the magnitude of the field from each wire. The field may point out at points in regions B and D as well, but the magnitude of the field will be the difference of the two contributions and thus smaller than in region C.

10. The answer is B. From the right hand rule for force you can see that both particles deflect in the same direction. Since they each move in a circle, they will collide when they reach the y-axis. As a result they will have traveled $\frac{1}{2}$ of a period before colliding. The period is $T = \frac{2\pi m}{qB}$, so B follows.

FREE RESPONSE

1. (a) The kinetic energy gained as the charges move to the grid will equal the potential energy lost.

$$\frac{1}{2}mv_0^2 = qV_g \Rightarrow v_0 = \sqrt{\frac{2qV_g}{m}}$$

(b) The charges will execute a semicircle as they leave the selector, bending in a counterclockwise sense.

(c) Using the centripetal force relation (Newton's second law), you have

$$qv_0B = m\frac{v_0^2}{R} \Rightarrow R = \frac{mv_0}{qB} = \sqrt{\frac{2mV_g}{qB^2}}$$

(d) As the charges move through the selector, the magnetic force qvB pushes them to the left. If you want the charges moving with speed v_0 to be undeflected, you must introduce an electric field directed to the right with magnitude satisfying

$$qv_0B = qE \Rightarrow E = v_0B$$

2. (a) Use superposition. Find the field due to each wire, using the long wire formula. For the 4 A current,

$$B = (2 \times 10^{-7})\frac{4}{2} = 4 \times 10^{-7} \text{ T directed into paper}$$

For the 6 A current,

$$B = (2 \times 10^{-7})\frac{6}{4} = 3 \times 10^{-7} \text{ T directed out of paper}$$

The net field is then $B_{net} = 1 \times 10^{-7}$ T directed into the paper.

(b) The electron is moving at right angles to the field, so the magnitude of the force is

$$F = qvB = (1.6 \times 10^{-19})(3 \times 10^5)(1 \times 10^{-7}) = 4.8 \times 10^{-21} \text{ N}$$

Since $\vec{v} \times \vec{B}$ is directed down, the negative electron is force up in the $+y$ direction.

3.　　(a)

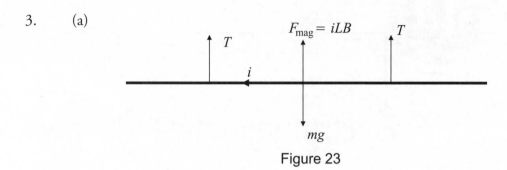

Figure 23

If the current flows to the left, the magnetic force will be directed up. Since there is no acceleration, Newton's second law gives

$$netF = 2T + iLB - mg = 0$$

If $T = 0$, then $i = \frac{mg}{LB}$

(b) Now the magnetic force is down, so the second law gives

$$netF = 2T - iLB - mg = 0 \Rightarrow T = \frac{1}{2}(iLB + mg) = mg$$

(c) The field at point P due to the wire is directed out with magnitude

$$B_w = k'\frac{i}{R} = k'\frac{mg}{LBR}$$

The charge will experience the total field due to the wire and the field $\vec{B}$. The two fields are in the same direction at P, so

$$B_P = B + B_w = B + k'\frac{mg}{LBR}$$

The positive charge is moving at right angles to this field so it feels the maximum force which will be directed down.

$$F = qvB_p = qv\left(B + k'\frac{mg}{LBR}\right)$$

Electromagnetic Induction

You've seen in previous chapters that electric and magnetic fields are intimately related to electric charges: Charges create the fields, and charges experience forces within the fields. In this chapter, you'll find out how electric and magnetic fields are intimately related to each other as well and how changing one of them can create the other. A very important topic for the test is the creation of induced voltages and currents in electric circuits.

Motional Induced Voltages

Consider a conducting rod of length L moving with speed v through a uniform magnetic field $\vec{B}$ such that the length cuts directly across the field lines (figure 1). The mobile electrons in the conductor will each experience a force $F = qvB$ directed down in the diagram.

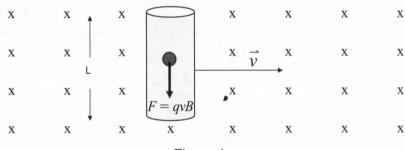

Figure 1

Because the electrons in the conductor aren't really free but are constrained to remain in the conductor (recall that a free electron moving this way would move in a circle), a fairly complex process is occurring within the conductor, but the net result is that electrons are forced down the rod, leading to a polarization or separation of charge within the rod. This polarization creates an electric field within the rod. Equilibrium will be quickly established, with the magnetic force down being balanced by the electric force up (figure 2):

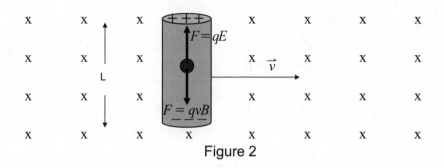

Figure 2

$$qE = qvB \Rightarrow E = Bv$$

The two ends of the rod will have a potential difference between them:

$$V_{in} = EL = BLv$$

The motion of the rod though the magnetic field has created a voltage difference across the rod, an **induced voltage**. If this rod is now connected to a circuit properly, the voltage can be used to create an electric current, and you'll have an electric generator, a device that converts mechanical energy to electrical energy. A simple system that does this is the so-called "rail system," shown in figure 3. Many B-level questions are framed in the context of this system, so be sure you understand it well.

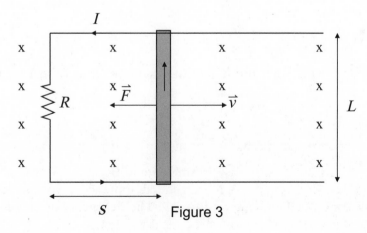

Figure 3

Notice that the additional rails (assumed to have negligible resistance) and resistor provide a return path for separated charge so a current will flow around the loop as pictured. Since the resistor is connected directly across the moving rail, you have

$$I = \frac{V_{in}}{R} = \frac{BLv}{R}$$

This is the induced current. Now you can see an interesting effect: The induced current will behave like any current in a magnetic field and feel a force $F = ILB$. The induced current, itself a product of the magnetic field (and the motion of the rod), will interact back with the field that helped create it in the first place. Using the right-hand rule, you can see that the force on the rail will be to the left, opposite to the direction the rail is moving. Notice that it was motion *to the right* that created the current, and the induced current flowed counterclockwise, creating a force *to the left* on the moving rail. In this case, the induced current flowed in such a way that it created a force that opposed the motion of the rail. This will be true in general and is summarized in **Lenz's law:**

The induced current in any system will always flow in such a way as to oppose the change that caused it. Lenz's law is consistent with the conservation of energy principle, as you'll see in this example. If the force on the rail were to the right, this would cause the rail to move faster, creating a larger current and an even bigger force. The tiniest push on the rail would then lead to very large currents and rail speeds, obviously violating the energy conservation principle.

Suppose some agent (for example, a person or a machine) pulls on the rail to keep it from slowing down. Then the agent must supply energy at the rate (power):

$$P_{\text{agent}} = F_{\text{agent}}\, v = (ILB)v = \left(\frac{BLv}{R}\right)LBv = \frac{B^2L^2v^2}{R}$$

On the other hand, as the current flows in the circuit, thermal energy will appear in the resistor at the rate:

$$P_R = I^2R = \left(\frac{BLv}{R}\right)^2 R = \frac{B^2L^2v^2}{R}$$

You can see that $P_{\text{agent}} = P_R$. You cannot get out any more electrical energy than you put in mechanically.

Magnetic Flux

Motional induced voltages are fairly easy to understand because you can think in terms of forces to derive the induced voltage. A more general approach involves introducing a new and rather abstract concept, the **magnetic flux**, Φ. The definition of magnetic flux has two ingredients:

1. magnetic field $\vec{B}$,
2. an area, A

From a conceptual point of view, the magnetic flux measures how much of the field cuts through an area (figure 4).

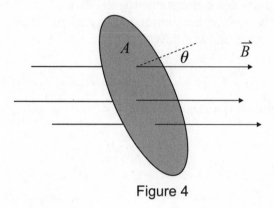

Figure 4

Quantitatively, you have the definition for a uniform field:

$$\Phi_B = \vec{B} \cdot \vec{A} = BA \cos \theta$$

The units of Φ_B are T • m^2, also called a **weber**. Here θ is the angle between the field and a line perpendicular to the area plane. Even if both the field and the area are large, Φ_B could be small if the angle is close to 90° and not much of the field cuts through the area.

On the B-level test, you'll have to be able to calculate magnetic flux for uniform fields. For nonuniform fields, you'd need calculus to do the calculation, so this won't be asked. But you can think conceptually about field lines cutting through areas even if the field isn't uniform, and you may be asked whether the flux is getting bigger or smaller.

Faraday's Law

So what does flux have to do with induced voltages? Let's re-examine the rail system, focusing on the flux through the current loop. In figure 3, the flux through the loop is given by

$$\Phi_B = BLs$$

In a small time Δt the flux will change, in this case increasing because the area is increasing. Let's calculate the rate at which the flux changes:

$$\frac{\Delta \Phi_B}{\Delta t} = BL \frac{\Delta s}{\Delta t} = BLv = V_{in}$$

You can see that the rate at which the flux changes is just the induced voltage. While it was derived for the special case of the rail system, the validity of this statement is much broader and is known as **Faraday's law**. When the magnetic flux through a loop changes, a voltage will be induced. For a single loop, you have

$$V_{in} = \frac{\Delta \Phi_B}{\Delta t}$$

If there are N loops wound in the same direction, each loop will have the preceding voltage induced, so that

$$V_{in} = N\frac{\Delta \Phi_B}{\Delta t}$$

Since you're looking at time intervals that may not be extremely small, these formulas give average values for the induced voltages. You can then find the average induced current in the circuit if the overall resistance is known.

Lenz's Law and Flux

A common question on the AP test involves determining the direction of the induced current. The easiest way to do this is to apply Lenz's law while thinking about the *magnetic field created by the induced current* and what this will do to the overall flux through the loop. Since the induced current will always flow in such a way as to oppose the change that caused it, the induced current will create its own field that will try to keep the flux from changing. To determine the direction of the field created by a current loop at points inside the circumference of the loop, you can use a variation of the long wire right-hand rule:

> **Loop right-hand rule:** Curl the fingers of the right hand around the loop in the direction of the current flow. The thumb will point in the direction of the magnetic field within the loop created by this current.

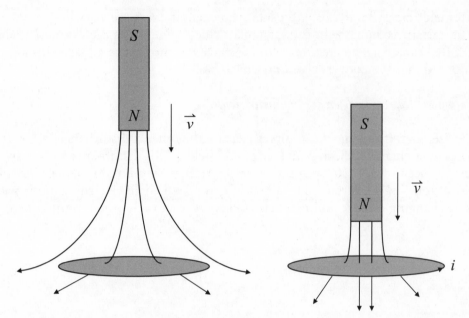

As flux into the loop increases, a current flows, creating its own field
that opposes the original change in flux.

Figure 5

In figure 5, the flux through the loop increased as the magnet fell. The induced current will
create an upward field to oppose the change. In terms of the loop right-hand rule, to get your
thumb to point up, the current must flow as shown in the figure.

Faraday's Law Generalized

As stated, Faraday's law will correctly give the induced voltages and currents associated with
changing magnetic flux. You might well ask, How does a changing magnetic flux actually
create the current? What is the mechanism? How do the electrons in the loop know about
the changing field inside the loop? If there's no loop present to experience the change, is there
no effect at all? For a complete answer, you need to have a grasp of the theory of special
relativity. But the short answer is that when the magnetic field changes at a point, an electric
field is created at that point. If a loop is present, this electric field can do work on charges
and drive a current, but even if no loop is present, the electric field is still created. You can
generalize Faraday's law to say that:

Changing magnetic fields create electric fields.

The electric fields created like this will usually be changing in time as well.

There's a certain asymmetry to this statement since it identifies the magnetic field as the special field that can create an electric field. Maxwell was the first to address this asymmetry, and he proposed that the converse could occur as well:

Changing electric fields create magnetic fields.

Maxwell realized that if each field can directly create the other, a disturbance in any field will produce a **wave** of changing electric and magnetic fields. This disturbance moves away from the source at a speed of $3 \times 10^8 \frac{m}{s}$, much like the ripples on a pond moving away from the point where a stone hit the surface. This phenomenon is called an **electromagnetic wave**, and it consists of changing electric and magnetic fields creating each other continuously.

KEY FORMULAS

Rail System Induced Voltage	$V_{in} = BLv$
Magnetic Flux	$\Phi_B = BA \cos \theta$
Faraday's Law	$V_{in} = N \dfrac{\Delta \Phi_B}{\Delta t}$

PRACTICE EXERCISES

SECTION I MULTIPLE CHOICE

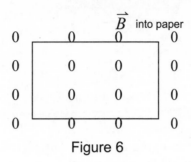

Figure 6

1. A rectangular loop of dimensions 0.04 m by 0.06 m is at rest in a uniform magnetic field of magnitude 0.5 T. The field is perpendicular to the plane of the loop coming out of the page. The magnetic flux through the loop is

   (A) $12 \text{ T} \cdot \text{m}^2$ (B) 0   (C) $0.12 \text{ T} \cdot \text{m}^2$ (D) $12 \times 10^{-4} \text{ T} \cdot \text{m}^2$ (E) $0.5 \text{ T} \cdot \text{m}^2$

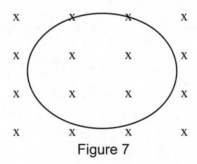

Figure 7

2. A flexible conducting loop is placed in a magnetic field with the plane of the loop perpendicular to the field. Which of the following will NOT induce a current in the loop?

   (A) increase the magnitude of the field
   (B) stretch the loop, making a larger circle
   (C) move the loop parallel to the field
   (D) remove the loop from the field
   (E) rotate the loop about a diameter

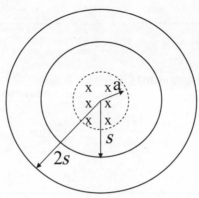

Figure 8

3. Two concentric loops have radii s and $2s$. A spatially uniform magnetic field over the range $r < a$ with $a < s$ is changing at a constant rate. The voltage induced in the outer loop is V_{in}. The voltage induced in the inner loop is

(A) 0   (B) $\dfrac{V_{in}}{2}$ (C) $\dfrac{V_{in}}{4}$ (D) $2V_{in}$ (E) V_{in}

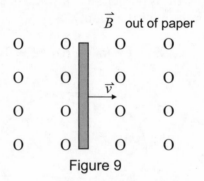

Figure 9

4. A wire of constant length is moving through a uniform magnetic field at a constant velocity with the velocity vector perpendicular to the field. A graph of the induced voltage between the ends of the wire as a function of time would look like

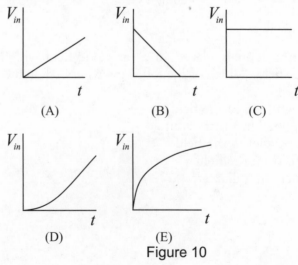

Figure 10

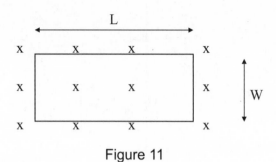

Figure 11

5. A rectangular loop of dimensions L and W and resistance R is stationary in a changing magnetic field. To produce a current I in the loop, the field must change at a rate of

(A) $\frac{LW}{IR}$ (B) $\frac{IR}{LW}$ (C) $\frac{L}{IR}$ (D) $\frac{IRL}{W}$ (E) $\frac{IRW}{L}$

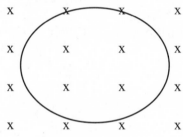

Figure 12

6. A magnetic field, perpendicular into the page to a circular loop, is decreasing as time goes on. In which direction will the current induced in the loop flow?

(A) counterclockwise
(B) clockwise
(C) No current will flow.
(D) out of the page
(E) into the page

Questions 7 and 8

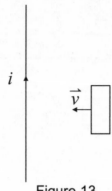

Figure 13

7. A rectangular loop is moving toward a long wire carrying current up as shown in the figure. In which direction will the induced current in the loop flow?

   (A) counterclockwise (B) clockwise (C) No current will flow.

   (D) out of the page (E) into the page

8. The force exerted on the loop by the long wire will be directed

   (A) into the page (B) out of the page (C) left (D) right (E) down

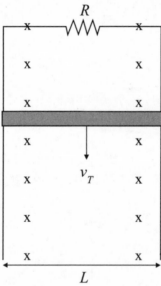

Figure 14

9. A conducting rail of mass m and length L slides vertically along frictionless rails connected by a resistance R. A uniform magnetic field $\vec{B}$ is directed perpendicular to the plane of the rails and into the paper as shown. When the falling rail has reached terminal speed v_T, the rate at which thermal energy appears in the resistor is

   (A) mgv_T (B) $\dfrac{BLv_T}{R}$ (C) $\dfrac{B^2L^2v_T}{R}$ (D) BLv_T (E) $\dfrac{mg}{BL}$

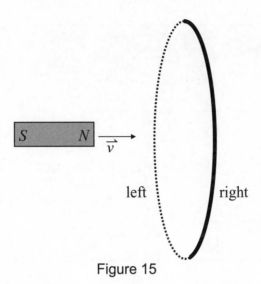

Figure 15

10. A bar magnet moves at constant speed through a circular conducting loop. Viewed from the left, the current flow in the loop will be

   (A) clockwise only
   (B) counterclockwise only
   (C) clockwise first, then counterclockwise
   (D) counterclockwise first, then clockwise
   (E) Current does not flow in the loop.

PRACTICE EXERCISES

SECTION II FREE RESPONSE

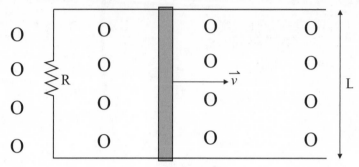

Figure 16

1. A conducting rail, positioned to slide without friction over fixed conducting rails separated by a distance L, is pulled along at a constant speed v by some external force $\vec{F}$. A uniform magnetic field $\vec{B}$ points out of the paper, perpendicular to the plane of the loop. The fixed rails are connected by a resistance R.

   (a) On the diagram, indicate the direction of the induced current flow.
   (b) Determine the magnitude of the induced current.
   (c) Determine the magnitude of force F needed to keep the rail moving at a constant speed.
   (d) The force $\vec{F}$ is suddenly removed. How much energy will be dissipated in the resistor as the rail slows to a stop?

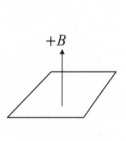

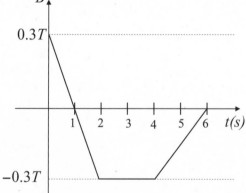

Figure 17

2. A square loop of resistance 0.5 Ω and side 0.6 m is oriented so that the plane of the loop is perpendicular to a magnetic field that is uniform spatially but changing in time as depicted in the graph below. The positive direction of $\vec{B}$ is up.

   (a) Calculate the flux through the loop at $t = 4$ s.
   (b) Find the induced voltage at $t = 5$ s.
   (c) On the axes below, sketch the induced current as a function of time. Indicate numerical values on the current axis and assume counterclockwise current is positive.

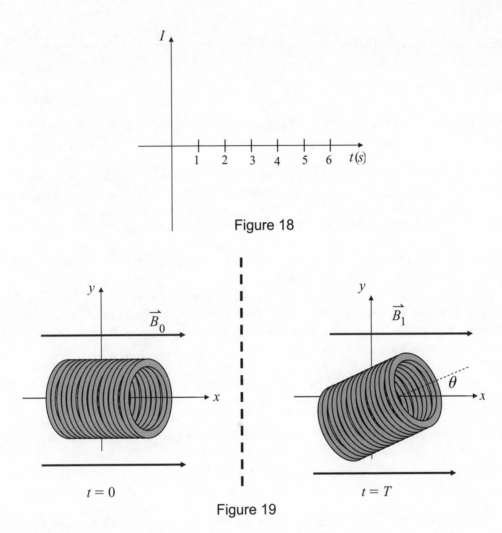

Figure 18

Figure 19

3. A length L of wire with cross sectional area a and resistivity ρ is wound around a hollow tube of radius R forming a coil. The two ends of the coil are connected and the coil is then aligned so that its axis lies along the x-axis of a coordinate system. A spatially uniform magnetic field B_0 parallel to the x-axis exists in this region. In a time T, the field strength changes to B_1 and the coil is rotated θ above the x-axis.

    (a) In terms of L and R, how many loops are in the coil?
    (b) What is the average induced voltage in the coil over the time T?
    (c) What is the average current that flowed during the time T?
    (d) The answer to (c) is independent of L, the length of the wire. Explain why this is so in physical terms.

Answers and Explanations

MULTIPLE CHOICE

1. The answer is D. The area of the loop is 24×10^{-4} m². Since $\Phi = BA$, the result follows by multiplying by 0.5 T.

2. The answer is C. Moving the loop parallel to the field won't change how much of the field cuts through the loop. All other possibilities given will change the flux, either by changing the field in the loop (A and D), the area (B), or the orientation of the field with respect to the area (E). Changing the flux will induce a current.

3. The answer is E. The changing flux through either loop is $\frac{\Delta B}{\Delta t}(\pi a^2)$. Since $a < s$, whatever flux cuts through the smaller loop will also cut through the larger loop. While the two loops will have the same induced voltage, in general they will have different currents induced because in general they will have different resistances. Within each loop, different electric fields will be induced as well, but only C-level students need to address this level of complexity.

4. The answer is C. As the wire cuts across the field, a voltage of $V_{in} = BLv$ is induced between the ends of the wire. All of these quantities are constant.

5. The answer is B. The induced voltage from the changing flux will produce a current $I = \frac{V_{in}}{R} = \frac{\frac{\Delta B}{\Delta t}(LW)}{R}$. Solving for $\frac{\Delta B}{\Delta t}$ gives the result.

6. The answer is B. Since the field is *decreasing* into the loop, by Lenz's law the induced current will flow to try to *increase* the field into the loop. The loop right-hand rule then gives a clockwise direction for the current flow.

7. The answer is A. As the loop moves closer to the wire, the field is getting stronger. This field points into the paper at the position of the loop, so the flux is increasing into the paper. Lenz's law then tells you that the induced current will create a field that points out of the paper, and the loop right-hand rule gives a counterclockwise direction.

8. The answer is D. This is the force direction that will oppose the change. You can analyze the segments of the loop to see how this happens. From question 7 you know the current flows counterclockwise. The two shorter-width sections will experience equal but opposite ilB forces. The length section closer to the long wire will feel an ilB force directed away from the long wire, using the force right-hand rule. While the other length section feels a force toward the long wire, the field is weaker at its position, so the net force is away.

9. The answer is A. At terminal speed, the work done by gravity will not increase the KE of the rail so all the work done by gravity will have to appear as thermal energy in the resistor. The power supplied by gravity is $P = Fv = mgv_T$.

10. The answer is D. As the north pole approaches from the left, the field will point left to right through the loop, and it will be getting stronger. To oppose this change, the loop will have to create a field that points right to left, and this is achieved with a counterclockwise current. As the magnet exits the loop, the field direction is determined by the closer south pole, so the field still points left to right through the loop, but now it is getting weaker. To oppose this change, a the loop will have to create a field that points left to right, achieved by a clockwise current.

FREE RESPONSE

1. (a) The current will flow clockwise around the rectangular loop. The area of the loop is getting larger, causing the flux out of the loop to increase. By Lenz's law, the induced current will flow to oppose the increase in flux, and this can be accomplished by creating a field *into the page*. The right-hand rule then gives the clockwise direction.

   (b) The induced voltage is $V_{in} = BLv$. The induced current will then be $I = \frac{BLv}{R}$, since the voltage drop across the resistor is V_{in}.

   (c) The moving rail will feel a force to the left because the current I flowing in the rail is experiencing the magnetic field $\vec{B}$. This force is $F_{left} = ILB$. An equal force will have to be applied to the right to keep the rail moving at constant speed. Substituting for I, you have

   $$F = \frac{B^2 L^2 v}{R}$$

   (d) At the instant the force is removed, the rail is moving at speed v and has kinetic energy $\frac{1}{2}mv^2$. Conservation of energy then says that all of this energy will eventually appear as thermal energy in the resistor, so the answer is $\frac{1}{2}mv^2$.

2. (a) At $t = 4$ s, the field is 0.3 T. The area of the loop is $(0.6 \text{ m})^2 = 0.36 \text{ m}^2$, so

   $$\Phi_B = BA = 0.3(0.36) = 0.108 \text{ webers}$$

(b) At $t = 5$ s, the field is changing at the rate of $\frac{0.3}{2} = 0.15\frac{\text{T}}{\text{s}}$. This is the slope of the last line segment in the graph. Since the area doesn't change, the flux will be changing at the rate

$$\frac{\Delta \Phi_B}{\Delta t} = \frac{\Delta B}{\Delta t} A = 0.15(0.36) = 0.054 \text{ V}$$

This is the induced voltage by Faraday's law.

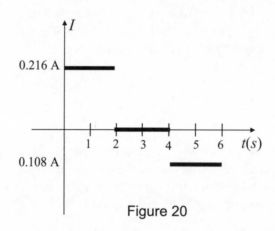

Figure 20

(c) Over the first 2 s, the field changes at the rate of $\frac{0.6}{2} = 0.3\frac{\text{T}}{\text{s}}$ (slope), and the induced voltage will be

$$\frac{\Delta \Phi}{\Delta t} = \frac{\Delta B}{\Delta t} A = 0.3(0.36) = 0.108 \text{ V}$$

The induced current then will be $I = \frac{V_{in}}{R} = \frac{0.108}{0.5} = 0.216$ A. By Lenz's law, this current will flow in such a way as to oppose the change in flux created by the decreasing field. This means the current will create a field in the + direction, and the right-hand rule then gives a counterclockwise direction for the flow. This is the + current direction.

Over the interval from 2–4 s, there's no change in flux, so the current will be 0. Over the last 2 seconds, you can see that the slope is just half of the slope over the first 2 seconds, so the induced current will be just half as much. In this case, however, the field is increasing, causing the flux up through the loop to increase. The induced current will flow to oppose this change in flux; this means that the current must flow clockwise, creating its own field down through the loop. This is the negative current direction.

3. (a) Since each loop in the coil has a circumference $2\pi R$, the number of loops is

$$N = \frac{L}{2\pi R}$$

(b) The initial flux is $NB_0 (\pi R^2)$ since the field is perpendicular to the plane of the loops. The part of the field that is perpendicular to this plane after time T is $B_1 \cos\theta$, so Faraday's law gives the average induced voltage.

$$V_{in} = \frac{\Delta\Phi}{\Delta t} = \frac{N\pi R^2(B_1\cos\theta - B_0)}{T} = \frac{LR(B_1\cos\theta - B_0)}{2T}$$

(c) Since the resistance of the length of wire is $r = \rho\frac{L}{a}$, Ohm's law gives the average current over the time interval.

$$i = \frac{V_{in}}{r} = \frac{aR(B_1\cos\theta - B_0)}{2\rho T}.$$

(d) As L increases, more loops can be formed implying a greater induced voltage, but increasing L also increases the resistance by the same factor. The net effect is that the ratio of voltage to resistance stays the same.

15

Waves

This chapter will introduce the phenomenon of waves, with particular emphasis on mechanical waves. A later chapter will focus on electromagnetic waves and light.

Traveling Waves

A **wave** is a disturbance in a medium that moves away from the origin of the disturbance with a characteristic speed v_w. If the disturbance takes place in a material medium like air or water, then forces on individual particles and their subsequent motion contribute to the wave behavior. These types of waves are called **mechanical waves** because their behavior is governed by the laws of mechanics. While individual particles take part in the wave motion, the particles themselves never move very far from their equilibrium positions. A mechanical wave is a correlated motion of many particles, resulting in the transfer of energy without the actual transfer of the medium particles themselves. Water waves and sound waves are both examples of mechanical waves.

In the previous chapter, you saw that the laws of electricity and magnetism allow for changing electric and magnetic fields to create each other. This mechanism also leads to wave behavior, an **electromagnetic wave**, which clearly isn't a mechanical wave. The wave consists of the oscillating fields themselves and can travel even in vacuum; no material particles are needed to sustain the wave.

As a mechanical wave travels through a medium, the manner in which the medium particles move falls into one of two categories. In a **transverse wave**, the medium particles move at right angles to the direction in which the wave travels. For example, when a string is plucked, the individual pieces of the string move up and down as the wave itself travels down the length of the string. In figure 1, point P on the string moves up and then down the dotted line as the wave travels to the right.

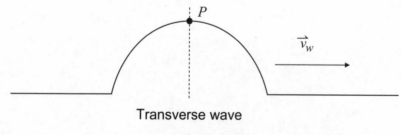

Transverse wave

Figure 1

If the medium particles move along the same line as the direction in which the wave travels, the wave is a **longitudinal wave**. Figure 2 shows a region of compression on a spring moving to the right. Point P will move left and right as the disturbance passes through it, so this is a longitudinal wave.

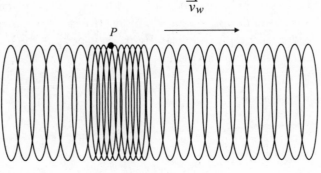

Longitudinal wave

Figure 2

A sound wave is an important example of a longitudinal wave. In air, it consists of regions of consecutive high and low pressure where the air molecules have been forced closer together or farther apart. Figure 3 depicts a sound wave traveling down a hollow tube. The air molecules themselves move back and forth along the tube axis. The overall size of the pressure changes is actually quite small, but your ears are very sensitive.

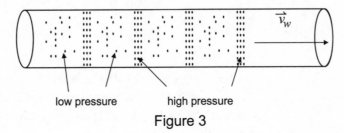

low pressure   high pressure

Figure 3

Electromagnetic waves are always transverse. The electric and magnetic fields oscillate perpendicular to the direction in which the wave travels. In fact, they're perpendicular to each other as well, so that $\vec{E}$, $\vec{B}$, $\vec{v}_w$ form a set of three mutually perpendicular vectors as shown in figure 4.

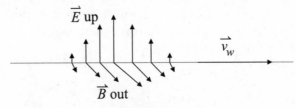

Figure 4

A wave created by a source that makes an identical disturbance at regular time intervals is called a **periodic wave**. For example, on a stretched string, you could move one end up and down, over and over again in an identical manner, sending identical wave forms down the length of the string. The tines of a vibrating tuning fork also will disturb the surrounding air in a way that creates regular patterns of high and low pressure moving away from the fork.

Describing and analyzing periodic waves is by far the most important aspect of waves for the B-level test. Consider the graph shown in figure 5. It depicts the disturbance of a periodic wave traveling down the x-axis at one instant of time.

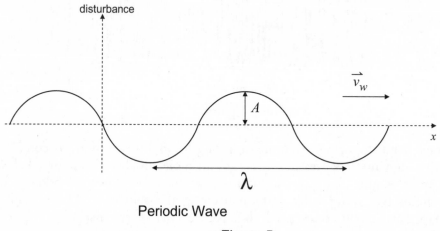

Periodic Wave

Figure 5

The quantity shown on the vertical axis measures the disturbance: For a water wave, it would be the height above still water; for a sound wave, it would be the slight pressure deviation from atmospheric pressure; for an electromagnetic wave, it would be the electric field component.

The maximum value of the disturbance is called the **amplitude A** of the wave. As you look at the wave in its entirety, you can see points along the wave where the medium particles (for a mechanical wave) at a given instant are moving in exactly the same way: They have the same displacement from their equilibrium position, and they have the same velocity. These particles are "in **phase**" with each other. For example, in a water wave, all the points at the top of the wave crests at a given instant are in phase. The distance between any two consecutive points that are in phase is called the **wavelength λ** of the wave. You can think of it as the distance between crests. For an electromagnetic wave, it would be the distance between consecutive maxima of the electric field.

If you watch a periodic water wave pass by, you can count the number of crests that pass you every second. This is called the **frequency f** of the wave and is defined analogously for any periodic wave. For the water wave, if 3 crests passed you in 1 second, it would mean that the water molecules in front of you actually oscillated up and down 3 times in 1 second. They would have a period of $\frac{1}{3}$ of a second. Generally, the frequency of the wave is the inverse of the medium particles' period of oscillation:

$$f = \frac{1}{T}$$

For an electromagnetic wave, it would be the period of the electric field oscillation, and the same equation would hold.

By the nature of how the wave moves, in 1 period of oscillation for a medium particle, the wave will advance 1 wavelength while moving at a constant speed v_w. For any periodic wave, you can say:

$$\lambda = v_w T = v_w \frac{1}{f}$$

$$v_w = \lambda f$$

This simple equation holds for sound, light, and any periodic wave.

EXAMPLE

What is the wavelength of the sound created by middle C on a piano, frequency 256 Hz, on a day when the speed of sound is 340 m/s?

$$v_w = \lambda f \Rightarrow \lambda = \frac{v_w}{f} = \frac{340}{256} = 1.33 \text{ m}$$

Doppler Effect

When a source of sound is moving, the frequency of the sound heard by a stationary observer will be different from the frequency heard by a source who is also stationary. Similarly, if the source is stationary and the observer moves, he or she again hears a different frequency. These are examples of the **Doppler effect**, which you have experienced if an ambulance has ever passed you with its siren on. Most B-level textbooks go into these effects in some detail and derive equations for the frequency shifts. For the B-level AP test, you really only need to understand the qualitative aspects of the phenomenon. Let's look at the effect, using sound waves as the concrete example. (Electromagnetic waves also exhibit a Doppler effect, but the explanation requires special relativity, which is outside the syllabus for the B-level test.)

MOVING SOURCE

A stationary source emits sound of frequency f and wavelength λ, as shown in figure 6a. You can assume that the speed of sound in air is a constant v. Since the source is emitting a periodic wave, you can say $v = \lambda f$.

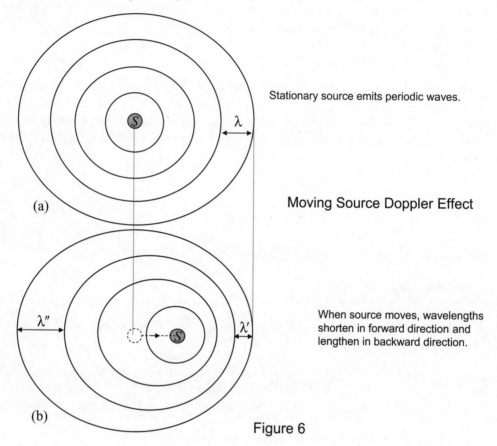

Stationary source emits periodic waves.

(a)

Moving Source Doppler Effect

When source moves, wavelengths shorten in forward direction and lengthen in backward direction.

(b)

Figure 6

If the source moves as shown in figure 6b, the wave crests in the forward direction will be closer together. That's because once the wave is emitted, it moves at the same speed as the waves emitted by the stationary source: The wave speed is independent of the motion of the source and depends on only the properties of the medium—in this case, air. That means the first crest emitted in the figure reaches the same point in the same time as the first crest emitted by the stationary source. The last crest emitted, however, is now farther to the right, so all the in-between crests have to be scrunched into a smaller length. Meanwhile, the wave traveling to the left will have its crests expanded for just the opposite reason. Of course, the wave is still periodic, and the wave speed is the same, so you have

$$v = \lambda'f' \qquad f' \text{ is larger in forward direction, since } \lambda' \text{ is smaller.}$$
$$v = \lambda''f'' \qquad f'' \text{ is smaller in forward direction, since } \lambda'' \text{ is larger.}$$

When an ambulance passes you with its siren on, you experience both effects.

MOVING OBSERVER

When the observer moves, there's no change in the wavelength of the wave. As shown in figure 7a, however, when the observer moves into the wave with velocity $\vec{v}_{ob}$, from his point of view it seems as if the wave is traveling past him faster, and more crests are passing his ear every second.

Moving Observer Doppler Effect

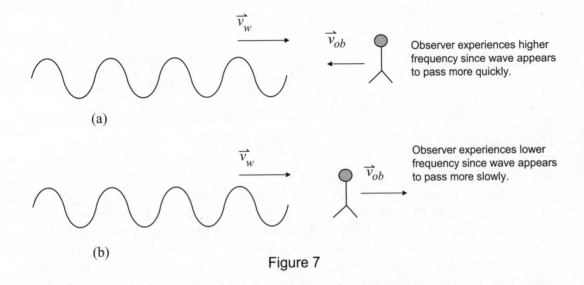

(a)

Observer experiences higher frequency since wave appears to pass more quickly.

(b)

Observer experiences lower frequency since wave appears to pass more slowly.

Figure 7

This periodic wave will seem to have a larger wave speed and a higher frequency, but it would have the same wavelength as a stationary observer would see it. Moving in the opposite direction, as in b, would lower the wave speed and frequency experienced by the observer.

$v' = \lambda f'$ f' is larger if the observer moves toward the source, since v' is larger.

$v'' = \lambda f''$ f'' is smaller if the observer moves away from the source, since v'' is smaller.

Superposition Principle and Interference

Suppose two pulses of the same orientation are sent down a string in opposite directions as shown in figure 8.

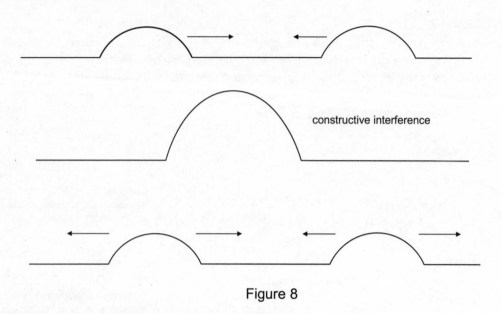

constructive interference

Figure 8

What will happen when they meet? Wave phenomena obey the superposition principle, a concept you learned about in electricity. In this context, the principle says that each wave travels as if the other one weren't present. When they occupy the same position, the amplitude of the combined wave is just the algebraic sum of the individual amplitudes. Eventually they pass through each other and travel on as if they never met. When the two waves are passing through each other, they are "interfering" with each other. Since the two combine to produce a larger amplitude, this is called **constructive interference**. Figure 9 shows two pulses of opposite orientation interfering. This is called **destructive interference**.

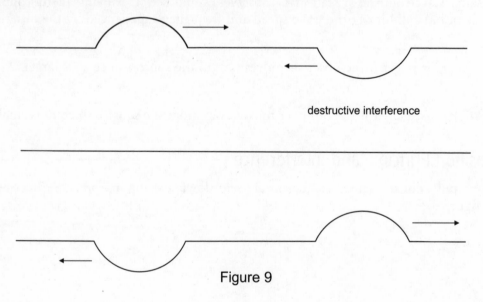

destructive interference

Figure 9

Wave Reflections

When a wave pulse moves down a string, after it reaches the end, it will reflect back again. The orientation of the reflected pulse will depend on whether the endpoint is fixed or free to move up and down. If the end is fixed, as an upward-oriented pulse encounters the endpoint, it pulls up on the fixed point; a Newton's third-law reaction force pulls down on the pulse, and it inverts. This is shown in figure 10a: A fixed endpoint will invert a pulse.

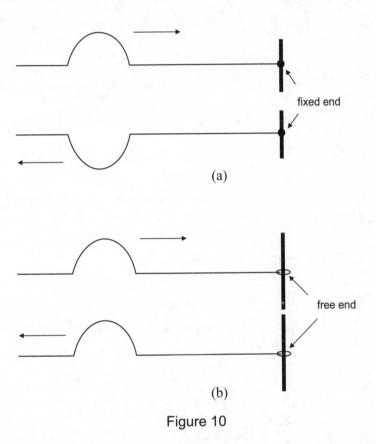

(a)

(b)

Figure 10

If a periodic wave moved down the string, each section of the wave would flip at the endpoint. Since the difference between a peak and a valley in a periodic wave is $\frac{1}{2}\lambda$, the wave has shifted by $\frac{1}{2}\lambda$. This is called a half wavelength **phase shift**.

If the endpoint is free to move—for example, by connecting with a loop to a vertical rod as shown in b—there is no reaction force, and the reflected pulse doesn't acquire a phase shift. The constraint imposed by the endpoint in this case is a special case of a **boundary condition**. In general, when waves move from one medium to another, a boundary condition will be imposed that will determine if the reflected wave inverts.

Standing Waves

When a periodic wave moves down a string, the reflected wave will also be periodic, as shown in the example (figure 11). These two waves will pass through each other and interfere in such a way that you won't be able to see any left or right motion of the wave.

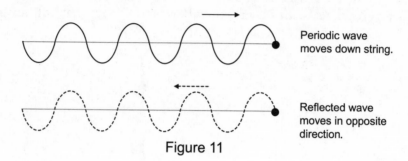

Periodic wave moves down string.

Reflected wave moves in opposite direction.

Figure 11

A stationary pattern will appear on the string, called a **standing wave**. At any given instant, you can record a snapshot of the wave currently on the string. Five such snapshots are shown in figure 12.

Superposition of original and reflected waves

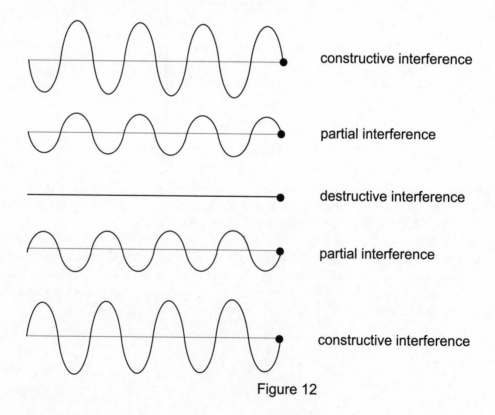

constructive interference

partial interference

destructive interference

partial interference

constructive interference

Figure 12

Notice that the interference ranges from constructive to destructive. Such patterns are often depicted as shown in figure 13, which is a kind of time average of all the patterns. At the **nodes** of the pattern, the amplitude of the superposed wave is always 0. These points never move on the string. At the **antinodes**, the string vibrates through the largest possible amplitude.

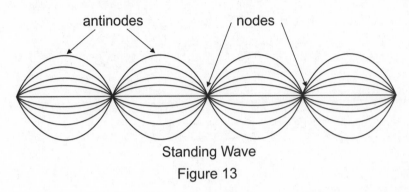

antinodes   nodes

Standing Wave

Figure 13

Standing waves can be set up in a wide range of circumstances. The necessary ingredients are two or more periodic waves of the same frequency. The waves can be supplied by several sources or by a single source of waves that are allowed to reflect at boundaries of the medium. You can determine the possible standing wave frequencies if you know the type of boundary conditions. For the B-level test, you'll have to be familiar with one-dimensional standing waves on strings and in air columns.

STRINGS

The wave speed on a uniform string is determined by the tension T, mass m, and length L of the string through the following formula:

$$v_{string} = \sqrt{\frac{T}{\frac{m}{L}}}$$

These parameters define the medium. The technique for determining the possible frequencies for standing waves involves two steps:

1. From the boundary conditions, determine the simplest standing wave. This is called the fundamental mode or the first harmonic. The wavelength will be determined by the length.

2. Using the basic equation $v = \lambda f$, solve for the frequency. For higher levels of excitation (more nodes), repeat steps 1 and 2 for the particular excitation.

EXAMPLE

Given a wave speed v for waves on a string of length L with fixed endpoints, determine all possible standing wave frequencies.

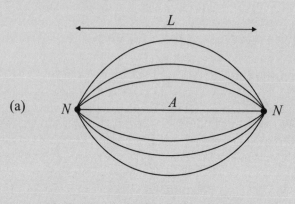

(a)

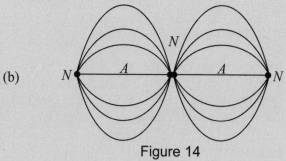

(b)

Figure 14

The boundary conditions of fixed endpoints force nodes at each end. The simplest standing wave will have 1 antinode between the ends, as shown in figure 14a. For any standing wave, there will always be $\frac{1}{4}\lambda$ between consecutive nodes and antinodes, so for this standing wave, the string length is $\frac{1}{2}\lambda$. Then you have

$$v = \lambda f = (2L)f_1 \Rightarrow f_1 = \frac{v}{2L} \quad \text{first harmonic}$$

The next simplest standing wave will have 1 more node and antinode, since you can't add one without the other. Figure 14b shows the form. For this standing wave, the length of the string is 1 wavelength, 4 N-A intervals. Then you have

$$v = \lambda f = (L)f_2 \Rightarrow \frac{v}{L} = 2f_1 \quad \text{second harmonic}$$

As you add more nodes, the frequencies increase by integral multiples of the lowest value:

$$f_n = nf_1$$

AIR COLUMNS

An air column of length L can support standing sound waves within it. Of course, the wave speed here will be the speed of sound, around 340 m/s at sea level and 20° C. The frequencies allowed in a given length of tube will depend on whether the tube ends are open or not. An open end will allow maximum movement of the air molecules so that a standing wave will have an antinode here. A closed end restricts the movement of the molecules, and a standing wave will have a node here. The technique for determining the allowed frequencies for a given length is exactly the same as for a string.

EXAMPLE

Find the allowed frequencies for standing sound waves in an air column of length L with one end open.

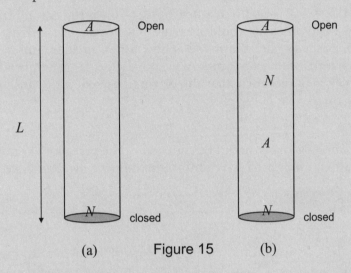

(a)   Figure 15   (b)

The simplest standing wave will have a node at the closed end and an antinode at the open end and nothing else. Figure 15a depicts the situation. The tube length is $\frac{1}{4}\lambda$, so you have

$$v = \lambda f = (4L)f_1 \quad \text{first harmonic}$$

The next simplest standing wave will have one more node and antinode as shown in b, making $L = \frac{3}{4}\lambda$. This gives you

$$v = \lambda f = \left(\frac{4}{3}L\right)f_2 \Rightarrow f_2 = 3\frac{v}{4L} = 3f_1 \quad \text{third harmonic}$$

As you add more nodes and antinodes, the frequencies increase by odd integer multiples of the lowest frequency:

$$f_n = nf_1 \quad n = 1, 3, 5 \ldots$$

The moral of the story for strings and air columns is that boundary conditions and simple counting, using $v = \lambda f$, will allow you to handle any possible case. You should also try some of the other possibilities, such as an air column open at both ends or a string with one end free.

Resonance

When you push someone on a swing, it's not hard to get the swinger moving in very large motions even if you don't push that hard. The trick is to push at just the right time, to match the frequency of your pushes to the frequency of the swinger's motion. This is a simple example of the phenomenon of **resonance**. In a resonance, large amplitudes of vibration are established through the repeated application of small impulses applied at a natural frequency of the excited system. The swing example has all of these ingredients. The swing itself is a pendulum with period $T = 2\pi\sqrt{\frac{L}{g}}$ and frequency $f = \frac{1}{T}$. This is the natural frequency of the system, the frequency with which it would oscillate if you just released the swinger from some height and never pushed again. But if you apply pushes, small impulses, at a frequency that just matches this natural frequency, you can eventually get large amplitudes. The key to understanding resonance is to recognize that the driving frequency, the pusher, must match a natural frequency of the system being excited:

$$f_{\text{driver}} = f_{\text{system}}$$

The simplest systems can have many natural frequencies. The preceding examples show that vibrating strings and air columns each have an infinite number of natural frequencies.

EXAMPLE

A string of length L with fixed endpoints and wave speed v_{st} is made to vibrate in its second harmonic, the first excitation beyond the lowest frequency. You want to use this vibrating string to create a standing wave in a hollow tube with only one end open by placing the string near the open end. What is the length of the shortest tube that will work?

The frequency of the string is $f_{\text{st}} = \frac{v_{\text{st}}}{L}$, from the previous example. The shortest air column will be vibrating in its lowest mode, a single node and antinode. You could excite longer tubes if you set up a standing wave in the tube with more than the smallest number of nodes and antinodes. The frequency for the tube will be from the previous example, $f_{\text{tube}} = \frac{v_{\text{sound}}}{4L_{\text{tube}}}$. At resonance, the frequencies are equal:

$$\frac{v_{\text{st}}}{L} = \frac{v_{\text{sound}}}{4L_{\text{tube}}} \Rightarrow L_{\text{tube}} = L\frac{v_{\text{sound}}}{4v_{\text{st}}}$$

Notice that the two waves involved, the string wave and the sound wave, have different wave speeds and wavelengths. At a resonance, what they have in common is their frequency.

Beats

When two waves of the same frequency pass through each other, you get a standing wave pattern. You saw this in the one-dimensional examples earlier where the two waves consisted of a wave made by a periodic disturbance and a wave reflected from a boundary. Similar patterns of nodes and antinodes can be set up in two and three dimensions as well. For example, two tuning forks of the same frequency will create a standing wave pattern; two small circular floats driven up and down at the same frequency will make a standing wave pattern in a wave tank. An interesting phenomenon occurs if the two interfering waves don't have exactly the same frequency but differ by just a small amount. In this case, the two interfering waves don't stay in step with each other. A point where constructive interference occurs at one instant will eventually experience destructive interference.

For example, suppose you have two tuning forks with frequencies 256 Hz and 252 Hz, respectively. If the tuning forks are struck independently, you might be able to discern the slight difference in pitch, but if they're struck simultaneously, you hear a sound that fades in and out in amplitude. At your eardrum, the two waves produced by the forks will interfere constructively some of the time and destructively at other times, producing a sound that gets alternately louder and softer. These alternating louder and softer sounds are called **beats**. The frequency with which the beats occur is the magnitude of the difference in the two wave frequencies interfering:

$$f_{\text{beat}} = |f_1 - f_2|$$

In the example, the beat frequency would be 4 Hz; the sounds would get louder and softer 4 times every second.

KEY FORMULAS	
Period Frequency	$f = \frac{1}{T}$
Periodic Wave	$v = \lambda f$
String Waves	$v_{\text{string}} = \sqrt{\dfrac{T}{\frac{m}{L}}}$
Resonance	$f_{\text{driver}} = f_{\text{system}}$
Beats	$f_{\text{beat}} = |f_1 - f_2|$

CHAPTER 15 PRACTICE EXERCISES

SECTION I MULTIPLE CHOICE

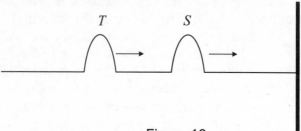

Figure 16

1. Two pulses on a string move to the right as shown in the figure. When pulse S reflects from the fixed end of the string and interferes with T, the shape of the resulting pulse is best described by

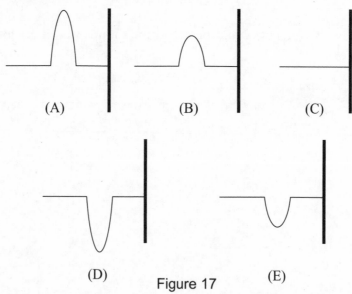

(A)   (B)   (C)

(D)   Figure 17   (E)

2. A sound source produces waves of frequency f on a day when the speed of sound is v_s. The sound experienced by a stationary observer as this source moves away from the observer will have frequency and wave speed f', v'_s. Which of the following is true?

(A) $f' > f$, $v'_s = v_s$ (B) $f' < f$, $v'_s = v_s$ (C) $f' < f$, $v'_s < v_s$
(D) $f' > f$, $v'_s > v_s$ (E) $f' > f$, $v'_s < v_s$

Questions 3 and 4

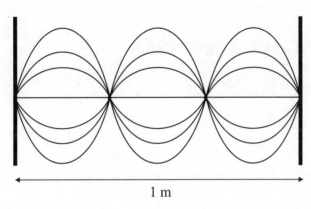

1 m

Figure 18

3. The standing wave shown in the figure has a frequency of 6 Hz. The wave speed on the string is most nearly

(A) 2 m/s   (B) 4 m/s   (C) 6 m/s   (D) 8 m/s   (E) 10 m/s

4. The fundamental frequency of the string is

(A) 3 Hz   (B) 1 Hz   (C) 6 Hz   (D) 12 Hz   (E) 2 Hz

5. A hollow tube of length 3 m is open at both ends. A sound source emitting waves of which wavelength will not produce a standing wave in the tube?

(A) 1 m   (B) 2 m   (C) 3 m   (D) 4 m   (E) 6 m

6. A sound source emitting waves of frequency 250 Hz is placed near a guitar that has 6 strings of length 0.9 m. When the source is turned off, you notice that one of the strings continues to vibrate with one antinode present. The wave speed on this string is most nearly

(A) 340 m/s   (B) 110 m/s   (C) 220 m/s   (D) 440 m/s   (E) 170 m/s

7. A piano tuner has a set of precision tuning forks. A colleague gives him a tuning fork with no frequency markings on it. When he sounds the unknown with a 496 Hz tuning fork, he hears a beat frequency of 3 Hz. When he sounds it with a 484 Hz tuning fork, he hears a beat frequency of 9 Hz. The frequency of the unknown tuning fork is

(A) 499 Hz   (B) 490 Hz   (C) 475 Hz   (D) 493 Hz   (E) 487 Hz

PRACTICE EXERCISES

SECTION II FREE RESPONSE

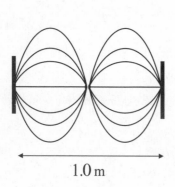

(a)

Figure 19

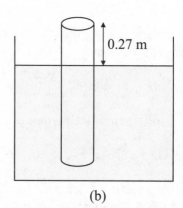

(b)

1. A sound source producing waves of frequency 600 Hz causes a 1.0 m string with fixed ends to vibrate in a standing wave pattern, shown in the figure on the left. When the same string is simply plucked so that it vibrates in its fundamental mode, it will first resonate with a long, hollow tube immersed in water when the tube is withdrawn 0.27 m from the water.

(a) Determine the wave speed on the string.
(b) Determine the speed of sound from the data given.
(c) If the string continues to vibrate in its fundamental mode, how far must the tube be raised out of the water to reach another resonance?

Answers and Explanations

MULTIPLE CHOICE

1. The answer is C. The reflected pulse S will invert upon reflection. As it passes through the pulse T, their opposite orientation will lead to destructive interference.

2. The answer is B. This is the moving source Doppler effect. As the source moves away from the observer, the wavelength gets longer, but the wave speed stays the same since the wave speed depends on only the medium properties. Since $v_s = \lambda' f'$, a larger wavelength means a lower frequency.

3. The answer is B. From the figure, you can see that the wavelength of the standing wave is $\frac{2}{3}$ m . Then, $v_{st} = \lambda f \Rightarrow v_{st} = \frac{2}{3}(6) = 4\frac{m}{s}$.

4. The answer is E. The fundamental mode will have one antinode between the two nodes at the ends. The full length of the string will support $\frac{1}{2}$ wavelength, so $\lambda = 2$ m. The wavespeed will still be 4 m/s, so you have $f = \frac{v_{st}}{\lambda} = \frac{4}{2} = 2\text{Hz}$.

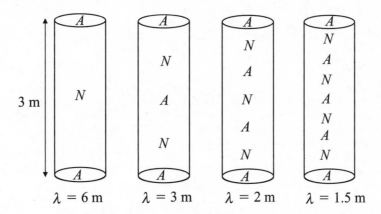

Figure 20

5. The answer is D. Since there must be an antinode at each end, the sequence of possible standing waves is shown in the figure. Because each N-A interval is $\frac{1}{4}\lambda$, simple counting leads to the wavelengths shown in the figure. 4 m isn't possible.

6. The answer is D. This is a resonance, so the frequency of the string wave will be 250 Hz. The string is vibrating in its fundamental mode, so the wavelength will be 1.8 m. Then, v = λf = (1.8)(250) = 450 Hz.

7. The answer is D. Since $f_{\text{beat}} = |f_1 - f_2|$, a beat frequency of 3 Hz with a 496 Hz fork means the unknown fork has a frequency of either 493 Hz or 499 Hz. A beat frequency of 9 Hz with a 484 Hz fork means the unknown fork is either 493 Hz or 475 Hz. Together, only 493 Hz is possible.

FREE RESPONSE

1. (a) From the figure, you can see that the wavelength of the standing wave is the same as the string length, 1.0 m. Since this is a resonance, the frequency of the string wave is the same as the sound source, so

$$v_{st} = \lambda f = (1.0)(600) = 600 \text{ m/s}$$

(b) The frequency of the string in the fundamental mode will be 300 Hz because the wavelength is now twice as long. This will also be the frequency of the standing sound wave set up in the tube. Since this tube has one end closed and one end open, the fundamental frequency is $f_1 = \frac{v_s}{4L}$. Then you have

$$300 = \frac{v_s}{4(0.27)} \Rightarrow v_s = 324 \text{ m/s}$$

(c) To excite another standing wave in the tube with the same frequency, you can draw it out of the water until the third harmonic of the new length matches the 300 Hz driving frequency. For a tube with one end closed, the third harmonic has a frequency of

$$f_2 = 3\frac{v_s}{4L}$$

Then you have

$$300 = 3\frac{v_s}{4L} = 3\frac{324}{4L} \Rightarrow L = 0.81 \text{ m}$$

16

Geometrical Optics

Light is a wave with a very short wavelength. In fact, the visible spectrum ranges from about 400 nm to about 700 nm. When a beam of light is interrupted by a screen with a small pencil hole in it, a well-defined beam filling the dimensions of the hole emerges on the other side of the screen. If you were to carefully inspect the region at the edge of the hole, you would see alternating bright and dark areas varying over a region comparable to the size of the wavelength of the light. These effects are called diffraction effects, and they're intimately connected to the wave nature of light. But as long as the hole itself doesn't become comparable in size to the wavelength, the diffraction effects are negligible, and you can treat the light as if it travels in straight lines. This approach to the study of light is called the geometrical optics approximation. As long as the light never encounters objects or apertures comparable in size to the wavelength of the light, this will be a valid description. And as you'll see, simple geometry and trigonometry will give you the behavior of a wide range of systems.

Wave Fronts and Rays

When light is emitted by a point source, it will move out and away from the source in ever-widening spheres. At a given instant, you can identify a connected region where the electric field has the same magnitude and direction and is changing in exactly the same way. This is a region of constant phase. To be concrete, you could imagine a region where the electric field component reached its maximum value. There are many such regions, each separated from the next by 1 wavelength. These connected regions of constant phase are called wave fronts. For water waves, you could consider wave fronts to be the wave crests. You can draw imaginary lines perpendicular to the **wave fronts** in the direction the wave is traveling, as in figure 1a on the next page. These lines are called the **rays**.

In the geometrical optics approximation, you can do all analysis in terms of rays. When the waves get far away from the point source, the curvature of the wave fronts is negligible. Such waves are called **plane waves** because the regions of constant phase are planes. Figure 1b depicts a plane wave; notice that the rays are parallel.

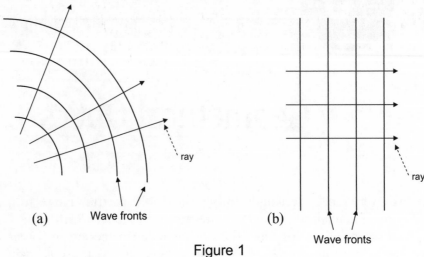

(a) Wave fronts   (b)   Wave fronts

Figure 1

Index of Refraction

When light enters a material medium, it's constantly being absorbed and re-emitted. This process slows down the wave. The ratio of the speed of light in a vacuum to that in a medium is called the **index of refraction** n of the medium.

$$n = \frac{\text{speed in vacuum}}{\text{speed in medium}} = \frac{c}{v}$$

The letter c is used to represent the speed of light in vacuum. Not all colors of light travel in a material at the same speed: The index of refraction varies slightly with wavelength (or frequency). This leads to a phenomenon called **dispersion**, where the various colors in a beam of light separate upon leaving the material. White light is an equal mixture of all colors, and dispersion is evident as white light passes through a prism.

Reflection

When a plane wave is incident upon a smooth surface that forms the boundary between two media, a portion of the wave will be reflected. In figure 2, the line perpendicular to the surface is called the **normal line**.

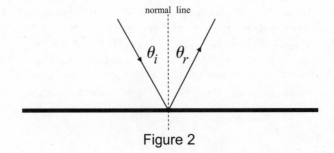

Figure 2

The incident ray, making an angle θ_i with the normal line, will reflect at the same angle, designated θ_r. This is the **law of reflection**:

$$\theta_i = \theta_r$$

This law is independent of wavelength; there is no color separation upon reflection.

Refraction

When a wave travels from one medium to another, there will always be a reflection at the interface between the two media. The wave can also be transmitted into the second medium. If the wave speeds in the two media are different, then the transmitted wave may be bent off its original direction. This is called **refraction**, and the wave has been refracted. You can see why this happens by looking at figure 3.

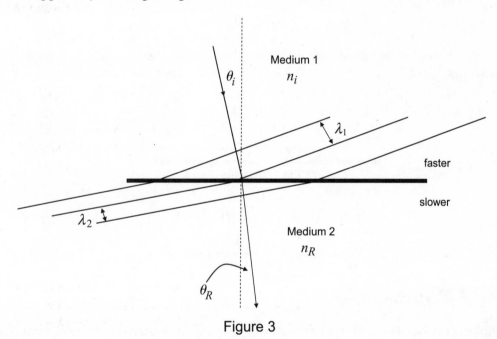

Figure 3

The incident wave moves in medium 1, where the wave speed v_1 is faster than v_2, the speed in medium 2. The frequency of both waves will be the same; the frequency and period of oscillation are determined by the source of the waves and won't be affected by transmission properties of the media. In 1 period of oscillation, each wave front progresses 1 wavelength. Since the wave moves more slowly in medium 2, the wavelength must be shorter here, and this can only mean that the wave fronts bend back as shown in the figure. Since each wave is periodic, you can relate their wavelengths:

$$v_1 = \lambda_1 f \qquad\qquad v_2 = \lambda_2 f$$

$$\Rightarrow \lambda_2 = \lambda_1 \frac{v_2}{v_1}$$

Everything covered so far about refraction applies to any type of wave. If you consider the case of light moving from a medium with index of refraction n_i to a medium with n_R, the definition of index of refraction gives you

$$\lambda_2 = \lambda_1 \frac{n_i}{n_R}$$

If medium 1 is vacuum where $n_i = 1$, or air where $n_i \cong 1$, then you can see that in the slower medium, the wavelength is reduced by the index of refraction:

$$\lambda_{medium} = \frac{\lambda_{vacuum}}{n} \qquad n = \text{index in medium}$$

When you analyze the rays, you can see that the incident ray is bent toward the normal line, making an angle θ_R called the angle of refraction. The incident and refracted angles are related by **Snell's law:**

$$n_i \sin \theta_i = n_R \sin \theta_R$$

If the wave moves from the slower medium into the faster medium, it will be bent away from the normal line. Snell's law will continue to relate the incident and refracted angles. The two possibilities are shown in figure 4.

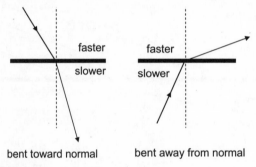

Figure 4

EXAMPLE

A monochromatic beam of light moves from air to glass, where the index of refraction for the beam is 1.5. If the incident angle is 30° measured with respect to the normal, what angle will the refracted beam make with the reflected beam?

You can use Snell's law to find the angle of refraction.

$$(1) \sin 30 = (1.5) \sin \theta_R \qquad \Rightarrow \theta_R = 19.2°$$

The reflected angle is the same as the incident angle, 30°. When it's added to the refracted angle, you have 49.2°. The angle between the reflected and refracted ray will be 180° minus this value:

$$\theta_{r-R} = 180 - 19.2 - 30 = 130.8°$$

Total Internal Reflection

When a ray crosses an interface going from a slower medium to a faster medium, it bends away from the normal line. Of course, some of the beam is reflected as well. The amount of energy in the transmitted beam decreases as the incident angle increases and the refracted angle approaches 90°. Figure 5 shows a typical situation.

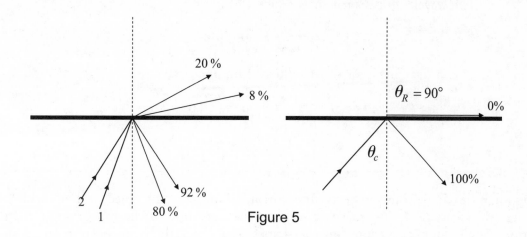

Figure 5

As the incident angle increases, the amount of energy, shown as a percent, decreases in the refracted beam and increases in the reflected beam. In the limit where the refracted beam is 90°, all the energy is reflected. This is called **total internal reflection**. You can use Snell's law to determine the **critical angle**, since you know the refracted angle is 90°.

$$n_i \sin\theta_i = n_R \sin 90 = n_R$$

$$\sin\theta_c = \frac{n_R}{n_i}$$

All rays that enter at this angle or greater will be totally reflected, with no transmission of energy into the optically faster medium.

A laser with wavelength 640 nm in vacuum is placed at the bottom of a pool. Find the wavelength of the light in the water ($n = 1.33$), and determine the angle with the normal to the surface that the laser must be placed so that the beam will not exit the surface?

The wavelength is smaller by a factor of n:

$$\lambda_{\text{water}} = \frac{640}{1.33} = 481 \text{ nm}$$

The critical angle for water follows from Snell's law:

$$\sin \theta_c = \frac{1}{1.33} \Rightarrow \theta_c = 48.6°$$

Mirrors

When light leaving a source reflects off a mirror, an image of the object will be formed. The nature and location of this image depend on the curvature of the mirror surface. In this section, you'll look at various mirror shapes and learn the nomenclature used in the description of images. In each case, imagine a source producing light that will eventually strike the mirror. A common convention is to depict the source as an arrow. While light from all parts of the arrow will strike the mirror, you'll focus on light leaving the tip of the arrow. Once you find the action of the mirror on these rays, you can determine all you need to know about the image.

PLANE MIRROR

Figure 6 shows two rays reflecting off the mirror surface. One reflects straight back on itself, and the other reflects below the center line in accordance with the law of reflection. Rays that are especially easy to depict, like the ones shown, are called **principle rays**. For any imaging system, if you can draw two principle rays that intersect, you have found the image.

Plane mirror

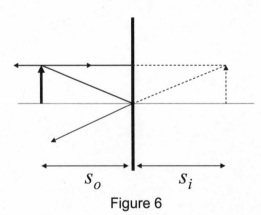

Figure 6

Notice that these two reflected rays never intersect. Your brain, however, interprets light as traveling in straight lines and will construct an image for you in this situation. The rays that began at the tip of the arrow upon reflection appear to come from a point behind the mirror, so you see an image of the tip behind the mirror. This type of image is called a **virtual image**. It can't be displayed on a screen, and rays don't really intersect. It's common to display the virtual image and the rays that extend back to it with dotted lines. For a plane mirror, the image distance s_i will equal the object distance s_o. There's no magnification; both image and object are the same size.

CONCAVE MIRROR

Figure 7 depicts a concave mirror. If the curvature is perfectly parabolic, all rays that are parallel to the axis of the mirror will reflect through a single point called the **focal point** of the mirror.

Concave Mirror

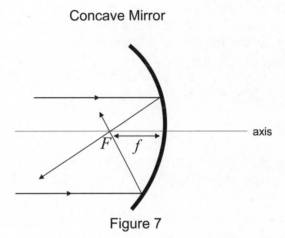

Figure 7

This is a simple consequence of the law of reflection. The distance from the focal point to the mirror along the axis is called the focal length, f. Since parabolic mirrors are harder to make than spherical mirrors, the latter are often used in practice. As long as a spherical mirror is small compared with its radius of curvature, it's a good approximation to a parabolic reflector. For a spherical mirror, you have the added condition that the focal length is $\frac{1}{2}$ the radius of curvature.

$$f = \frac{R}{2} \qquad \text{spherical mirror}$$

Figure 8 depicts image formation for a concave mirror.

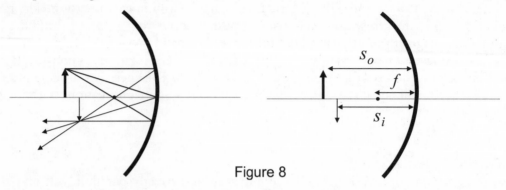

Figure 8

Three principle rays are shown: a ray parallel to the axis reflects through the focal point, a ray that passes first through the focal point reflects parallel to the axis, and a ray that strikes the mirror at the axis reflects below the axis according to the law of reflection. Notice that the rays converge at a point in front of the mirror. Since the rays actually do come together here, a screen placed at that point would show the image. This is called a **real image**. Since the image has an opposite orientation, it is **inverted**. If you call the image distance from the mirror s_i, the object distance s_o, and the focal length f, a straightforward geometric analysis involving similar triangles gives you the relation:

$$\frac{1}{f} = \frac{1}{s_i} + \frac{1}{s_o}$$

The size of the image will differ from the object. The magnification factor is determined by the ratio of the image and object lengths:

$$m = -\frac{s_i}{s_o}$$

When m is negative, the image is inverted; when m is positive, the image is upright.
When the object is inside the focal length, a concave mirror will form a virtual image.
Figure 9 shows the principle rays used to locate the image, which will appear to be behind the mirror. The same equations govern the image position and size. When you solve for the image distance, it will be negative, indicating it's behind the mirror. This will make m positive, indicating the image is **upright**.

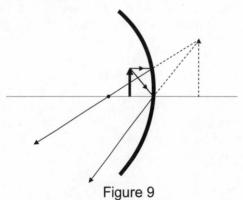

Figure 9

CONVEX MIRROR

When rays parallel to the axis of a convex mirror reflect, they diverge and appear to originate from a point behind the mirror. This is the focal point for a concave mirror, shown in figure 10a. An object in front of the mirror will form a virtual image behind the mirror, as shown in figure 10b.

Convex mirror

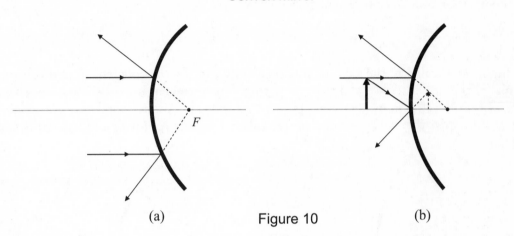

(a)   Figure 10   (b)

The same equations govern the position and size of the image if you interpret the focal length to be a negative number. Then you might say the focal length is − 3 cm for a particular convex mirror.

EXAMPLE

A convex mirror has a focal length of − 10 cm. An object 4 cm high is placed 20 cm in front of the mirror. Find the position and size of the image. Describe the nature of the image.

Using the formula, you have

$$\frac{1}{f} = \frac{1}{s_i} + \frac{1}{s_o} \Rightarrow \frac{1}{-10} = \frac{1}{20} + \frac{1}{s_i}$$

$$s_i = -6.67 \text{ cm}$$

$$m = -\frac{s_i}{s_o} = -\frac{(-6.67)}{20} = +0.33$$

You have a virtual image located 6.67 cm behind the mirror. Since the magnification is positive, it is upright and its size will be (0.33)(4) = 1.33 cm.

Lenses

Like mirrors, lenses can alter the path of light rays and form images. While mirrors rely on reflection, lenses use refraction to bend light. The types of images formed will depend on the curvature of the lens. The language used to describe the images is exactly the same as that used for mirrors, and as you'll see, there's a great simplifying feature: The same equations govern the position and size of the image.

CONVEX LENS

When a light ray parallel to the axis encounters a convex or converging lens, it bends toward the normal at the first interface and then away from the normal as it exits the lens, as shown in figure 11a. Both refractions bend the light toward the axis. All rays parallel to the axis will be bent and focused through the same point, called the focal point of the lens (shown in figure 11b).

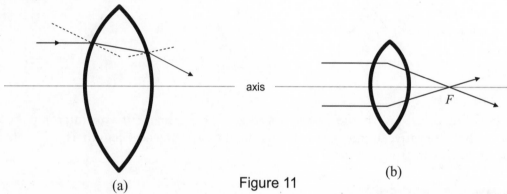

(a)   Figure 11   (b)

Since the rays arriving at the lens from distant objects are nearly parallel, distant objects will form images very close to the focal length. Rather than show the light bending at each interface, it's common practice to show it bending once at the center of the lens, even though this isn't really what happens. Like the concave mirror, the convex lens will form either a real or a virtual image, depending on whether the object is outside or inside the focal length. The two possible configurations are shown with principle rays in figure 12. For a thin lens, a ray striking the lens at the axis will emerge undeflected. A principle ray of this type is shown in each figure.

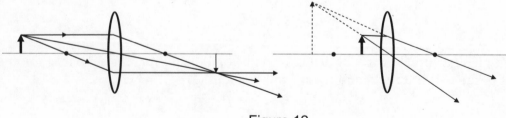

Figure 12

You'll also see that a ray that passes through the focal point before it passes through the lens will emerge parallel to the axis after passing through the lens. In general, the rays you draw will also depict light traveling in the other direction if you reverse the direction of the ray. For a convex lens, the focal length is positive. The image distance will be positive for a real image formed on the opposite side of the lens as the object; it will be negative for a virtual image formed on the same side of the lens as the object. Once again, the basic equations are

$$\frac{1}{f} = \frac{1}{s_i} + \frac{1}{s_o} \qquad m = -\frac{s_i}{s_o}$$

EXAMPLE

An object 6 cm tall is placed 2 cm in front of a convex lens with focal length 10 cm. Determine the position, size, and nature of the image.

Applying the basic equations, you have

$$\frac{1}{10} = \frac{1}{s_i} + \frac{1}{2} \Rightarrow s_i = -2.5 \text{ cm image is virtual}$$

$$m = -\frac{-2.5}{2} = 1.25 \quad \text{image is upright since } m \text{ is positive}$$

The size of the image will be $(1.25)(6) = 7.25$ cm

CONCAVE LENS

Figure 13a shows that a ray parallel to the axis of a concave or diverging lens will bend the light toward the normal at the first interface and away from the normal at the second.

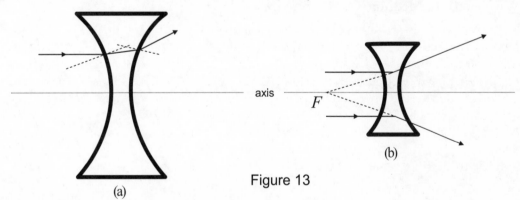

Figure 13

At each interface, the ray is bent away from the axis, causing rays parallel to the axis to diverge as if they originated at from a single point on the incoming side of the lens. This point is called the focal point for a concave or diverging lens, and this behavior is shown in figure 13b. Image formation and principle rays are shown in figure 14. By itself, a concave lens will form only a virtual image. The usual equations govern the position and size of the image, with the assumption that f is negative for this type of lens, so you can talk about a diverging lens with focal length -5 cm.

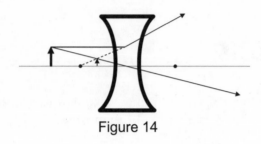

Figure 14

KEY FORMULAS

Index of Refraction	$n = \dfrac{c}{v}$
Wavelength in Medium	$\lambda' = \dfrac{\lambda_{\text{vac}}}{n}$
Law of Reflection	$\theta_i = \theta_r$
Snell's Law of Refraction	$n_i \sin\theta_i = n_R \sin\theta_R$
Critical Angle	$\sin\theta_c = \dfrac{n_R}{n_i}$
Spherical Mirror	$f = \dfrac{R}{2}$
Image Equation	$\dfrac{1}{f} = \dfrac{1}{s_i} + \dfrac{1}{s_o}$
Magnification	$m = -\dfrac{s_i}{s_o}$

CHAPTER 16

PRACTICE EXERCISES

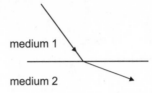

Figure 15

1. A light ray crosses an interface from medium 1 to medium 2 as shown in figure 15. Which of the following is true for the light in medium 2?

   (A) wave speed faster, wavelength shorter
   (B) wave speed faster, wavelength longer
   (C) wave speed slower, wavelength shorter
   (D) wave speed slower, wavelength longer
   (E) wave speed slower, wavelength unchanged

2. Eyeglasses make use of which property exhibited by light?

   (A) dispersion   (B) reflection   (C) refraction   (D) interference   (E) diffraction

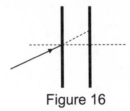

Figure 16

3. A light ray encounters a glass plate with parallel faces surrounded by air as shown in figure 16. The diagram that most accurately depicts the emerging ray is

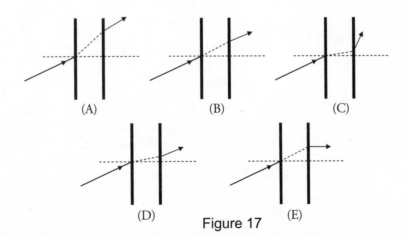

(A)   (B)   (C)

(D)   **Figure 17**   (E)

mirror

Figure 18

4. An arrow-shaped object is placed in front of a plane mirror as shown in figure 18. The image would look most like

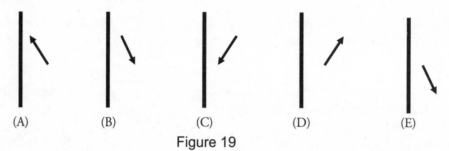

(A)   (B)   (C)   (D)   (E)

Figure 19

5. An illuminated arrow is placed 2 cm in front of a diverging lens with focal length − 6 cm. The image is

(A) real, inverted, smaller than the object
(B) virtual, inverted, larger than the object
(C) virtual, upright, larger than the object
(D) real, upright, larger than the object
(E) virtual, upright, smaller than the object

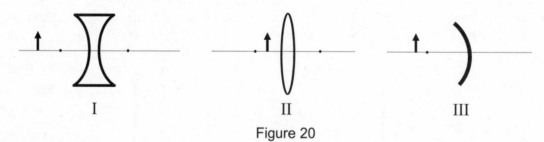

I   II   III

Figure 20

6. An object is placed in front of three different optical devices, two lenses and a mirror, with focal points as shown in figure 20. Which will produce a real image?

(A) I only   (B) II only   (C) III only   (D) I and II   (E) II and III

7. A concave mirror with radius of curvature 1.5 m is used to collect light from a distant source. The distance between the image formed and the mirror is closest to

   (A) 0.75 m   (B) 1 m   (C) 1.5 m   (D) 2 m   (E) 3 m

8. A student sets up an optics experiment with a converging lens of focal length 10 cm. He places an illuminated arrow 2 cm high at 15 cm from the lens along the lens axis. The size of the image is most nearly

   (A) 0.5 cm   (B) 1 cm   (C) 2 cm   (D) 3.5 cm   (E) 4 cm

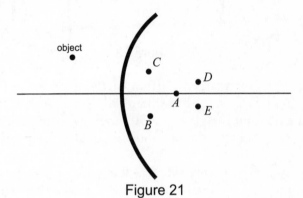

Figure 21

9. An object is placed in front of a concave mirror as shown in figure 21. The location of the image is closest to

   (A) *A*   (B) *B*   (C) *C*   (D) *D*   (E) *E*

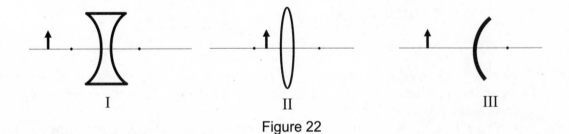

Figure 22

10. For which cases will the image of the arrow shown in figure 22 be virtual and smaller than the object?

   (A) I only   (B) II only   (C) III only   (D) I and II   (E) I and III

PRACTICE EXERCISES

SECTION II FREE RESPONSE

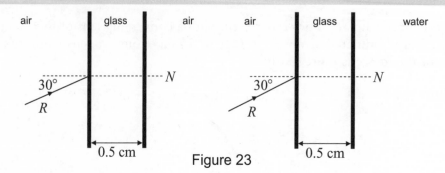

Figure 23

1. The figures above show an enlarged portion of the glass wall of a fish tank, currently empty so that air ($n = 1$) is on either side of the glass ($n = 1.5$). The glass is 0.5 cm thick. A ray R is incident on the glass at a 30° angle with the normal line as shown.
   (a) On the first figure, continue the ray, showing qualitatively what happens at the next interface.
   (b) At what distance above the normal line N will the transmitted ray emerge out of the glass?
   (c) Determine the incident angle at the second interface that will ensure total internal reflection. Could the initial ray R have its incident angle adjusted to make this happen? Explain.
   (d) Suppose the tank is filled with water ($n = 1.33$). On the second figure provided, continue the ray, showing qualitatively what happens at the glass-water interface.

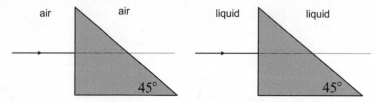

Figure 24

2. A ray of light of wavelength 680 nm (red) enters an isosceles right prism as shown in the figure above. The index of refraction for this wavelength is 1.22 in the prism. Assume air surrounds the prism.
   (a) On the first figure, continue the ray to the next interface and show the behavior qualitatively at this interface.
   (b) Find the wavelength of the light in the prism.
   (c) Determine the angle that the ray leaving the prism makes with the original direction of the ray, shown as a dotted line in the figure.
   (d) Violet light of wavelength (in air) 460 nm with an index of refraction 1.26 is added to the ray so that both colors are in the ray. Determine the angular separation of the two rays as they leave the prism.
   (e) The prism is now immersed in a transparent liquid with an index of refraction that is 1.50 for both colors. On the second figure, continue the ray and show the qualitative behavior at the second interface.

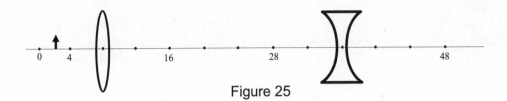

Figure 25

3. A converging lens with focal length 4 cm has an object placed 6 cm in front of it as pictured. A diverging lens with focal length − 8 cm is placed 28 cm behind the first lens.
   (a) Determine the position of the image formed by the first lens.
   (b) On the figure, draw the rays needed to display this image.
   (c) What is the magnification of this image?
   (d) Determine the position of the image formed by the second lens.
   (e) On the figure, sketch the rays needed to display this image.
   (f) Find the overall magnification of this lens system. What is the nature of the final image?

Answers and Explanations

MULTIPLE CHOICE

1. The answer is B. The ray is bending away from the normal line in medium 2, indicating that the index of refraction in medium 2 is less than that in medium 1. For concreteness, you could think of medium 1 as glass and medium 2 as air. The wave is moving faster with a longer wavelength.

2. The answer is C. Eyeglasses focus light with lenses, which focus by refraction.

3. The answer is D. At the first interface, it bends toward the normal, so the ray will exit below the dotted line extension of the original ray. Upon refraction, it will bend away from the normal just enough to be parallel to the original ray, because the incident angle at the second interface is the refracted angle at the first interface.

4. The answer is D. A plane mirror creates an upright virtual image with no magnification. You could draw two rays to check this. The object and image distance for each point on the arrow will then be equal.

5. The answer is E. A diverging lens (negative focal length) will always create an upright, virtual image in front of the object, as you can see by simple ray tracing. Since the image distance is smaller than the object distance, the image will be smaller as well.

6. The answer is C. A single concave lens produces only virtual images. An object placed inside the focal length of a convex lens will result in a virtual image. This eliminates I and II. An object outside the focal length of a concave mirror will produce an inverted, real image.

7. The answer is A. Distant objects will be imaged near the focal point since the rays are nearly parallel when they arrive at the mirror. The focal length of a spherical mirror is $\frac{1}{2}$ the radius of curvature.

8. The answer is E. Use the image equation to find the image distance, and then use the magnification equation.
$$\frac{1}{10} = \frac{1}{15} + \frac{1}{s_i} \qquad s_i = 30 \text{ cm}$$
$$m = -\frac{30}{15} = -2 \qquad \text{The size of the inverted image is 4 cm.}$$

9. The answer is C. A convex (diverging) mirror will produce upright, virtual images smaller than the object, as you can see with simple ray tracing, using two principle rays.

10. The answer is E. Diverging elements like I and III will always produce smaller virtual images. II will produce a virtual image, but it will be larger. This is basically a magnifying glass.

FREE RESPONSE

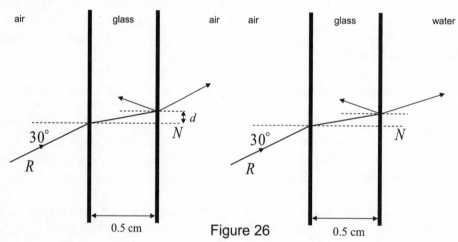

Figure 26

1. (a) The figure shows the reflected and refracted rays. You can find the refracted angle at the first interface from Snell's law.
$$1 \sin 30 = 1.5 \sin \theta_{R1} \qquad \Rightarrow \theta_{R1} = 19.5°$$

Since the glass surfaces are parallel, this will become the incident angle of the second interface. Then you can use Snell's law to find the second refracted angle.

$$1.5 \sin\theta_{R1} = 1 \sin\theta_{R2} \quad \Rightarrow \theta_{R2} = 30°$$

The exiting ray is parallel to the original ray.

(b) From geometry, you have
$$\tan\theta_{R1} = \tan 19.5 = \frac{d}{0.5} \quad \Rightarrow d = 0.18 \text{ cm}$$

(c) For total internal reflection at the glass-air interface, you must have
$$1.5 \sin\theta_c = 1 \sin 90 \quad \Rightarrow \theta_c = 41.8°$$

The refracted beam exits at a limiting angle of 90° as the critical angle approaches. Since the exiting ray and the initial ray will be parallel, as shown in b, to get total internal reflection at the second interface would require a 90° incident angle at the first interface, indicating that the ray didn't actually enter the glass. You can get very close to total internal reflection at the second interface, but you'll never quite reach it.

(d) At the second interface, the reflection is the same. The ray that refracts into the water, however, won't bend away from the normal as much because the index of refraction doesn't change as much at a glass-water interface.

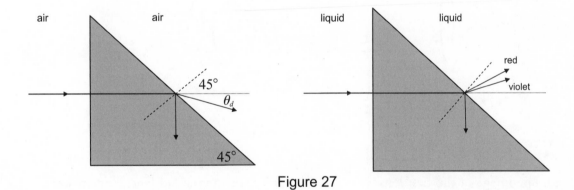

Figure 27

2. (a) The exiting ray bends away from the normal line. The reflected ray goes straight down because the incident and reflected angles are both 45°. Notice that the angle of refraction is 45° plus the deviation angle θ_d.

(b) The wavelength shortens in the slower medium by a factor of the index of refraction.

$$\lambda' = \frac{680}{1.22} = 557 \text{ nm}$$

(c) Use Snell's law.
$$1.22 \sin 45 = 1 \sin\theta_R \qquad \Rightarrow \theta_R = 59.6°$$

Then, $\theta_d = 14.6°$.

(d) Find the refracted angle for the violet ray and determine the difference in the two refraction angles.
$$1.26 \sin 45 = 1 \sin\theta_R' \qquad \Rightarrow \theta_R' = 63.0°$$

The difference or angular separation is $63 - 59.6 = 3.4°$

(e) At the second interface, the reflections will be the same for both rays because the law of reflection is independent of wavelength. Since the rays are entering a medium that has a greater index of refraction, they will bend toward the normal line. The red ray experiences the greater deflection, since the change in refraction index is greater for it.

3. (a) Use the image equation.
$$\frac{1}{4} = \frac{1}{6} + \frac{1}{s_i} \qquad \Rightarrow s_i = 12 \text{ cm}$$

(b) Figure 28

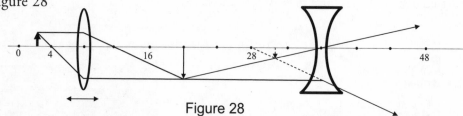

Figure 28

(c) $m_1 = -\frac{s_i}{s_o} = -\frac{12}{6} = -2$

(d) The image of the first lens will act as the object of the second lens. This makes the object distance 16 cm. Then you have
$$\frac{1}{-8} = \frac{1}{16} + \frac{1}{s_i} \qquad \Rightarrow s_i = -5.33 \text{ cm}$$

(e) See figure 28.

(f) The magnification of the second lens will be $m_2 = -\frac{-5.33}{16} = +\frac{1}{3}$. The overall magnification will be the product of the two separate values.
$$m = m_1 m_2 = \frac{-2}{3}$$

The image is virtual and inverted.

CHAPTER 17

Wave Optics

When light encounters a screen with a hole in it the size of a pencil, a well-defined beam emerges on the other side of the screen with a cross section the same size as the hole. A second screen following the first would display a dot apparently no larger than the size of the hole. But if the hole were made smaller and smaller until it began to become comparable to the size of the light wavelength, you would find that the dot would be considerably larger than the size of the hole. How do you account for this? After the light left the hole, it entered the region that you would normally associate with the shadow cast by the screen. This bending of light around obstacles and into the so-called shadow region is called diffraction, which is exhibited by all waves. You can ignore diffraction if the wavelength is small compared with any obstacles or openings the wave might encounter, but if that's not the case, any wave will diffract into the shadow region. In this chapter, you'll look at both the diffraction and interference of light in detail. It's important for you to have a solid qualitative understanding of the phenomena involved, but you'll also need quite a bit of quantitative detail as well.

Huygens's Principle

In 1690, Christian Huygens proposed a constructive method to explain the propagation of light. To apply the method, imagine every point on a given wave front as an emitter of spherical wavelets, so-called **Huygens emitters**. In a given time, these wavelets will move out a certain distance from the emitter. The new wave front will be the envelope of the wavelets, obtained by drawing a tangent to each wavelet at the position it has reached in the time given. The method is shown in figures 1 and 2. Notice that plane waves remain plane waves and spherical waves remain spherical waves if the properties of the medium don't change.

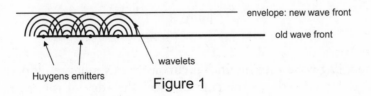

envelope: new wave front

old wave front

wavelets

Huygens emitters

Figure 1

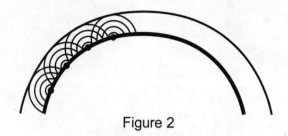

Figure 2

Huygens's principle is remarkable for several reasons. It was proposed at a time when there was hot debate over whether light was indeed a wave. As you'll see, it predicts the fundamental wave property of diffraction. With some modifications, it has a solid basis in the mathematical description of waves; for example, it's now known that the emitters don't emit equal amplitudes in all directions. And as a tool for predicting the basic behavior of waves, it's conceptually simple and easy to apply.

Diffraction

Figure 3 depicts a plane wave incident upon an opaque barrier with an opening comparable in size to the wavelength. As the wave that isn't blocked moves through the opening, the Huygens emitters along this shortened wave front will emit spherical wavelets directed not only in the forward direction, but also into the shadow region behind the barrier.

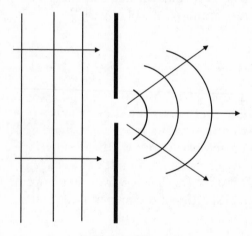

Figure 3

The result is an outgoing wave with significant curvature. A similar result occurs when the wave encounters an edge. Figure 4 shows the emitters near the edge of the interrupted wave front emitting into the shadow region.

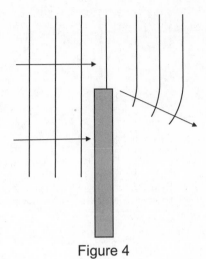

Figure 4

This bending of the light into the shadow region of an obstacle is called **diffraction**. It's worth noting that this bending has nothing to do with refraction. The bending occurs within the same medium, while refraction bending involves passing from one medium to another. In diffraction, the amount of bending that occurs depends on the ratio of the wavelength to the characteristic size of the object. For example, as the wavelength in figure 3 is lengthened, keeping the width of the opening fixed, the outgoing wave will produce much more curvature. One of the reasons that the wave nature of light was so hotly contested among the physicists of Huygens's time was that since the wavelength is so small, the diffraction effects weren't readily observed. It's understandable that many believed light wasn't a wave.

Two-Slit Interference

The definitive proof that light is a wave came with the experiment of Thomas Young. He interrupted a plane wave front with two small openings, spaced very close to each other. The resulting spherical waves produced by each opening moved through each other and produced an interference pattern of bright and dark fringes. With this demonstration, the question of whether or not light was a wave was closed; only waves behave this way.

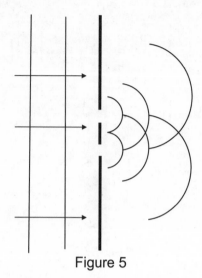

Figure 5

The basic setup is shown in figure 5, where it's clear the outgoing wave fronts are interfering. To analyze this interference quantitatively, let's assume point openings for the slits and a monochromatic light source, and let's choose an arbitrary point on a screen behind the slits as shown in figure 6.

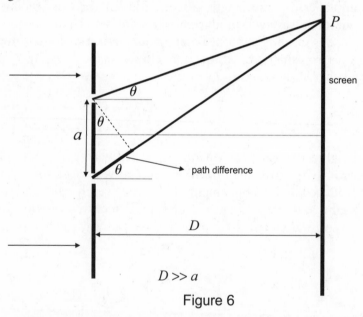

Figure 6

Because of diffraction, rays will reach the point P from both openings. The light that gets to P originated from the same wave front passing through the two slits, so the two rays are initially in phase with each other. But since the two rays travel different distances to get to P, there will be a phase difference in the two rays when they reach this point. At a given instant, one ray may have an electric field maximum at P while the other might have its field at a different value.

Figure 6 is drawn so that you can see where the rays reach the screen. In reality, the distance D between slits and screen is much larger than a, the spacing between the slits. So even though the two rays do come together at a great distance at the screen, they can be considered nearly parallel. The extra length that one ray travels compared with the other is called the **path difference**. From the geometry, you can see that

$$path\ difference = a\sin\theta$$

For the two rays to interfere constructively, the path difference must be an integral multiple of the wavelength. This ensures that the two waves have maximum on maximum, minimum on minimum at P. In the language of standing waves, this will insure an antinode at P.

$$a\sin\theta = N\lambda \quad N = 0, 1, 2\ \ldots\ \text{maxima}$$

For the two waves to interfere destructively, forming an antinode, you must have the maximum of one ray sitting on the minimum of the other. This means

$$a\sin\theta = \frac{1}{2}\lambda, \frac{3}{2}\lambda, \frac{5}{2}\lambda\ldots = \left(N + \frac{1}{2}\right)\lambda \quad N = 0, 1, 2\ \ldots\ \text{minima}$$

As you look up and down the screen, you see alternating bright and dark fringes. In the straight-ahead direction, $\theta = 0$, and there's no path difference for any wavelength, so there's always a maximum here. This corresponds to $N = 0$ in the maxima formula, and it's called the **central maximum**. Move up or down the screen, and you next encounter a maximum when the two rays differ in path length by 1 wavelength, $N = 1$. These are called **first order maxima**. Similar nomenclature is used for the minima. Figure 7 depicts this description.

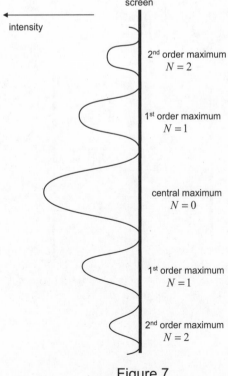

Figure 7

Since the position at which the maxima and minima occur depends on the wavelength, light composed of different colors will separate upon moving through the slits, and the screen will show separated maxima for the various colors.

EXAMPLE

Light consisting of red ($\lambda = 640$ nm) and blue ($\lambda = 440$ nm) is incident upon a double slit with spacing 4×10^{-5} m. A screen is located 2 m behind the slits. Determine the distance on the screen between the first order red maximum and the first order blue maximum.

You can use the basic equation to find the angles relative to the forward direction at which the two maxima form.

$$a\sin\theta = \lambda \qquad N = 1$$

$$a\sin\theta_R = \lambda_R$$
$$(4 \times 10^{-5})\sin\theta_R = 6.4 \times 10^{-7}$$
$$\sin\theta_R = 0.016$$
$$\theta_R = 0.92°$$

$$a\sin\theta_B = \lambda_B$$
$$(4 \times 10^{-5})\sin\theta_B = 4.4 \times 10^{-7}$$
$$\sin\theta_B = 0.011$$
$$\theta_B = 0.63°$$

The basic geometry is shown in figure 8, so you have

$$\tan\theta_R = \frac{x_R}{2}$$
$$0.016 = \frac{x_R}{2}$$

$$\tan\theta_B = \frac{x_B}{2}$$
$$0.011 = \frac{x_B}{2}$$

Then, $x_R - x_B = 0.032 - 0.022 = 0.010$ m

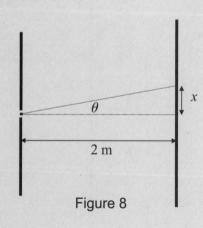

Figure 8

Diffraction Grating

A **diffraction grating** is an optical device with many equally spaced slits, as opposed to the two slits of the basic Young's apparatus. A grating gives better resolution of the maxima; rather than the spread of each maximum as shown in figure 7, each maximum formed by a grating with many slits will have a width that is more pointlike. The condition on the spacing of the grating and the maxima formation, however, is exactly the same as for the two slit apparatus. Figure 9 shows rays emerging from a grating. Notice that consecutive rays will all have the same path difference. This means that if ray 2 travels 1 more wavelength than ray 1, thus interfering constructively at the screen, then ray 3 will travel 2 extra wavelengths and will also interfere constructively. If two consecutive rays interfere constructively, then all the rays will, so you have

$$a\sin\theta = N\lambda \qquad N = 0, 1, 2 \ldots \text{ grating maxima}$$

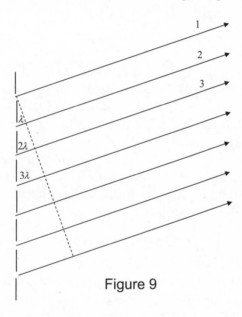

Figure 9

Single-Slit Diffraction

So far, the slits of the Young's apparatus or the grating have been treated as point emitters, comprising a single Huygens emitter. In reality, a slit that is comparable in size to the wavelength will have many such emitters along the width of the slit. As a wave front encounters the slit, these emitters will produce rays that can interfere with each other. Figure 10 shows a single slit and 8 emitters producing nearly parallel rays in a given direction.

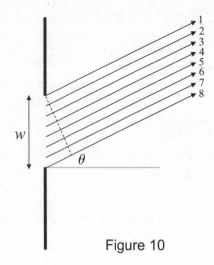

Figure 10

If you focus on ray 1 at the top of the slit, and ray 5 at the middle of the slit, you can see that if their path difference is $\frac{1}{2}\lambda$, they will cancel out when brought together at the screen. But if they cancel out, then so will the pairs 2 and 6, 3 and 7, and 4 and 8, since they will have the same path difference. It shouldn't be surprising that you'll get a pattern of maxima and minima very similar to the two slit pattern discussed earlier.

While the patterns look similar, the single slit diffraction pattern of a given slit width is more gently varying than the two slit pattern of similar slit width, and the intensity of the maxima outside the central maximum is much less. The formula that determines the single slit diffraction *minima* is similar to the formula for multiple slit *maxima*:

$$w\sin\theta = N\lambda \quad N = 1, 2, \ldots$$

Here w is the width of the slit. Notice that $N = 0$ is not allowed because a maximum always forms at $\theta = 0$. As the width of the slit is decreased for a fixed wavelength, the pattern spreads out more and more. You should understand the conceptual aspects of this formula, but in the past, the AP test hasn't included free response questions that require using it quantitatively.

Thin Film Interference

Figure 11 shows two glass plates with a wedge of air between them. The size of the air wedge is greatly exaggerated in the figure; in reality, the plates are nearly parallel, and the maximum spacing across the wedge is not many multiples of a wavelength.

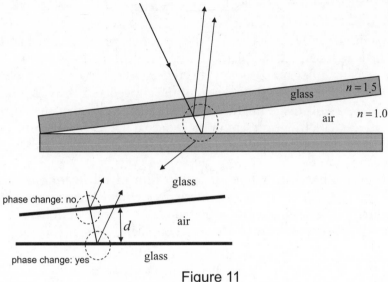

Figure 11

When the plates are illuminated with monochromatic light, a ray that's incident upon the first glass-air interface will be partially reflected and partially transmitted. The transmitted ray can continue and be reflected at the next air-glass interface. This reflected ray can then interfere with the ray reflected at the first interface.

Notice that the second ray travels an extra distance $2d$ (the angles of the incident and reflected rays are greatly exaggerated here). This produces a phase difference in the two rays. If there were nothing else happening, you'd expect that a separation of $2d = N\lambda$ would lead to constructive interference. But there *is* something else happening. Just as a wave on a string will invert upon reflection at a fixed end, so too will a light wave invert upon reflection at an interface where the incident medium has a smaller index of refraction than the refracted medium. As shown in the insert, at the first interface, the ray is moving from glass into air. Since the index of refraction of glass is greater than that of air, there will be no inversion of the reflected wave here.

At the next interface, however, the ray is moving from air to glass. Since the index of refraction of air is less than that of glass, there will be an inversion of the reflected wave here. The inversion of the wave amounts to an extra $\frac{1}{2}\lambda$ phase difference between the incident and reflected waves. Notice also that only reflected rays can acquire such an extra phase shift. Since the two rays have an extra $\frac{1}{2}\lambda$ phase difference between them, the condition for constructive interference becomes

$$2d = \left(N + \tfrac{1}{2}\right)\lambda \qquad N = 0, 1, 2 \ldots \qquad \text{constructive interference}$$

For destructive interference, you need the physical distance $2d$ to be an integral multiple of the wavelength. Then the extra $\frac{1}{2}\lambda$ from the reflection will be just enough to get the two rays to cancel out.

$$2d = N\lambda \qquad N = 0, 1, 2, \ldots \text{ destructive interference}$$

Since d varies along the air wedge, an observer will see a series of bright and dark fringes if he or she observes the light reflected off the plates. Each successive dark fringe corresponds to one extra wavelength of path difference between the two reflected rays. By simply counting the fringes, the observer can determine the thickness of the air wedge at the wide end, where a thin object like a hair or a slice of tissue might be placed. Notice also that the narrow end of the wedge will always have a dark fringe present in the reflected light. Here there's a reflection phase change, but no physical path difference.

When light reflects off a soap bubble or a thin film of oil floating on water, a similar phenomenon occurs, but there's one added subtlety. Figure 12 shows the situation. Think concretely and assume you're dealing with a soap bubble, so that the film has $n = 1.33$, with air ($n = 1$) on either side, the outside and inside of the bubble.

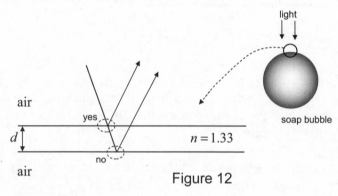

Figure 12

There will be a phase shift in the reflected ray at the first interface, but not at the second. This means the situation is the same as that for the air wedge, except that the physical path difference takes place inside the film of the bubble. Since the index of refraction is larger here, the wavelength is smaller, and more wavelengths will fit into the path difference. You'll need to be careful to use the value of the wavelength in the medium where the physical path difference occurs. In the case of figure 12, you have

$$2d = N\lambda_{\text{medium}} = N\frac{\lambda}{n} \qquad\qquad \text{destructive}$$

$$2d = \left(N + \frac{1}{2}\right)\lambda_{\text{medium}} = \left(N + \frac{1}{2}\right)\frac{\lambda}{n} \qquad\qquad \text{constructive}$$

EXAMPLE

Suppose your bubble has a thickness of 400 nm. What wavelengths of visible light will be diminished in the reflected light? What wavelengths will be enhanced?

For the diminished wavelengths, you must have destructive interference. Since d isn't 0, try $N = 1, 2, \ldots$ and see which λs correspond to visible light.

$$2(400) = N\frac{\lambda}{1.33}$$

$N = 1 \Rightarrow \lambda = 1{,}066 \text{ nm} \qquad N = 2 \Rightarrow \lambda = 533 \text{ nm}$

$N = 3 \Rightarrow \lambda = 355 \text{nm}$

Only the $N = 2$ value is visible.

For the enhanced wavelengths, you need constructive interference.

$$2(400) = \left(N + \frac{1}{2}\right)\frac{\lambda}{1.33}$$

$N = 0 \Rightarrow \lambda = 2{,}133 \text{ nm} \qquad N = 1 \Rightarrow \lambda = 711 \text{ nm}$

$N = 2 \Rightarrow \lambda = 407 \text{nm}$

The $N = 1$ is at the extreme red end, while the $N = 2$ is at the extreme violet end. All others will be out of the visible range.

There's no one-size-fits-all formula for these reflective interference problems. That's because, depending on the various media involved, there could be zero, one, or two phase shifts involved. For example, a soap film on glass involves a progression from air ($n = 1$) to soapy water ($n = 1.33$) to glass ($n = 1.5$). Both reflected rays would get a phase shift, so the preceding formulas for destructive and constructive interference would change places. The best thing to do is approach each problem of this type with the knowledge that three ingredients are involved:

1. physical path difference
2. reflective phase changes
3. wavelength change in medium

You must then put the ingredients together logically.

KEY FORMULAS

Multiple Slit Interference Maxima $\qquad a\sin\theta = N\lambda \qquad N = 0, 1, 2 \ldots$

Multiple Slit Interference Minima $\qquad a\sin\theta = \left(N + \frac{1}{2}\right)\lambda \qquad N = 0, 1, 2 \ldots$

Single Slit Diffraction Minima $\qquad w\sin\theta = N\lambda \qquad N = 1, 2 \ldots$

PRACTICE EXERCISES

SECTION 1 MULTIPLE CHOICE

1. A two slit interference experiment is performed with slit spacing a and wavelength λ. As the spacing is increased, holding λ fixed, which of the following is true?
    I. The width of the central maximum will decrease.
    II. The width of the central maximum will increase.
    III. There will be more interference fringes formed.

    (A) I only   (B) II only   (C) III only   (D) I and III   (E) II and III

2. A Young's apparatus consisting of two identical narrow slits is illuminated with light of wavelength λ. If the spacing between the slits is 3.7λ, the maximum number of interference maxima observed will be

    (A) 0   (B) 1   (C) 3   (D) 6   (E) 7

3. A single slit with width w produces a diffraction pattern on a screen when illuminated with light of a given wavelength. The entire experiment is then immersed in water with the same light source. Which of the following is true?

    (A) The diffraction pattern will contract.
    (B) The diffraction pattern will expand.
    (C) The diffraction pattern will be unchanged.
    (D) The diffraction pattern will disappear.
    (E) The central maximum becomes less intense than the secondary maxima.

4. Two parallel glass plates are separated by an air space 300 nm thick. When illuminated with various monochromatic light sources from directly above the plates, which wavelength will produce the least amount of reflected light?

(A) 400 nm   (B) 450 nm   (C) 500 nm   (D) 550 nm   (E) 600 nm

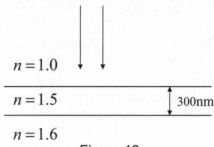

Figure 13

5. Light of several wavelengths is incident from above on a thin film of index 1.5 and thickness 300 nm that's coated on a surface with index 1.6. Which wavelength will produce the most reflected light?

(A) 400 nm   (B) 450 nm   (C) 500 nm   (D) 550 nm   (E) 650 nm

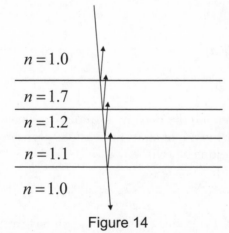

Figure 14

6. Three layers of transparent material with different indices of refraction are laminated to form a single device. When illuminated from above, reflections will occur at the various interfaces. The number of reflected rays experiencing a phase shift is

(A) 0   (B) 1   (C) 2   (D) 3   (E) 4

PRACTICE EXERCISES

SECTION II FREE REPONSE

1. Light consisting of two wavelengths, 500 nm and 600 nm, is incident upon a screen that has two narrow slits separated by a distance a. A second screen is placed 1 m behind the first screen. It's observed that the shorter wavelength has its first order maximum form on the second screen 0.015 m above the center of the central maximum.
   (a) Determine the spacing between the two slits.
   (b) Determine the distance from the central maximum to the first order maximum of the longer wavelength.
   (c) One of the slits is covered up. Describe any changes in the pattern appearing on the second screen.

2. A thin film with index of refraction 1.4 is to be coated onto a glass surface, index of 1.5, to remove red light of wavelength 600 nm from the reflections.
   (a) What is the minimum film thickness that will do the job?
   (b) At this thickness, will there be any visible wavelengths that will be enhanced in the reflected light?

Answers and Explanations

MULTIPLE CHOICE

1. The answer is D. Rearranging the maxima formula, you have $\sin\theta = \frac{N\lambda}{a}$. Making a larger will make θ smaller, so the width of all its dimensions decreases. The largest order maximum can be determined by looking at a 90° angle.

   $a \sin 90 = N\lambda \quad \Rightarrow N = \frac{a}{\lambda}$ Thus as a gets larger, N also gets larger.

2. The answer is E. From the previous explanation, you have at 90°

   $$N = \frac{a}{\lambda} = 3.7$$

   This means that the fourth order maximum doesn't form. There are 3 maxima for each order, one on each side of the central maximum, and when they're added to the central maximum itself you have a total of 7.

3. The answer is A. Rewriting the diffraction minima formula, you have
$$\sin\theta = \frac{N\lambda}{w}$$
As w gets bigger, θ will get smaller, indicating a contracting pattern.

4. The answer is E. There will be a phase shift at only one interface, where the ray moves from air to glass. For a minimum to occur, you need the physical path difference, $2d = 600$ nm, to be a multiple of the wavelength. E obviously satisfies this for $N = 1$.

5. The answer is B. There will be two phase shifts that compensate for each other when the rays are brought back together. For constructive interference, you need the two rays to have the 600 nm path difference in the film be an integral multiple of the wavelength in the film. The wavelength in the film is $\lambda' = \frac{\lambda}{1.5}$. For B, this gives you 300 nm, and the path difference is two wavelengths.

6. The answer is B. Only at the first interface do you have a ray going from a lower index medium to a higher index medium.

FREE RESPONSE

1. (a) You can use geometry to find the angle for the first maximum, then use the maxima formula to find the spacing.

$$\tan\theta = \frac{0.015}{1} \quad \Rightarrow \quad \theta = 0.859°$$

$$a\sin(0.859) = 500 \times 10^{-9} \quad \Rightarrow \quad a = 3.33 \times 10^{-5} \text{ m}$$

It's worth noting that the small angle approximation can often be used in these problems. In this approximation, $\sin\theta \cong \tan\theta$, and you can use the tangent in the maxima formula directly and avoid actually solving for the angle.

(b) Using your result and the small angle approximation, you have

$$a\sin\theta \cong a\tan\theta = 600 \times 10^{-9}$$

$$3.33 \times 10^{-5} \frac{x}{1} = 600 \times 10^{-9} \quad \Rightarrow \quad x = 0.018$$

(c) With one slit covered, you have a single slit diffraction pattern for each wavelength. Each color will have a broad central maximum, with the first order minimum occurring at different positions. The other maxima will also occur at different positions, but they'll be much less intense than the central maximum.

2. (a) There will be a phase shift at each reflection, since each interface involves moving to a medium with a higher index of refraction. The effects of the phase changes then cancel out in determining maxima and minima. To get a minimum in the 600 nm light, you need the path difference to be $\frac{1}{2}$ the wavelength in the film. Then you have

$$2d = \frac{1}{2}\frac{600}{1.4} \Rightarrow d = 107 \text{ nm}$$

(b) For maxima to occur, you need the path difference in the film to be an integral multiple of the wavelength in the film, so

$$2(107) = N\frac{\lambda}{1.4} \quad N = 1, 2 \ldots$$

For $N = 1$, this gives you 300 nm, out of the visible range. All other enhanced wavelengths will also be in the ultraviolet, so the answer is no, there are no visible wavelengths enhanced in the reflected light.

CHAPTER 18

The Quantum World

As you look at matter in smaller and smaller sizes, you'll find that the properties of the individual constituents are significantly different from those you're familiar with in the scale of the everyday world. When you throw a ball through an open window, for example, you can watch it travel in a well-defined path, in this case a parabola if gravity is the only influence on the ball. Your observation of its path has no effect on the ball. As it passes through the open window, there's no particular effect, and the ball continues as if it were traveling in open space above the Earth's surface.

But similar experiments performed with molecular, atomic, and subatomic particles would have significantly different outcomes. You cannot observe an electron trajectory as it travels between two points. "Observation" always involves some sort of interaction with the subject, and at the level of electrons, any observation produces significant change in what's being observed. If you directed a beam of electrons at a small opening analogous to your ball and window, you'd find that it's impossible to predict exactly where the electron will end up on the other side of the opening. How can passing through an empty space impart unpredictable behavior? This chapter will develop some of the concepts you'll need to address these phenomena.

The Photoelectric Effect

Within a metal, many of the electrons are very mobile and not bound to any one atom. These conduction electrons, while more or less free to move within the metal, can't simply fly out at the surface. There's a minimum energy that they need to acquire to escape, called the **work function**, ϕ, of the material. A typical value for the work function is a few electron-volts (eV). One **electron-volt** is the amount of energy gained or lost by an electron as it moves through 1 volt potential difference. The conversion is

$$\Delta U = q\Delta V = (1.6 \times 10^{-19})(1) = 1.6 \times 10^{-19} \, \text{J} = 1 \, \text{eV}$$

The electron-volt is useful for describing energy changes on the atomic scale. When light is incident upon a metal surface, you might expect the oscillating electric field in the beam to set these electrons into oscillation as well, transferring energy to them. The **intensity** of a light beam is proportional to $\vec{E}^2$, the square of the electric field strength in the beam, and it's a measure of the rate at which energy in the beam reaches a surface. As you increase the light's intensity, the amplitude of these oscillations will increase, and you'd expect that if you made the intensity high enough, the electrons would gain enough energy to be ejected. In principle, there should be no limit on the energy the electrons might absorb; if you increase the intensity, you increase the field strength, creating larger forces on the electrons so that more energy will be transferred to them. This prediction is based on treating light as a wave that propagates through the interaction between the electric and magnetic fields.

But this prediction is incorrect. To describe this effect quantitatively, consider the experimental setup in figure 1. You shine light onto a metal surface.

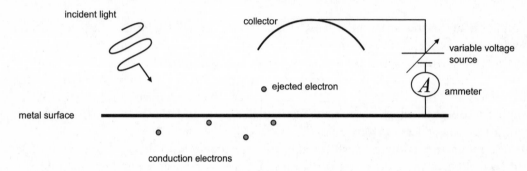

Figure 1

The light is under your control: You can set the frequency (wavelength, color) and the intensity. If electrons are ejected, you can count them by collecting them and passing them back to the surface through an ammeter. The current displayed by the ammeter is directly proportional to the number of ejected electrons. You can be sure you'll collect them if you place the collector at higher potential relative to the metal surface. The negative electrons will be pulled into the collector and forced into the ammeter circuit. You can set the potential of the collector with a variable voltage source. If you're interested in the energy of the ejected electrons, you could make the potential of the collector more and more negative with respect to the surface. Eventually, you'll reach a voltage level where the electrons ejected can no longer reach the collector. The minimum potential on the collector that will do this is called the **stopping potential**, V_{stop}. The maximum kinetic energy of the ejected electrons will then be

$$KE_{electron} = qV_{stop} \qquad\qquad q = 1.6 \times 10^{-19}\ C$$

Because of the definition of the electron-volt, the stopping potential expressed in volts will have the same numerical value as the electron energy expressed in eV. For example, a stopping potential of 1.7 V implies a maximum electron energy of 1.7 eV.

Suppose you set up the experiment with a metal that has a work function of 2.5 eV. When you shine dim red light of wavelength 650 nm on the surface, no electrons are ejected. Increasing the intensity *has no effect*. If dim light of a given color can't eject electrons, no matter how intense the light is made, it will still not eject electrons. Thinking of light as a wave with an oscillating electric field carrying energy proportional to $\vec{E}^2$ can't explain this.

As you shorten the wavelength (increase the frequency), you find that eventually you reach a **threshold** where electrons start to be ejected. At this frequency value, electrons will be ejected no matter how dim the light is! At threshold, even the dimmest light will immediately produce a response in the ammeter. Increasing the frequency further, you'll find that electrons continue to be ejected for all intensities. Increasing the intensity at a given frequency above threshold increases the number of ejected electrons: The ammeter gives a higher reading. For a fixed frequency above threshold, you can measure the energy in the ejected electrons as intensity is varied. For dim light, the ammeter gives a low reading, and you can determine the stopping potential by adjusting the voltage source until the ammeter reads 0. Increasing the intensity, you get many more ejected electrons and the ammeter may jump off scale, but you can bring it to 0 with *the same stopping potential*. This indicates that the ejected electrons' energy doesn't depend on the intensity, which flies in the face of the wave picture. Since the more intense light has a larger electric field, it should transfer more energy to the electrons.

The puzzle of the **photoelectric effect** was resolved by Albert Einstein in 1905. He proposed that electrons don't absorb light energy continuously as the wave model would predict, but that they absorb the energy in discrete bundles called **photons**. The photon is the basic unit of electromagnetic energy, the **quantum** of electromagnetic energy. The energy of a photon is proportional to the frequency of the light:

$$E_{\text{photon}} = hf \qquad h = 6.63 \times 10^{-34} \, \text{J} \cdot \text{s}$$

The constant h is called **Planck's constant**. Its extremely small value means that at the macroscopic level, the granular nature of light is totally unobservable. Increasing the intensity of the light at a fixed frequency increases the number of photons, but they will all have the same energy.

How does this explain the photoelectric effect? For your metal with 2.5 eV work function, a single photon would need energy of 2.5 eV to eject an electron. The photons in a beam with wavelength 650 nm have energy:

$$E_{\text{photon}} = hf = \frac{hc}{\lambda} = \frac{(6.63 \times 10^{-34})(3 \times 10^8)}{650 \times 10^{-9}} = 3.06 \times 10^{-19} \, \text{J} = 1.91 \, \text{eV}$$

These photons will be absorbed, but they don't have enough energy to eject electrons.

It's often useful to avoid constantly converting from eV to joules in these calculations. If you express the product hc in eV • nm instead of J • m, you have

$$hc = 1.99 \times 10^{-25} \, \text{J} \cdot \text{m} = 1{,}240 \, \text{eV} \cdot \text{nm}$$

Once you have the wavelength of a photon in nm, you can immediately get its energy in eV. For the above example, you have

$$E_{\text{photon}} = \frac{hc}{\lambda} = \frac{1{,}240}{650} = 1.91 \, \text{eV} \quad \text{(much quicker)}$$

To begin to eject electrons, the photons would need a shorter wavelength and energy just equal to the work function. This is called the **threshold wavelength**.

$$E_{photon} = \phi \text{ (at threshold)}$$

$$\lambda_{th} = \frac{hc}{E_{photon}} = \frac{hc}{\phi}$$

The corresponding frequency is called the **threshold frequency**. For the example, you can find the threshold wavelength:

$$\lambda_{th} = \frac{hc}{\phi} = \frac{1,240}{2.5} = 496 \text{ nm}$$

Once you go above threshold with even shorter wavelengths, the ejected electrons will have energy left over because the photon they absorbed had energy greater than the work function. Conservation of energy implies:

$$KE_{electron} = E_{photon} - \phi = hf - \phi$$

A graph of this relationship is shown in figure 2. Notice that the y-intercept is given by the work function, the x-intercept is the threshold frequency, and the slope is Planck's constant.

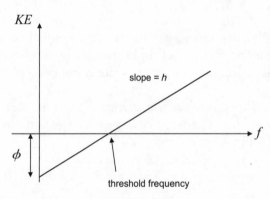

Figure 2

It's observed that for a certain metal surface illuminated with decreasing wavelengths of light, electrons are first ejected when the light has a wavelength of 550 nm. Find the work function of the material and determine the stopping potential when light of wavelength 400 nm is incident on the surface.

At threshold, the work function is equal to the energy of the incident photon.

$$\phi = \frac{hc}{\lambda_{th}} = \frac{1{,}240}{550} = 2.25 \text{ eV}$$

The KE of the ejected electrons will be the difference in the incident photon energy and the work function.

$$KE = E_{photons} - \phi = \frac{hc}{\lambda} - 2.25$$

$$KE = \frac{1{,}240}{400} - 2.25 = 0.85 \text{ eV}$$

The stopping potential will be 0.85 volts.

The photoelectric effect was the first phenomenon to demonstrate that light had a "particle" nature to it. If you ordinarily think of particles as objects that are localized in some small region of space, you're faced with resolving a paradox. Young's experiment clearly demonstrated that light acts as a wave, and a wave by its very nature is spread out in space. That's how it went through both slits. Now the photoelectric effect seems to be saying that light can behave as a particle and isn't spread out in space. This is a manifestation of **wave-particle duality**, and you'll look into it in more detail soon.

The Compton Effect

Einstein's explanation of the photoelectric effect addresses the interaction between electrons and light. It says that in the interaction, the light is absorbed in little bundles. But does the light exist as little bundles in other types of interactions? In the **Compton effect**, x-rays—a form of electromagnetic energy more energetic than light—are scattered off electrons. The scattered x-rays were found to have a longer wavelength. You could explain the phenomenon if you assumed the x-rays were a collection of photons acting like particles having an elastic collision with the electron. A schematic of the experiment is shown in figure 3.

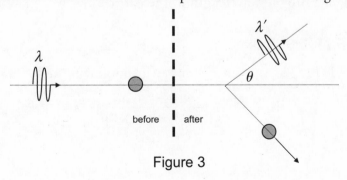

Figure 3

To apply collision theory to this situation, you need an expression for the photon momentum. Einstein's theory of special relativity predicts a very general relation between the energy of any particle, its momentum, and its rest mass. The rest mass m_0 of a particle is the mass you would measure if the particle weren't moving with respect to you.

$$E = \sqrt{p^2 c^2 + m_0^2 c^4}$$

Photons always move at the speed of light, and such particles don't have a rest mass. So for a photon, you can write

$$E = pc$$

Since you have another expression for the photon energy in terms of its wavelength, you can combine them to get

$$E = \frac{hc}{\lambda} = pc \;\Rightarrow\; p = \frac{h}{\lambda}$$

Applying momentum and energy conservation to the collision, you can accurately predict the wavelength shift in the x-rays as the observation angle θ is changed. The photoelectric effect can be explained by treating light as a particle that's completely absorbed in the interaction. The Compton effect can be explained by treating light as a particle that can transfer energy and momentum, but that isn't completely absorbed. Taken together, they provide solid evidence for the particle nature of light.

Matter Waves

In 1924, Louis De Broglie proposed that light was not the only phenomenon to exhibit wave particle duality. He said that material particles like electrons and atoms, which are recognized as being particles, can exhibit wave behavior. To make this statement, he had to define a meaningful wavelength for a material particle; the quintessential wave properties of diffraction and interference require that the wavelength be comparable to the slit width or slit spacing. To define a wavelength, De Broglie used the photon to make an analogy: If the photon has a momentum related to its wavelength through the equation $p = \frac{h}{\lambda}$, then perhaps material particles with momentum $p = mv$ have a wavelength that satisfies the same relation:

$$\lambda = \frac{h}{p} = \frac{h}{mv}$$

This is called the **De Broglie wavelength** of the particle.

EXAMPLE

What is the De Broglie wavelength for a neutron moving at 10^3 m/s?

$$\lambda = \frac{h}{mv} = \frac{6.63 \times 10^{-34}}{(1.66 \times 10^{-27})(10^3)} = 0.4 \text{ nm}$$

X-rays have a wavelength comparable in size to 0.4 nm. When x-rays are incident on various crystalline compounds that have ionic spacing on the order of their wavelength, such as salt, you'll see a diffraction pattern. This isn't surprising since x-rays, like light, exhibit wave behavior. According to De Broglie, neutrons moving at 10^3 m/s should exhibit a similar diffraction pattern, and indeed they do. There is a certain symmetry to nature, and light isn't special in exhibiting wave-particle duality. Material particles will also exhibit this duality. Notice that diffraction effects will be important only when the wavelength is comparable to the size of any objects or openings encountered. For a ball (mass = 0.1 kg) moving through an open window with a speed of 40 m/s, the De Broglie wavelength will be

$$\lambda = \frac{h}{mv} = \frac{6.63 \times 10^{-34}}{(0.1)(40)} = 1.66 \times 10^{-34} \text{ m}$$

Clearly, this is so small that diffraction is out of the question.

Wave-Particle Duality

The past few sections of this chapter have alluded to wave-particle duality. Now let's focus on some of the surprising ramifications of this phenomenon. If you fire classical particles like pellets from an air gun at a two slit apparatus and record the pattern of hits created on a screen behind the slits, you get a simple pattern of two regions behind the slits where the pellets hit, shown in figure 4. You could ask what pattern would be seen on a screen if you use a light source so dim that only 1 photon per second is emitted; this photon will be absorbed on the screen long before the next photon is emitted.

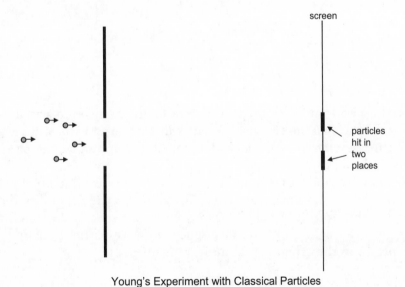

Young's Experiment with Classical Particles

Figure 4

You could frame the same question in terms of electrons as well: If the source emits only 1 electron per second, what pattern will eventually emerge on the screen? In each case, there's no possibility of any interaction between one particle and the next.

The surprising result is that after a reasonable time when many particles have eventually hit the screen, the classic Young's two slit interference pattern emerges. There are maxima where it is very probable for the particles to end up and minima where they don't end up, depicted in figure 5. But if any attempt is made to determine which slit the particles go through before they reach the screen, perhaps by placing detectors after each slit, the interference pattern is lost and the classic particle pattern of figure 4 emerges.

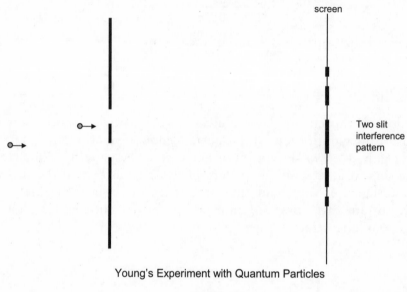

Young's Experiment with Quantum Particles

Figure 5

As long as you don't perform experiments that require the particles to actually be localized at a specific point in space, an interference pattern will emerge and you will see wave behavior. If you do make measurements of the particles' position, you localize the particles and you'll observe particle behavior.

Electrons, photons, and other quantum particles won't exhibit both behaviors in the same experiment. To see wave behavior, you must allow for the possibility that the particles go through either slit. To see particle behavior, you must specifically determine which slit each particle goes through. This is the essence of wave-particle duality: The behavior manifested depends on the experimental measurements made.

Atomic Energy Levels

An electron that's zipping along in space, not interacting with anything else, has KE only. There are no restrictions on the possible values of this energy as long as they are positive, since KE can't be negative. But when an electron is bound to a nucleus in an atom, there are restrictions on what energies it can have. The bound electron in the atom can have only specific values of total energy. These specific values are called the **atomic energy levels**. They're determined by the interaction of the electron with the nucleus and all the other electrons in the atom. Because the levels are like uneven ladder steps, not a continuum, the levels are quantized. If you let infinity be the zero of electric potential energy, then an electron bound to a nucleus will have a negative total energy. This just means that energy has to be added to get it to zero energy—to get it out to infinity and escape the nucleus.

To be concrete, imagine a hypothetical atomic electron with energy levels depicted in figure 6. When the electron has its lowest possible energy, it is in its **ground state**. There's no lower energy available to the electron, so this state is stable: An electron in the ground state will persist indefinitely in this state unless energy is added.

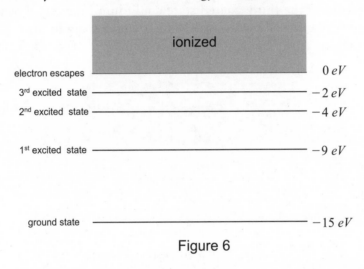

Figure 6

It's possible for the electron to absorb energy, but it has to come in just the right packages. If your electron is in the ground state at −15 eV, it can absorb 6 eV of energy to get to the first excited state, or 11 eV of energy to get to the second excited state. But it couldn't absorb 5 eV if it were in the ground state because there's no −10 eV level for it to go to. If the electron is in the ground state, it must absorb 15 eV of energy to escape the nucleus. This is called the **ionization energy** of the electron.

There are no restrictions on energy absorption as long as the energy is enough to knock the electron out of the atom. For example, an electron in the second excited state can absorb 2 eV to get to the third excited state, or it can absorb any energy greater than 4 eV to escape the nucleus.

Line Spectra

The excited states of an atomic electron aren't stable. In time, the electron will make a transition to a lower level. When this occurs, the electron will end up with less energy. Where does the excess energy go? It's carried away by a single photon. For every transition, 1 photon is emitted, and this photon will have energy equal to the energy lost by the electron in making the transition.

$$E_{photon} = -\Delta E_{electron}$$

For example, if your electron were in the first excited state, upon jumping to the ground state it would emit a single photon with energy 6 eV. You can easily calculate the wavelength of this photon:

$$\lambda = \frac{hc}{E_{photon}} = \frac{hc}{-\Delta E_{electron}} = \frac{1,240}{6} = 207 \text{ nm}$$

This corresponds to ultraviolet light. When an electron is at a higher level, there are more possibilities. An electron in the third excited state could jump directly down to the ground state, emitting a single photon of energy 13 eV, or it could **cascade** through several states, emitting as many photons as the transitions it makes. Figure 7 depicts a 3-photon cascade.

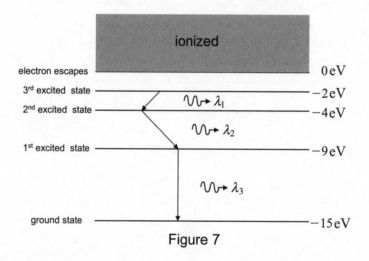

Figure 7

The arrows indicate the transition made by the electron, and the photons are shown moving off to the right. You can easily calculate the wavelengths of the emitted photons using $\lambda = \frac{hc}{-\Delta E_{electron}}$

$$\lambda_1 = \frac{1,240}{2} = 620 \text{ nm} \quad \lambda_2 = \frac{1,240}{5} = 248 \text{ nm} \quad \lambda_3 = \frac{1,240}{6} = 207 \text{ nm}$$

Notice that λ_1 is in the visible part of the spectrum. If you had a large collection of atoms with electron energy levels like the example, and if you excited the atoms by adding energy to them somehow, all possible transitions would be constantly occurring. The photons emitted by your collection would have only the specific wavelengths permitted by the various electron transitions allowed. You could analyze the various wavelengths emitted by passing the light through a diffraction grating. Each visible wavelength would show up as a distinct line on the screen behind the grating. If you used a plastic transmission grating, looking at the light through it, you would see distinct lines for each color off to the left or right of the central maximum. This phenomenon is called the **emission spectrum** of the atom.

Because each atom has different energy levels, each atom will have a distinct emission spectrum, an atomic fingerprint. In the example, only one visible wavelength is emitted, so you would see the one red line. If white light consisting of all visible wavelengths is passed through a gas of atoms, the electrons can absorb photons with wavelengths that match the possible electron transitions. After the light has passed through the gas, this absorption will produce gaps in the transmitted light, as you can see by passing the transmitted light through a diffraction grating. This is just the reverse of the emission process, and the spectrum of gaps produced is called the **absorption spectrum**. The absorption spectrum and emission spectrum of a given atom correspond to exactly the same wavelengths. Together they are often referred to as **line spectra**.

KEY FORMULAS

Photon Energy	$E_{\text{photon}} = hf = \dfrac{hc}{\lambda}$
Threshold Condition	$E_{\text{photon}} = \phi$
Maximum Ejected KE	$KE_{\text{electron}} = qV_{\text{stop}}$
Photoelectric Energy Condition	$KE_{\text{electron}} = hf - \phi = \dfrac{hc}{\lambda} - \phi$
Photon Momentum	$p = \dfrac{h}{\lambda}$
De Broglie Wavelength	$\lambda = \dfrac{h}{mv}$
Photon Emission	$E_{\text{photon}} = -\Delta E_{\text{electron}}$
Emission Wavelengths	$\lambda = \dfrac{hc}{-\Delta E_{\text{electron}}}$

CHAPTER 18 PRACTICE EXERCISES

SECTION I MULTIPLE CHOICE

1. In a photoelectric experiment performed above threshold, as the intensity of the incident light increases, which of the following is true?

   (A) The stopping potential for ejected electrons increases.
   (B) The De Broglie wavelength of the ejected electrons decreases.
   (C) The number of electrons ejected increases.
   (D) The number and energy of the electrons ejected are not affected.
   (E) The kinetic energy of the ejected electrons decreases.

2. A photoelectric effect experiment performed with a fixed light intensity is producing ejected electrons. As the wavelength of the incident light is continuously increased, which of the following is true?

   (A) The stopping potential for ejected electrons increases.
   (B) The number of electrons ejected increases.
   (C) The number and energy of the electrons ejected are not affected.
   (D) Electrons ejected will remain constant in number until a sudden stoppage.
   (E) The De Broglie wavelength of the ejected electrons decreases.

3. Two metals, labeled S and T, are used in separate photoelectric effect experiments. S has a smaller work function than T. Which graph best represents the electron energy vs. frequency plots for the two experiments?

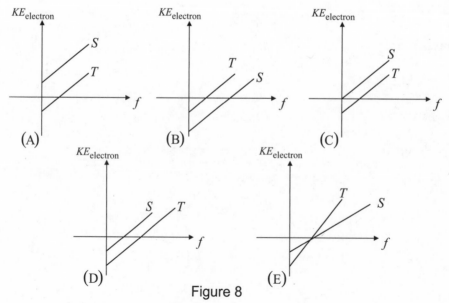

Figure 8

4. An electron with initial kinetic energy E is accelerated so that its kinetic energy is doubled. If its original De Broglie wavelength was λ, its De Broglie wavelength after the energy increase is

(A) λ　(B) 2λ　(C) $\sqrt{2}\lambda$　(D) $\dfrac{\lambda}{2}$　(E) $\dfrac{\lambda}{\sqrt{2}}$

5. The De Broglie wavelength of a neutron happens to have the same numerical value as the wavelength of a photon. Which of the following is true?

(A) The neutron and photon have the same speed.
(B) The neutron and photon have the same energy.
(C) The neutron and photon have the same frequency.
(D) The neutron and photon have the same momentum.
(E) The neutron and photon have the same mass.

6. Two monochromatic beams of light have different frequencies, with beam R having twice the frequency of beam S. If p_R is the momentum of photons in beam R and p_S is the momentum of photons in beam S, which of the following is true?

(A) $p_R = 2p_S$　(B) $p_R = \dfrac{1}{2}p_S$　(C) $p_R = p_S$　(D) $p_R = \dfrac{p_S}{\sqrt{2}}$　(E) $p_R = \sqrt{2}p_S$

Questions 7 and 8

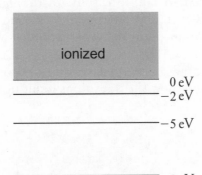

Figure 9

7. A hypothetical atom has an electron energy level diagram as shown. If a gas of these atoms were excited, which of the following photon energies would you expect to be emitted?

(A) 2, 3, and 4 eV only　(B) 3 and 4 eV only　(C) 3, 4, and 7 eV only
(D) 2, 3, 4, and 7 eV only　(E) 2, 3, and 7 eV only

8. Photons of a continuous range of energies from 2 eV to 5 eV are sent through a gas of these atoms. If the atomic electrons in the gas are distributed over all possible energy levels, the photons that can be absorbed have what energy?

(A) All energies can be absorbed.　(B) 4 eV only　(C) 2 eV and 4 eV only
(D) 2, 3, and 4 eV only　(E) 3 and 4 eV only

CHAPTER 18 · PRACTICE EXERCISES

SECTION II FREE RESPONSE

1. In a photoelectric experiment, it's observed that incident light of wavelength 520 nm requires a stopping potential of 1.4 V.
   (a) Determine the momentum of the incident photons.
   (b) Determine the work function of the metal surface.
   (c) Find the stopping potential when light of wavelength 420 nm is incident on the surface.

2. An x-ray with wavelength 5×10^{-11} m collides head-on with a stationary electron. After the collision, the photon is headed in the opposite direction with a wavelength 5.24×10^{-11} m.
   (a) Determine the initial energy of the photon.
   (b) Determine the final energy of the photon.
   (c) Determine the initial momentum of the photon.
   (d) Determine the final momentum of the photon.
   (e) Determine the final momentum of the electron.

3. The ground state energy of an atomic electron is determined to be -6.4 eV. When a gas of these atoms, initially in their ground state, is illuminated with monochromatic ultraviolet light of wavelength 200 nm, some of the light is adsorbed, and subsequent emissions of 200 nm, 310 nm, and 564 nm are detected.
   (a) Determine the minimum photon wavelength that would ionize an electron in its ground state.
   (b) On the figure below, draw an energy level diagram consistent with the data. Show the energy of each state, and show the transitions resulting in each of the photon emissions.

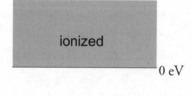

ionized

0 eV

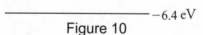

−6.4 eV

Figure 10

Answers and Explanations

MULTIPLE CHOICE

1. The answer is C. Below threshold, the intensity will have no effect. Above threshold, increasing the intensity increases the number of photons hitting the surface, so more electrons are ejected. Since all the ejected electrons have absorbed the same energy photon, the stopping potential and the De Broglie wavelength of the electrons are unaffected by the intensity.

2. The answer is D. As the wavelength is increased, the incident photon energy decreases. Eventually the photon energy will go below threshold, and no electrons will be ejected.

3. The answer is D. The slope of any such graph is Planck's constant, so the lines must be parallel. The magnitude of the work function is the negative of the y-intercept, with the smaller work function then closer to the origin.

4. The answer is E. You can combine the formulas for the De Broglie wavelength and kinetic energy.

$$E = \frac{1}{2}mv^2 \Rightarrow v = \sqrt{\frac{2E}{m}}$$

$$\lambda = \frac{h}{mv} = \frac{h}{\sqrt{\frac{2E}{m}}}$$

As E doubles, the wavelength decreases by $\frac{1}{\sqrt{2}}$.

5. The answer is D. Since $\lambda = \frac{h}{p}$ for both the neutron and the photon, the answer follows.

6. The answer is A. You can combine the momentum relation for a photon with the standard relation between wavelength and frequency.

$$p = \frac{h}{\lambda} = \frac{hf}{c} \text{ since } c = \lambda f$$

This means that momentum and frequency are directly proportional.

7. The answer is C. The excited atoms will populate all the levels. There are two excited states and one ground state, so there will be transitions from $-2\,\text{eV} \rightarrow -9\,\text{eV}$, $-2\,\text{eV} \rightarrow -5\,\text{eV}$, and $-5\,\text{eV} \rightarrow -9\,\text{eV}$, corresponding to the $-\Delta E_{\text{electron}}$ of 7, 3, and 4 eV, respectively.

8. The answer is A. Since the electrons in the gas could be in any of the allowed states, those in the second excited state at -2 eV can absorb a 2 eV photon, which will ionize it, or anything greater than 2 eV, since there are no restrictions on the energy of the electron if it isn't bound in an atom.

FREE RESPONSE

1. (a) $p = \frac{h}{\lambda}$ $\Rightarrow p = \frac{6.63 \times 10^{-34}}{520 \times 10^{-9}} = 1.28 \times 10^{-27} \frac{J \cdot s}{m}$

(b) Use the energy relation for the photoelectric effect. The ejected electrons will have a kinetic energy of 1.4 eV, since the stopping potential is 1.4 V.

$$KE = \frac{hc}{\lambda} - \phi$$

$$1.4 = \frac{1,240}{520} - \phi \qquad\qquad \Rightarrow \phi = 0.98 \text{ eV}$$

(c) Use the energy relation again with your value for the work function.

$$KE = \frac{hc}{\lambda} - \phi$$

$$KE = \frac{1,240}{420} - 0.98 \qquad\qquad \Rightarrow KE = 1.97 \text{ eV}$$

The stopping potential is 1.97 V.

2. This is a head-on Compton collision. You can use the basic formulas to find the energies and momenta of the photon. Conservation of momentum will allow you to determine the final momentum of the electron.

(a) $E_0 = \frac{hc}{\lambda_0} = \frac{1,240}{0.05} = 2.48 \times 10^4 \text{ eV}$

(b) $E_f = \frac{hc}{\lambda_f} = \frac{1,240}{0.0524} = 2.37 \times 10^4 \text{ eV}$

(c) $p_0 = \frac{h}{\lambda_0} = \frac{6.63 \times 10^{-34}}{5 \times 10^{-11}} = 1.33 \times 10^{-23} \frac{J \cdot s}{m}$

(d) $p_f = \frac{h}{\lambda_f} = \frac{6.63 \times 10^{-34}}{5.24 \times 10^{-11}} = 1.26 \times 10^{-23} \frac{J \cdot s}{m}$

(e) The momentum lost by the photon will equal that gained by the electron. Since the electron was initially at rest, the momentum gained will equal its final momentum.

$$p_{\text{electron}} = -\Delta p_{\text{photon}} = -(-1.26 - 1.33) \times 10^{-23} = 2.59 \times 10^{-27} \frac{J \cdot s}{m}$$

3. (a) The electron in the ground state needs to gain 6.4 eV to be ionized. This corresponds to a photon wavelength:

$$\lambda = \frac{hc}{-\Delta E_{\text{electron}}} = \frac{1,240}{6.4} = 194 \text{ nm}$$

(b) The three photon wavelengths correspond to energies:

$$E_{\text{photon}} = \frac{hc}{\lambda} = \frac{1,240}{\lambda} \quad E_{200} = 6.2 \text{ eV} \quad E_{310} = 4.0 \text{ eV} \quad E_{564} = 2.2 \text{ eV}$$

These energies correspond to the energy changes for the electron. To emit a 6.2 eV photon, the electron must jump from a level of energy -0.2 eV to the ground state. Similar reasoning leads to figure 11.

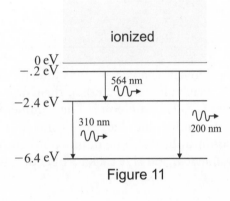

Figure 11

CHAPTER 19

Nuclear Physics

With the recent elimination of radioactivity and half life questions, the nuclear physics material on the AP test has been significantly reduced. This chapter will outline what you'll still need to know about the topic.

The Nucleus

The nucleus consists of positively charged protons and neutrons carrying no electric charge, bonded together in a very small volume. Because of their similar nuclear properties, the protons and neutrons are sometimes called **nucleons**. The number of protons is called the **atomic number**, Z, and its value determines the charge of the nucleus. The total number of protons and neutrons is called the **mass number**, A. The number of neutrons will be the difference $A - Z$. A nucleus with a given value of Z and A is called a nuclide and is designated by

$$_Z^A X$$

where X is the chemical symbol of the element. For example, the iron nucleus containing 56 nucleons is designated by

$$_{26}^{56} \text{Fe}$$

In a neutral atom, the number of electrons will equal Z. Since chemical properties are determined by the outer shell electrons, the neutrons don't figure into the chemical properties of an element. For a given value of Z, several nuclides may be possible, each with a different number of neutrons. These are called **isotopes** of the element. Isotopes of a given element have the same chemical properties.

Because of the short distances between the nucleons, the Coulomb interaction results in enormous repulsive forces between the protons. If you could build a stable nucleus from scratch, you'd have to put in a lot of energy to bring the protons in close to each other. When they get really close, however, a short-range force called the **strong nuclear force** comes into play. Unlike the electric force, which is mediated by massless photons, the strong force is mediated by particles that do have a mass. That's why the force comes into play only when nucleons are close together.

While the Coulomb force affects only protons, the strong force affects protons and neutrons equally, so adding neutrons can help hold together a nucleus: The neutrons provide attractive forces and no repulsive forces. For example, a nucleus consisting of just 2 protons isn't stable, but if 2 neutrons are added, forming ^4_2He, you get a very stable, tightly bound nucleus. The strong nuclear force is much stronger than the electric repulsive force, and this is what holds together the nucleus, keeping it from flying apart due to the Coulomb repulsion. Although you do have to add energy to bring free protons together to form the nucleus, as the nucleons get very close to each other they will attract each other, and energy will be released. For a stable nucleus, more energy is released as the nucleons finally come together than had to be put in to overcome the Coulomb repulsion.

The difference in the energy of the free nucleons and the bound nucleus is called the **binding energy** of the nucleus. If you know the mass of a nucleus and how many protons and neutrons it contains, you can use the Einstein **mass-energy equivalence principle** to determine the binding energy. This relation tells you that mass and energy can be converted into each other.

$$\Delta E = \Delta mc^2 \qquad c = 3 \times 10^8 \text{ m/s}$$

If you compare the mass of a nucleus with the mass of all the nucleons that make it up, you'll find the nucleus to have less mass. The Δm in this case is the difference and ΔE is the binding energy, the energy that must be added to remove all the nucleons and get them far away from each other. When you're working with mass differences in nuclear physics, the unified atomic mass unit is a useful unit. Its value is

$$1\text{u} = 1.66 \times 10^{-27} \text{kg}$$

If 1 atomic mass unit is converted to energy, energy is released:

$$\Delta E = \Delta mc^2 = (1.66 \times 10^{-27})(3 \times 10^8)^2 = 1.49 \times 10^{-10} \text{ J} = 931 \text{ MeV}$$

In the last step, the energy is expressed in MeV (10^6 eV), a useful energy scale for nuclear physics. If you know the change in mass in atomic mass units, you can multiply by 931 to find the energy gain or release in MeV.

EXAMPLE

Determine the binding energy of $^{12}_6\text{C}$. The mass of the nucleus, proton, and neutron are 12.0000 u, 1.0078 u, and 1.0087 u, respectively.

The nucleus consists of 6 protons and 6 neutrons, so the mass of the free nucleons is

$$M_{\text{nucleons}} = 6(1.0078) + 6(1.0087) = 12.0990 \text{ u}$$

The difference between the free nucleon mass and the carbon nucleus is

$$\Delta m = M_{\text{nucleons}} - M_{\text{nucleus}} = 12.0990 - 12.0000 = 0.0990 \text{ u}$$

Then the binding energy is

$$\Delta E = 0.0990(931) = 92.2 \text{ MeV}$$

Nuclear Reactions

A nuclear reaction involves two or more nuclear particles coming together to form nuclear products. The reactants and products may not be complete nuclei. In these reactions, single protons, neutrons, and electrons may be involved. To keep track of charge and number of nucleons in these reactions, you can designate these single particles as

$$_1^1p \ \text{proton} \qquad _0^1n \ \text{neutron} \qquad _{-1}^0e \ \text{electron}$$

Neutral non-nucleons can also be involved, designated as

$$\gamma \ \text{photon} \qquad \nu \ \text{neutrino} \qquad \overline{\nu} \ \text{antineutrino}$$

The **neutrino** and its antiparticle are very low mass particles involved in nuclear reactions. Notice that these particles have no sub- or superscripts, since they carry no charge and aren't nucleons.

In a nuclear reaction, both electric charge and total nucleon number are conserved quantities. Let's look at a couple of examples of nuclear reactions to see what happens.

Nuclear fission is a type of reaction where a large nucleus is cleaved by a neutron. A typical example is

$$_0^1n + {}_{92}^{235}U \rightarrow {}_{56}^{141}Ba + {}_{36}^{92}Kr + 3{}_0^1n + \text{energy}$$

In this process, a neutron hits the uranium isotope, which then splits into isotopes of barium and krypton. Also produced are 3 more neutrons, which can move off and cause more reactions like this; a large amount of energy is also released. Notice that the bottom numbers add up to the same value on each side of the equation:

$$0 + 92 = 56 + 36 + 3(0)$$

This is a reflection of charge conservation: You began with a charge of $+92$, and you end with the same. Notice also that the top numbers on each side of the equation add up:

$$1 + 235 = 141 + 92 + 3(1)$$

In a nuclear reaction, the total number of nucleons stays the same.

Another type of nuclear reaction is **nuclear fusion**. Here, two smaller nuclei come together to form a larger nucleus. A typical example is

$$_1^2H + {}_1^1p \rightarrow {}_2^3He + \gamma$$

In this process, an isotope of hydrogen with 1 neutron (called a deuteron) collides with a proton to produce an isotope of helium. A high-energy photon is also produced. Once again, notice that the top and bottom numbers balance on the two sides of the equation. Since the photon doesn't carry a charge or nucleon number, you can ignore it in balancing.

EXERCISE

In a possible fission of $^{235}_{92}$ by a neutron, two large fragments, one of which is $^{140}_{54}Xe$, are produced along with 2 neutrons, and considerable energy is released. Determine the atomic number and mass number of the other fragment.

Just balance the reaction:

$$^{1}_{0}n + {}^{235}_{92}U \rightarrow {}^{140}_{54}Xe + {}^{A}_{Z}? + 2{}^{1}_{0}n + energy$$

On the bottom, you have

$$0 + 92 = 54 + Z \Rightarrow Z = 38$$

On the top, you have

$$1 + 235 = 140 + A + 2(1) \Rightarrow A = 94$$

Energy in Nuclear Reactions

When energy is released in a nuclear reaction, some of it is carried away by the smaller particles created in the process, and some of it appears as kinetic energy of the nuclei created. Using the mass-energy equivalence relation along with momentum conservation, you can analyze the decay of a stationary nucleus in some detail. Since the initial momentum is 0, you have a condition on the final velocities of the particles. The difference in mass between the initial nucleus and the products is the source of the kinetic energy of the products. While radioactivity has been eliminated as a topic on the AP test, you still might have to analyze a decay in which a helium nucleus is emitted, so let's look at an example.

EXAMPLE

A stationary radium nucleus decays according to the equation

$$^{223}_{88}Ra \rightarrow {}^{219}_{86}Rn + {}^{4}_{2}He$$

The mass of the helium nucleus is 4.0026 u, and its kinetic energy is 5.72 MeV. The mass of the radon nucleus is 219.0095 u.

(a) Determine the speed of the helium nucleus.

(b) Determine the speed of the radon nucleus.

(c) Determine the mass of the radium nucleus.

(a) To find the speed of the helium, just use the KE formula, being careful about the units.

$$KE = (5.72)(1.6 \times 10^{-13}) = \frac{1}{2}mv^2 = \frac{1}{2}(4.0026)(1.66 \times 10^{-27})v^2$$

$$v = 1.66 \times 10^7 \, \frac{m}{s}$$

(b) Use momentum conservation.

$$P_i = P_f$$

$$0 = m_{Rn}v_{Rn} + m_{He}v_{He} \qquad \Rightarrow \quad v_{Rn} = -\frac{m_{He}}{m_{Rn}}v_{He}$$

$$v_{Rn} = -\frac{4.0026}{219.009}(1.66 \times 10^7) = 3.03 \times 10^5 \, \frac{m}{s}$$

(c) The radium nucleus will have a mass equal to the mass on the right side plus the Δm associated with the KE of the products. The KE of the radon is small compared with the helium, since the speed is squared.

$$KE_{Rn} = \frac{1}{2}m_{Rn}v_{Rn}^2 = \frac{1}{2}(219.0095)(1.66 \times 10^{-27})(3.03 \times 10^5)^2 = 1.67 \times 10^{-14} \, J = 0.10 \, MeV$$

Then, the total KE is

$$KE_{tot} = 5.72 + 0.10 = 5.82 \, MeV$$

From the mass-energy relation, you know that 931 MeV corresponds to a mass of 1 u, so

$$\Delta m = \frac{5.82}{931} = 0.0063 \, u$$

Finally, you can determine the radium mass:

$$m_{Ra} = m_{Rn} + m_{He} + \Delta m$$

$$m_{Ra} = 2.19.0095 + 4.0026 + 0.0063$$

$$m_{Ra} = 223.0184 \, u$$

KEY FORMULAS

Mass-Energy Equivalence $\qquad\qquad\qquad\qquad \Delta E = \Delta mc^2$

PRACTICE EXERCISES

SECTION I MULTIPLE CHOICE

1. In the reaction $^2_1H + {}^3_1H \rightarrow {}^4_2He + {}^1_0n$, which of the following is true?
    I.   The hydrogen isotopes must have a great deal of kinetic energy for the reaction to occur.
    II. This is an example of nuclear fission.
    III. This is an example of nuclear fusion.

    (A) I only   (B) II only   (C) III only   (D) I and II   (E) I and III

2. Tritium is an isotope of hydrogen containing 2 neutrons. If m_p, m_n, and m_{tr} are the masses of the proton, neutron, and tritium nucleus, respectively, which of the following is true?

    (A) $m_{tr} = 2m_n + m_p$ (B) $m_{tr} = 2m_n - m_p$ (C) $m_{tr} > 2m_n + m_p$
    (D) $m_{tr} < 2m_n + m_p$ (E) $m_{tr} = 2m_n$

3. For a particular nucleus, the difference between its mass and the sum of its individual nucleon masses is 0.01 u. The binding energy of the nucleus is most nearly

    (A) 0.01 MeV   (B) 0.1 MeV   (C) 1 MeV   (D) 10 MeV   (E) 100 MeV

$$^1_0n + {}^{235}_{92}U \rightarrow {}^{132}_{50}Sn + {}^{101}_{42}Mo + \text{neutrons} + \text{energy}$$

4. The number of neutrons produced in the above reaction is

    (A) 1   (B) 2   (C) 3   (D) 4   (E) 5

5. $^{252}_{98}Ca$ can undergo a nuclear reaction with $^{10}_5B$ to produce a single nucleus and 5 neutrons. The final nucleus could best be represented by

    (A) $^{252}_{103}X$ (B) $^{262}_{103}X$ (C) $^{262}_{108}X$ (D) $^{267}_{103}X$ (E) $^{257}_{103}X$

PRACTICE EXERCISES

SECTION II FREE RESPONSE

1. In a nuclear decay of $^{228}_{90}$Th with mass 228.0287 u, a stationary thorium nucleus decays, yielding a helium nucleus $^4_2$He with mass 4.0026 u and kinetic energy 5.42 MeV, and another product.
   (a) Determine the Z and A values of the other product.
   (b) Determine the momentum of the other product.
   (c) Ignoring the recoil kinetic energy of the other product, determine the mass of the other product.

Answers and Explanations

MULTIPLE CHOICE

1. The answer is E. The hydrogen must have large KE to overcome the Coulomb repulsion of the protons. A nuclear fusion process involves light nuclei combining to form heavier ones, as in this example.

2. The answer is D. The nucleus contains 1 proton and 2 neutrons. The mass of the nucleus is less than the sum of the individual components by an amount equal to the mass equivalent of the binding energy.

3. The answer is D. One atomic mass unit converts to roughly 1,000 MeV, so 0.01 u corresponds to about 10 MeV.

4. The answer is C. Balancing the top numbers (mass numbers) gives you
$$1 + 235 = 132 + 101 + x \quad x = 3$$

5. The answer is E. The reaction equation is
$$^{252}_{98}\text{Ca} + {}^{10}_{5}\text{B} \rightarrow 5{}^1_0\text{n} + {}^A_Z X$$
   The top numbers give
$$252 + 10 = 5(1) + A \qquad \Rightarrow A = 257$$
   The bottom numbers give
$$98 + 5 = 0 + Z \qquad \Rightarrow Z = 103$$

FREE RESPONSE

1. (a) The equation takes the form

$$^{228}_{90}\text{Th} \rightarrow {}^{4}_{2}\text{He} + {}^{A}_{Z}X$$

Balancing the top and bottom numbers yields $Z = 88$, $A = 224$ (radium isotope).

(b) Use momentum conservation, first finding the speed of the helium from its KE, being careful of units.

$$KE = (5.42 \times 10^6 \text{eV})\left(1.6 \times 10^{-19}\, \tfrac{\text{J}}{\text{eV}}\right) = \tfrac{1}{2}mv^2 = \tfrac{1}{2}(4.0026\text{u})\left(1.66 \times 10^{-27}\, \tfrac{\text{kg}}{\text{u}}\right)v^2$$

$$v = 1.62 \times 10^7 \text{ m/s}$$

$$P_i = P_f$$

$$0 = m_{\text{He}}v_{\text{He}} + p_X$$

$$\Rightarrow p_X = -(4.0026)(1.66 \times 10^{-27})(1.62 \times 10^7) = 1.08 \times 10^{-19}\, \tfrac{\text{kg} \cdot \text{m}}{\text{s}}$$

(c) If you ignore the kinetic energy of the recoiling product, energy conservation and the mass-energy equivalence relation yield

$$m_{\text{Th}} = m_{\text{He}} + m_X + \Delta m$$

$$228.0287 = 4.0026 + m_X + \frac{5.42}{931}$$

$$m_X = 224.0203 \text{ u}$$

CHAPTER 20

AP Physics and the Laboratory

Since 1996, the AP Physics Exam has increased its focus on the lab aspect of the AP curriculum. The test now includes free-response questions that require you to be familiar with common lab apparatus and how it's used. At the B level, the lab questions ask you to design a lab setup that will measure a certain property, perhaps with restrictions on the types of measuring instruments that can be used. Typically the questions call for a written description, a diagram, and an analysis showing how the instrument readings lead to the final measurement result. There are many possible correct answers to these questions. Let's look at some examples.

Figure 1

1. You're given a transparent, semicircular disc with radius 5 cm and thickness 1 cm and an unknown index of refraction (figure 1). It's your task to determine the index of refraction, using common laboratory equipment.

(a) List the devices and instruments you will need in your setup.

(b) Make a sketch of your apparatus, labeling the devices and instruments. On the diagram, label any variable quantities that you'll be using in equations.

(c) Describe how you will perform the experiment.

(d) Show how the measurements you make lead to the value for the index of refraction.

Possible Response

(a) meter stick, pen laser, white screen, metal stand with rod and rod holder
(b) figure 2

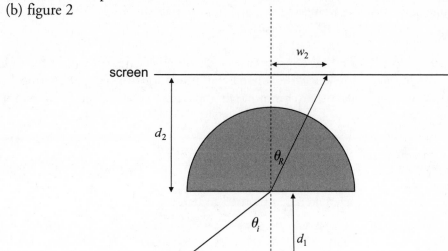

Figure 2

(c) Place the disc on a flat, horizontal surface. Put the pen laser into a rod holder and adjust the height so that the beam will be at the same level as the disc. Move the laser and holder to a point where there's an incident angle θ_i and aim the beam to hit dead center on the disc. You could determine this by measuring 5 cm from one end and 0.5 cm from the top side. You can figure out θ_i by measuring w_1 and d_1 with a meter stick. Since the beam hits dead center, it exits the disc along a normal line, so there's no further bending beyond the bending that occurs at the first interface. You can determine the angle θ_R by measuring w_2 and d_2. Repeat this procedure for several incident angles.

(d) Trigonometry determines the angles.

$$\tan\theta_i = \frac{w_1}{d_1} \qquad\qquad \tan\theta_R = \frac{w_2}{d_2}$$

Assuming air has an index $n_{air} = 1$, Snell's law tells you that

$$\sin\theta_i = n\sin\theta_R$$

If you calculate the sines for each trial, and plot $\sin\theta_i$ on the vertical and $\sin\theta_R$ on the horizontal, the slope of the resulting line will be the index of refraction.

Comments

    If you used a single trial and Snell's law directly, there would be less precision in the result. If the beam didn't enter at the center point, the exiting beam would bend at the circular interface; you would have to make more measurements to get all the angles. In principle, this could still be done.

2. You're given a simple pendulum that consists of a small spherical mass m attached to a long piece of string. You're also supplied with a metal stand and rods to hang the string from. Using this apparatus along with other common lab apparatus, you're asked to determine g, the acceleration due to gravity.

   (a) List any other measuring devices and equipment you need.
   (b) Describe how you would perform the lab. If you wish, you can make a sketch to clarify your description.
   (c) Show how the data you have taken can be used to determine g.

Possible Response

   (a) meter stick, stopwatch
   (b) For small amplitudes, the period is independent of the amplitude. With the pendulum attached to its support, measure the length of the string. Pull it out a small angle and release, starting the stopwatch. Record the time T_5 for 5 complete oscillations. Repeat these procedures for several measured lengths of the pendulum.
   (c) The experimental value for the period will be

$$T = \frac{T_5}{5}$$

Theoretically, you would expect the period to be related to the length by the equation

$$T = 2\pi \sqrt{\frac{l}{g}}$$

You can reorganize this to get

$$l = \left(\frac{g}{4\pi^2}\right) T^2$$

If you plot the length on the vertical axis and T^2 on the horizontal, you get a straight line with slope $\frac{g}{4\pi^2}$. Graphically determine the slope, equate it to $\frac{g}{4\pi^2}$, and solve for g.

Comments

Once again, it's better to use several data points and a graph rather than a single point and the equation. Depending on your calculator and your proficiency with it, you could fit the T vs. length data directly with a power fit and then extract g from the coefficient in the equation. You would have more precision in the answer if the length in the period formula were replaced with $l + r$, where r is the radius of the spherical mass. This would be the distance from the pivot to the center of mass.

In recent years, lab questions involving Archimedes' principle, specific heat of a liquid, spring constant, initial speed of a projectile, and more have been on the test. In preparing for these questions (there won't be more than one per year), be sure to look over your lab work and focus on the capabilities of the apparatus you used: how it works and what it measures.

Here are two more problems, with explanations at the end of the chapter. Try doing them yourself, even referring to notes or books, before looking at the method described here. There will be more than one correct procedure for most lab questions.

CHAPTER 20 PRACTICE EXERCISES

1. You are given several 20 cm × 30 cm sheets of conducting paper, and your task is to determine the resistivity of the paper. You're told that the paper is 0.12 mm thick, and you have the following equipment available:

   variable power supply
   voltmeter
   ammeter
   connecting wires and clips
   meter stick
   scissors and utility knife

   Describe a procedure that will allow you to determine the resistivity using these instruments only. Sketch a diagram showing your setup, and clearly label its components. Explain how to use your measurements to obtain the resistivity value.

2. You're given a wooden block of mass 0.200 kg in the shape of a rectangular solid and a flat, wooden plank 1 m long, with a width 3 times the width of the block. You're asked to determine the coefficient of kinetic friction between the block and the plank.

   (a) List the measuring devices and equipment you will need.
   (b) Make a sketch of your setup, clearly labeling all the components.
   (c) Describe how you would perform the experiment.
   (d) Show how the coefficient of friction can be determined from the measurements made.

Answers and Explanations

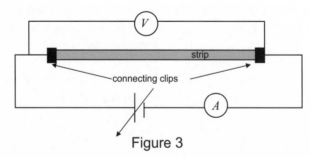

Figure 3

1. Possible Response
   Cut a strip of the material 1 cm wide by 20 cm long and connect it as shown in figure 3. The electric current will conduct down the length of this "wire" that has a cross-sectional area

   $$A = (\text{width})(\text{thickness}) = (0.01)(1.2 \times 10^{-4}) = 1.2 \times 10^{-6} \text{ m}^2$$

For the initial length of 0.2 m, determine the resistance of the strip by making several measurements of voltage and current, using the variable power supply to change the voltage. From a plot of V vs. I with V on the vertical axis, determine the slope, which will be the resistance.

Repeat this procedure several times, cutting off a centimeter of length on the strip each time and recording the length value. This will produce a set of resistance vs. length data. Plot this data with R on the vertical axis and length on the horizontal, and determine the slope of the line. Since you know that $R = \rho\frac{l}{A}$, the slope will be equal to $\frac{\rho}{A}$, from which you can get the resistivity since you know A.

2. Possible Response

The appropriate techniques all involve determining the acceleration. You can do this in a number of ways, ranging from low-tech "dot timers" using paper strips and carbon paper, to high-tech sonic rangers and smart pulleys. The AP test writers have emphasized that students should be familiar with technology, so let's look at an approach using a smart pulley.
(a) weights, string, smart pulley, graphing calculator software
(b) figure 4

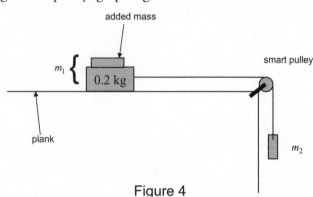

Figure 4

(c) Set up the wood block and plank as shown in the figure. Attach a known mass m_2 with a string over a smart pulley. Set up the graphing calculator software to receive smart pulley input, and release the masses. Determine the acceleration from the slope of the
  v vs. t graph displayed by the calculator readout. Repeat this procedure several times, each time adding some mass to the wood block. The added mass and the original block are designated m_1.
(d) The normal force N between the block and the plank is
  $$N = m_1g$$
You can calculate the friction force between the block and plank from the masses and the measured acceleration, using Newton's third law applied to the system:
  $$netF = ma$$
  $$m_2g - f = (m_1 + m_2)a$$
  $$f = m_2g - (m_1 + m_2)a$$
Each trial will give you a new value of f and N. If you plot the friction force on the vertical axis and the normal force on the horizontal, the slope will equal the coefficient of friction.

COMMENTS

The same apparatus and analysis technique would need to be modified only slightly to accommodate some other method of measuring acceleration. While a single data point can be used to get a value of μ, the graph provides higher precision.

TABLE OF INFORMATION

CONSTANTS AND CONVERSION FACTORS

1 unified atomic mass unit	$1u = 1.66 \times 10^{-27}$ kg
	$= 931$ MeV/c^2
proton mass	$m_p = 1.67 \times 10^{-27}$ kg
neutron mass	$m_n = 1.67 \times 10^{-27}$ kg
electron mass	$m_e = 9.11 \times 10^{-31}$ kg
magnitude of electron charge	$e = 1.60 \times 10^{-19}$ C
Avogadro's number	$N_0 = 6.02 \times 10^{23}$ mol^{-1}
universal gas constant	$R = 8.31$ J/(mol.K)
Boltzmann's constant	$k_B = 1.38 \times 10^{-23}$ J/K
speed of light	$c = 3 \times 10^8$ m/s
Planck's constant	$h = 6.63 \times 10^{-34}$ J.s
	$= 4.14 \times 10^{-15}$ eV.s
	$hc = 1.99 \times 10^{-25}$ J.m
	$= 1.24 \times 10^3$ eV.nm
vaccum permittivity	$\varepsilon_0 = 8.85 \times 10^{-12}$ C^2/N.m^2
Coulomb's law constant	$k = \dfrac{1}{4\pi\varepsilon_0}$
	$= 9.0 \times 10^9$ N.m^2/C^2
vacuum permeability	$\mu_0 = 4\pi \times 10^{-7}$ (T.m)/A
magnetic constant	$k' = \dfrac{\mu_0}{4\pi}$
	$= 10^{-7}$ (T.m)/A
universal graviational constant	$G = 6.67 \times 10^{-11}$ m^3/kg.s^2
acceleration due to gravity at Earth's surface	$g = 9.8$ m/s^2
1 atmosphere pressure	1 atm $= 1.0 \times 10^5$ N/m^2
	$= 1.0 \times 10^5$ Pa
1 electron volt	1 eV $= 1.60 \times 10^{-19}$ J

UNITS

Name	Symbol
meter	m
kilogram	kg
second	s
ampere	A
kelvin	K
mole	mol
hertz	Hz
Newton	N
pascal	Pa
joule	J
watt	W
coulomb	C
volt	V
ohm	Ω
henry	H
farad	F
tesla	T
degree Celsius	°C
electron-volt	eV

PREFIXES

Factor	Prefix	Symbol
10^9	giga	G
10^6	mega	M
10^3	kilo	k
10^{-2}	centi	c
10^{-3}	milli	m
10^{-6}	micro	μ
10^{-9}	nano	n
10^{-12}	pico	p

VALUES OF TRIGONOMETRIC FUNCTIONS FOR COMMON ANGLES

θ	$\sin\theta$	$\cos\theta$	$\tan\theta$
0°	0	1	0
30°	$\dfrac{1}{2}$	$\dfrac{\sqrt{3}}{2}$	$\dfrac{\sqrt{3}}{3}$
37°	$\dfrac{3}{5}$	$\dfrac{4}{5}$	$\dfrac{3}{4}$
45°	$\dfrac{\sqrt{2}}{2}$	$\dfrac{\sqrt{2}}{2}$	1
53°	$\dfrac{4}{5}$	$\dfrac{3}{5}$	$\dfrac{4}{3}$
60°	$\dfrac{\sqrt{3}}{2}$	$\dfrac{1}{2}$	$\sqrt{3}$
90°	1	0	∞

The following conventions are used in this examination.

I. Unless otherwise stated, the frame of reference of any problem is assumed to be inertial.

II. The direction of any electric current is the direction of flow of positive charge (conventional current).

III. For any isolated electric charge, the electric potential is defines as zero at an infinite distance from the charge.

IV. For mechanics and thermodynamics questions, W represents the work done *on* a system.

ADVANCED PLACEMENT PHYSICS B EQUATIONS

Newtonian Mechanics

$v = v_0 + at$

$x = x_0 + v_0 t + \frac{1}{2}at^2$

$v^2 = v_0^2 + 2a(x - x_0)$

$\sum \vec{F} = \vec{F}_{net} = m\vec{a}$

$F_{fric} \leq \mu N$

$a_c = \dfrac{v^2}{r}$

$\tau = rF\sin\theta$

$\vec{p} = m\vec{v}$

$\vec{J} = \vec{F}\Delta t = \Delta \vec{p}$

$K = \frac{1}{2}mv^2$

$\Delta U_g = mgh$

$W = \vec{F} \cdot \Delta \vec{r} = F\Delta r\cos\theta$

$P_{av} = \dfrac{W}{\Delta t}$

$P = \vec{F} \cdot \vec{v} = Fv\cos\theta$

$\vec{F}_s = -k\vec{x}$

$U_s = \frac{1}{2}kx^2$

$T_s = 2\pi\sqrt{\dfrac{m}{k}}$

$T_p = 2\pi\sqrt{\dfrac{l}{g}}$

$T = \dfrac{1}{f}$

$F_G = -\dfrac{Gm_1 m_2}{r^2}$

$U_G = -\dfrac{Gm_1 m_2}{r}$

a = acceleration
F = force
f = frequency
h = height
J = impulse
K = kinetic energy
k = spring constant
l = length
m = mass
N = normal force
P = power
p = momentum
r = radius or distance
$\vec{r}$ = position vector
T = period
t = time
U = potential energy
v = velocity or speed
W = work done on system
x = position
μ = coefficient of friction
θ = angle
t = torque

Electricity and Magnetism

$F = \dfrac{1}{4\pi\varepsilon_0}\dfrac{q_1 q_2}{r^2}$

$\vec{E} = \dfrac{\vec{F}}{q}$

$U_E = qV = \dfrac{1}{4\pi\varepsilon_0}\dfrac{q_1 q_2}{r}$

$E_{avg} = -\dfrac{V}{d}$

$V = \dfrac{1}{4\pi\varepsilon_0}\sum \dfrac{q_i}{r_i}$

$C = \dfrac{Q}{V}$

$C = \dfrac{\varepsilon_0 A}{d}$

$U_C = \frac{1}{2}QV = \frac{1}{2}CV^2$

$I_{avg} = \dfrac{\Delta Q}{\Delta t}$

$R = \dfrac{\rho l}{A}$

$V = IR$

$P = IV$

$C_p = \sum_i C_i$

$\dfrac{1}{C_s} = \sum_i \dfrac{1}{C_i}$

$R_s = \sum_i R_i$

$\dfrac{1}{R_p} = \sum_i \dfrac{1}{R_i}$

$F_B = qvB\sin\theta$

$F_B = BIl\sin\theta$

$B = \dfrac{\mu_0 I}{2\pi r}$

$\varphi_m = \vec{B} \cdot \vec{A} = BA\cos\theta$

$\varepsilon_{avg} = -\dfrac{\Delta \varphi_m}{\Delta t}$

$\varepsilon = Blv$

A = area
B = magnetic field
C = capacitance
d = distance
E = electric field
ε = emf
F = force
I = current
l = length
P = power
Q = charge
q = point charge
R = resistance
r = distance
t = time
U = potential energy
V = electric potential or potential difference
v = velocity or speed
ρ = resistivity
φ_m = magnetic flux

Fluid Mechanics and Thermal Physics

$p = p_0 + \rho g h$

$F_{\text{buoy}} = \rho V g$

$A_1 v_1 = A_2 v_2$

$p + \rho g h + \frac{1}{2}\rho v^2 = const.$

$\Delta l = \alpha l_0 \Delta T$

$p = \dfrac{F}{A}$

$pV = nRT$

$K_{\text{avg}} = \dfrac{3}{2} k_B T$

$v_{\text{rms}} = \sqrt{\dfrac{3RT}{M}} = \sqrt{\dfrac{3k_B T}{\mu}}$

$W = -p\Delta V$

$\Delta U = Q + W$

$e = \left| \dfrac{W}{Q_H} \right|$

$e_C = \dfrac{T_H - T_C}{T_H}$

A = area

e = efficiency

F = force

h = depth

K_{avg} = average molecular kinetic energy

l = length

M = molecular mass

m = mass of sample

n = number of moles

p = pressure

Q = heat transferred to system

T = temperature

U = internal energy

V = volume

v = velocity or speed

v_{rms} = root-mean-square velocity

W = work done on a system

y = height

α = coefficient of linear exp.

μ = mass of molecule

ρ = density

Atomic and Nuclear Physics

$E = hf = pc$

$K_{\text{max}} = hf - \phi$

$\lambda = \dfrac{h}{p}$

$\Delta E = (\Delta m)c^2$

E = energy

f = frequency

K = kinetic energy

m = mass

p = momentum

λ = wavelength

φ = work function

Waves and Optics

$v = \lambda f$

$n = \dfrac{c}{v}$

$n_1 \sin\theta_1 = n_2 \sin\theta_2$

$\sin\theta_C = \dfrac{n_2}{n_1}$

$\dfrac{1}{s_i} + \dfrac{1}{s_o} = \dfrac{1}{f}$

$M = \dfrac{h_i}{h_o} = -\dfrac{s_i}{s_o}$

$f = \dfrac{R}{2}$

$d \sin\theta = m\lambda$

$x_m \approx \dfrac{m\lambda L}{d}$

d = separation

f = frequency or focal length

h = height

L = distance

M = magnification

m = an integer

n = index of refraction

R = radius of curvature

s = distance

v = speed

x = position

λ = wavelength

θ = angle

Geometry and Trigonometry

Rectangle

$A = bh$

Triangle

$A = \dfrac{1}{2}bh$

Circle

$A = \pi r^2$

$C = 2\pi r$

Parallelepiped

$V = lwh$

Cylinder

$V = \pi r^2 l$

$S = 2\pi r l + 2\pi r^2$

Sphere

$V = \dfrac{4}{3}\pi r^3$

$S = 4\pi r^2$

Right Triangle

$a^2 + b^2 = c^2$

$\sin\theta = \dfrac{a}{c}$

$\cos\theta = \dfrac{b}{c}$

$\tan\theta = \dfrac{a}{b}$

A = area

C = circumference

V = volume

S = surface area

b = base

h = height

l = length

w = width

r = radius

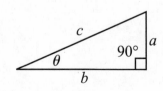

Physics B
Practice Exam

AP PHYSICS B TEST I

SECTION I—MULTIPLE CHOICE

Time: 90 minutes

70 Questions

Points: 90

Directions: Each of the questions or incomplete statements below is followed by 5 suggested answers or completions. Select the one that is best in each case.

Note: To simplify calculations, you may use $g = 10$ m/s^2 in all calculations.

Questions 1 and 2

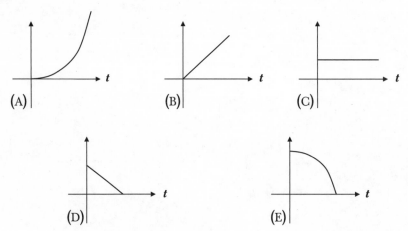

1. Which graph best represents the displacement of an object accelerating uniformly from rest?

   (A) A   (B) B   (C) C   (D) D   (E) E

2. Which graph could represent the momentum of an object after it has been thrown straight up in the air?

   (A) A   (B) B   (C) C   (D) D   (E) E

3. A book rests on a flat horizontal table. Which of the following is true?
   I. The reaction force to the weight is the normal force.
   II. The book exerts a force on the Earth equal in magnitude to the weight of the book.
   III. The book exerts a force on the table equal in magnitude to the weight of the book.

   (A) I only   (B) II only   (C) III only   (D) II and III only   (E) I, II, and III

GO ON TO THE NEXT PAGE

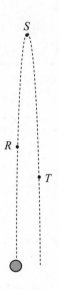

4. An object is projected straight up and passes through the points R, S, and T before returning to the ground, moving under only the influence of gravity. Which of the following best represents the acceleration at each point?

	R	S	T
(A)	↓	0	↓
(B)	↓	0	↑
(C)	↑	0	↓
(D)	↓	↓	↓
(E)	↓	↓	↑

GO ON TO THE NEXT PAGE

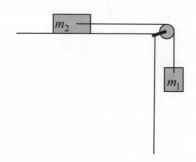

5. Two masses are connected by a light string over an ideal pulley. m_2 slides on a smooth surface. The acceleration of m_2 is

(A) $\dfrac{m_2}{m_1}g$ (B) $\dfrac{m_1}{m_2}g$ (C) $\dfrac{m_1-m_2}{m_1+m_2}g$ (D) $\dfrac{m_2}{m_1+m_2}g$ (E) $\dfrac{m_1}{m_1+m_2}g$

6. A 0.25 kg mass is hung vertically from a spring and allowed to come to rest. If the spring stretches 0.05 m, the value of the spring constant is most nearly

(A) 2.5 N/m   (B) 5 N/m   (C) 25 N/m   (D) 50 N/m   (E) 0.5 N/m

7. The following hypothetical situation is described by a physics teacher: Two equal mass objects moving at the same speed collide head-on and rebound with speeds equal to twice their initial speeds. Which of the following is true?

     I. Since momentum wasn't conserved, there must have been external forces acting.
     II. Energy stored in the masses must have been released.
     III. This is an example of an elastic collision.

(A) I only   (B) II only   (C) III only   (D) I and II only   (E) I and III only

GO ON TO THE NEXT PAGE

Questions 8 and 9

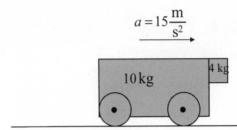

The 4 kg mass doesn't slip as the two masses accelerate at 15 m/s^2.

8.   The force exerted by the 10 kg mass on the 4 kg mass is best represented by

   (A) ↑   (B) ↗   (C) →   (D) ↖   (E) ←

9.   From the information given, what can be determined about the coefficient of static friction between the two masses?
   (A) No information can be determined because the system is moving.
   (B) The coefficient of static friction is less than the coefficient of kinetic friction.

   (C) $\mu = \dfrac{2}{3}$ (D) $\mu \leq \dfrac{2}{3}$ (E) $\mu \geq \dfrac{2}{3}$

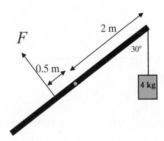

10.   A uniform plank 4 m long is pivoted about its center to an angle of 30° with the vertical. What magnitude of force must be applied 0.5 m from the pivot to maintain equilibrium with a 4 kg mass hanging from one end?
   (A) 80 N   (B) 20 N   (C) 40 N   (D) 60 N   (E) 100 N

GO ON TO THE NEXT PAGE

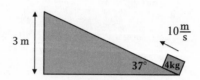

11. A 4 kg mass initially moving at 10 m/s at the bottom of a 37° incline barely makes it to the top before coming to rest. The work done by friction is most nearly

(A) 200 J   (B) −200 J   (C) −120 J   (D) 80 J   (E) −80 J

12. A 60 kg student runs up the stairs from the basement to the third floor in 10 s. If the height change between floors is 4 m, the average power output of the student was closest to

(A) 1,000 W   (B) 10,000 W   (C) 700 W   (D) 7,000 W   (E) 70 W

Questions 13 and 14

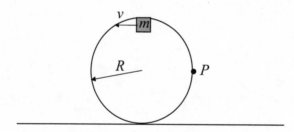

13. A toy car is at the top of a loop-the-loop moving with speed v such that the track exerts a non-zero force on the car. The force exerted on the car by the track at this point has a value

(A) $\dfrac{mv^2}{R}$ (B) $\dfrac{mv^2}{R} - mg$ (C) $mg - \dfrac{mv^2}{R}$ (D) $\dfrac{mv^2}{R} + mg$ (E) mg

GO ON TO THE NEXT PAGE

14. Which of the following is true at *P*, located halfway up the loop?
    I. The force of gravity and the normal force are equal in magnitude.
    II. The centripetal force is supplied by the normal force only.
    III. The centripetal force is equal to the difference in the normal force and the force of gravity.

    (A) I only   (B) II only   (C) III only   (D) I and II only   (E) I and III only

15. A neutral conducting sphere hangs vertically by an insulating thread. A nonconducting sphere of the same radius and carrying a charge $+Q$ is placed close to the first sphere. Which of the following is true?
    I. The neutral sphere will experience 0 force.
    II. The neutral sphere will be attracted to the charged sphere.
    III. Charges on the neutral sphere will reposition in response to the charged sphere.

    (A) I only   (B) II only   (C) III only   (D) I and III only   (E) II and III only

Questions 16 and 17

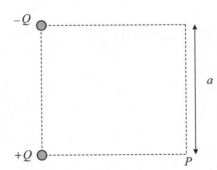

Two charges are fixed at the corners of a square of side *a* as shown in the figure.

16. The direction of the electric field at point *P* is best represented by

    (A) ↑   (B) ↗   (C) ↘   (D) ↘   (E) ↙

17. The potential energy of a charge *q* placed at the center of the square is

    (A) $k\dfrac{qQ}{\sqrt{2}a}$ (B) $k\dfrac{2qQ}{\sqrt{2}a}$ (C) $k\dfrac{4qQ}{\sqrt{2}a}$ (D) 0   (E) $k\dfrac{qQ}{2\sqrt{2}a}$

GO ON TO THE NEXT PAGE

Questions 18–20

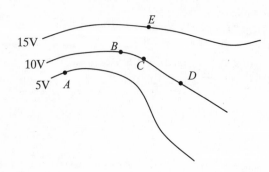

The figure shows several equipotential surfaces.

18. At which point is the electric field strongest?

(A) A (B) B (C) C (D) D (E) E

19. The work it would take to move $a + 2\,C$ from C to D is closest to

(A) $+\,20\,\text{J}$ (B) $-\,20\,\text{J}$ (C) 0   (D) $+\,10\,\text{J}$ (E) $-\,10\,\text{J}$

20. An electron released from rest at point C would most likely pass through which point a short time later?

(A) A (B) B (C) C (remain here)   (D) D (E) E

21. 10^8 electrons move through a section of wire every 10 s. The electric current in the wire is closest to

(A) $10^8\,\text{A}$ (B) $10^7\,\text{A}$ (C) $10^{-11}\,\text{A}$ (D) $10^{-12}\,\text{A}$ (E) $10^{-8}\,\text{A}$

22. At a depth of 5 m in a static fluid open to the atmosphere, the pressure is determined to be 3×10^4 Pa above atmospheric pressure. The density of the fluid is closest to

(A) $600\ \dfrac{\text{kg}}{\text{m}^3}$ (B) $300\ \dfrac{\text{kg}}{\text{m}^3}$ (C) $6{,}000\ \dfrac{\text{kg}}{\text{m}^3}$ (D) $1{,}000\ \dfrac{\text{kg}}{\text{m}^3}$ (E) $3{,}000\ \dfrac{\text{kg}}{\text{m}^3}$

GO ON TO THE NEXT PAGE

23. A rectangular solid of cross-sectional area A and thickness t floats in a fluid of density ρ_f such that only a portion h of the thickness is below the surface of the fluid. The density of the solid is

(A) $\dfrac{t-h}{h}\rho_f$ (B) $\dfrac{t-h}{t}\rho_f$ (C) $\dfrac{t}{h}\rho_f$ (D) $\dfrac{h}{t}\rho_f$ (E) $\dfrac{th}{A}\rho_f$

24. When a mass with density ρ is hung vertically from a spring with spring constant k, it is found to stretch the spring a distance x_1. With the spring attached, the mass is then lowered into a fluid with density $\rho_f < \rho$, and the spring stretch is now x_2. The volume of the fluid displaced by the mass is

(A) $\dfrac{k(x_2 - x_1)}{\rho g}$ (B) $\dfrac{k(x_2 - x_1)}{\rho_f g}$ (C) $k(x_2 - x_1)\rho g$ (D) $k(x_2 - x_1)\rho_f g$ (E) $\dfrac{kx_2}{\rho_f g}$

25. A liquid is enclosed in a cylindrical container with a piston that can move vertically, and it's currently adjusted to barely touch the top of the fluid. As the piston is forced further into the fluid, which of the following is true?

(A) The pressure in the fluid remains the same.
(B) The pressure increase in the fluid is the same at all points in the fluid.
(C) The pressure increase in the fluid is greatest near the piston.
(D) The pressure increase in the fluid is greatest near the bottom of the container.
(E) The pressure increase in the fluid is greatest at the sides of the container.

26. A gas is rapidly compressed adiabatically. Which of the following is true?

(A) The internal energy decreased, and the pressure increased.
(B) The temperature increased, and the pressure decreased.
(C) Heat energy flowed into the system.
(D) Heat energy flowed out of the system.
(E) The internal energy increased, and the temperature increased.

27. An object is observed to float when placed in a fluid. Which of the following is true?
  I. The density of the fluid is greater than the density of the object.
  II. As it floats, the object will displace an amount of water having a mass equal to the mass of the object.
  III. When completely submerged, the object will displace an amount of water having a volume equal to the volume of the object.

(A) I only   (B) I and II only   (C) I and III only   (D) II and III only   (E) I, II, and III

GO ON TO THE NEXT PAGE

28. Which of the following can be easily used to relate the energy content at different points in a fluid?

    (A) Bernoulli's principle   (B) Pascal's principle   (C) Archimedes' principle
    (D) uncertainty principle   (E) Fermat's principle

29. Which of the following processes involves a heat transfer to a cool metal rod?
      I. Place the rod in direct sunlight.
      II. Hammering the rod.
     III. Place the rod in a hot water bath.

    (A) I and III only   (B) I and II only   (C) I, II, and III   (D) III only   (E) II and III only

30. The conduction electrons in a metal are sometimes approximated as behaving as an ideal gas. This isn't a good approximation because

    (A) the temperature of the metal isn't hot enough to support a gas
    (B) the electrons are too big
    (C) there isn't enough space in the metal for a gas to move
    (D) the electrons will exert long-range forces on each other
    (E) electrons cannot have elastic collisions with each other

31. For an isothermal process involving an ideal gas, which of the following is true?

    (A) The pressure must increase.
    (B) The internal energy remains the same.
    (C) The volume must decrease.
    (D) The volume must increase.
    (E) The entropy remains the same.

32. An object is placed inside the focal length of a converging mirror. Which of the following is true?

    (A) A real image smaller than the object is formed in front of the mirror.
    (B) A virtual image smaller than the object is formed behind the mirror.
    (C) A real image larger than the object is formed in front of the mirror.
    (D) A virtual image larger than the object is formed behind the mirror.
    (E) A virtual image equal in size to the object is formed behind the mirror.

GO ON TO THE NEXT PAGE

33. An object is placed outside the focal length of a diverging mirror. Which of the following is true?

    (A) A real image smaller than the object is formed in front of the mirror.
    (B) A virtual image smaller than the object is formed behind the mirror.
    (C) A real image larger than the object is formed in front of the mirror.
    (D) A virtual image larger than the object is formed behind the mirror.
    (E) A virtual image equal in size to the object is formed behind the mirror.

34. An object is placed at a distance $2f$ from a converging lens, where f is the focal length. The object is moved slowly inward to a distance $\frac{3}{2}f$. Which of the following is true for the image?

    (A) The image changed from a real image to a virtual image.
    (B) The image changed from an upright image to an inverted image.
    (C) The image remained real but got smaller.
    (D) The image remained real but got larger.
    (E) The image remained virtual but got smaller.

35. An object is placed at a distance $\frac{1}{2}f$ from a diverging lens where f is the focal length. The object is moved slowly outward to a distance $2f$. Which of the following is true for the image?

    (A) The image changed from a virtual image to a real image.
    (B) The image changed from an upright image to an inverted image.
    (C) The image remained virtual but got smaller.
    (D) The image remained virtual but got larger.
    (E) The image remained real but got larger.

36. In a photoelectric experiment, it's found that a certain wavelength of light will not cause any electrons to be ejected. To begin to cause electrons to be ejected, what must be done?

    (A) Increase the wavelength of the light.
    (B) Increase the intensity of the light.
    (C) Increase the potential of the collector.
    (D) Decrease the frequency of the light.
    (E) Decrease the wavelength of the light.

GO ON TO THE NEXT PAGE

37. A focused beam of electrons is passed through a single slit that's very large compared with the De Broglie wavelength of the electron. When a screen is placed behind the slit, which of the following is true?

   (A) The electrons will strike points on the screen directly behind the slit.
   (B) The electrons will exhibit a wavelength shift.
   (C) A distinct pattern of maxima and minima will appear on the screen.
   (D) The electrons will scatter off Huygens emitters within the slit.
   (E) A diffraction pattern will appear if the electron energies are above threshold.

38. In a nuclear reaction, a boron nucleus $^{10}_{5}\text{B}$ collides with another particle, producing one lithium nucleus $^{7}_{3}\text{Li}$ and a helium nucleus $^{4}_{2}\text{He}$. The other particle is a

   (A) neutron   (B) proton   (C) photon   (D) electron   (E) $^{4}_{2}\text{He}$

39. How many neutrons are produced in the following nuclear reaction?

   $$^{1}_{0}\text{n} + {}^{235}_{92}\text{U} \rightarrow {}^{140}_{54}\text{Xe} + {}^{94}_{38}\text{Sr} + ?\text{neutrons}$$

   (A) 0   (B) 1   (C) 2   (D) 3   (E) 4

40. A mass is dropped from rest off the edge of a building. The graph that best depicts the power delivered to the mass as a function of time is

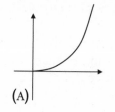
(A)

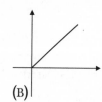
(B)

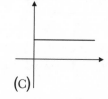
(C)

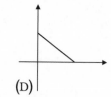
(D)

(E)

GO ON TO THE NEXT PAGE

41. Falling freely from rest for 1 s, a 2 kg mass collides in midair with a 3 kg mass that is instantaneously at rest. If the two masses stick together, their speed just after the collision is most nearly

    (A) 10 m/s   (B) 0.2 m/s   (C) 5 m/s   (D) 4 m/s   (E) 1 m/s

42. A 4 kg mass moving in one dimension with a velocity of $+10$ m/s is decelerated in 2 s to a speed of $+3$ m/s by a constant force. The value of the force is

    (A) -14 N   (B) -26 N   (C) -28 N   (D) 14 N   (E) 26 N

43. A 4 kg mass moving east at 10 m/s collides with a 1 kg mass moving north at 40 m/s. The two masses stick together. Just after the collision, the speed of the combined object is

    (A) $8\,\dfrac{m}{s}$ (B) $8\sqrt{2}\,\dfrac{m}{s}$ (C) $16\,\dfrac{m}{s}$ (D) $50\,\dfrac{m}{s}$ (E) $30\,\dfrac{m}{s}$

44. A 2 kg mass and a 6 kg mass are at rest on a smooth horizontal surface. With a light spring placed between them, the two masses are pushed together, compressing the spring. Then they're released, allowing the masses to fly apart and leaving the spring behind. Which of the following is true?

    (A) The 6 kg mass exerts a larger force on the spring than the 2 kg mass.
    (B) The two masses separate with equal speeds.
    (C) Energy and momentum are conserved. The 2 kg mass moves off at 4 times the speed of the 6 kg mass.
    (D) Energy is not conserved, but momentum is conserved. The 2 kg mass moves off at 3 times the speed of the 6 kg mass.
    (E) When the 2 kg mass has traveled 12 m, the 6 kg mass has traveled 4 m.

45. A 2 kg mass is moving in an x-y plane. At one instant it is at the point (3, 4) moving in the negative y-direction with a speed of 7 m/s. The magnitude of its angular momentum about the origin is

    (A) $14\,\dfrac{kg \cdot m^2}{s}$ (B) $56\,\dfrac{kg \cdot m^2}{s}$ (C) $70\,\dfrac{kg \cdot m^2}{s}$ (D) $42\,\dfrac{kg \cdot m^2}{s}$ (E) 0

GO ON TO THE NEXT PAGE

46. Two 4 Ω and one 100 Ω resistors are connected in parallel. Their equivalent resistance is closest to

    (A) 2 Ω   (B) 4 Ω   (C) 108 Ω   (D) 1 Ω   (E) 0.5 Ω

Questions 47–49

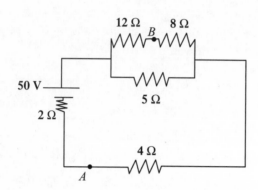

A 50 V battery with internal resistance 2 Ω is connected to several resistors as shown.

47. The terminal voltage of the battery is

    (A) 48 V   (B) 40 V   (C) 50 V   (D) 52 V   (E) 60 V

48. The power consumed by the 5 Ω resistor is

    (A) 80 W   (B) 5 W   (C) 50 W   (D) 125 W   (E) 200 W

49. An ideal voltmeter connected between A and B would read

    (A) 50 V   (B) 8 V   (C) 40 V   (D) 20 V   (E) 28 V

50. Fluid is flowing horizontally in a pipe system. At one point where the pipe radius is 0.04 m, the flow speed is 3 m/s. If the pipe narrows to 0.01 m, the flow speed will be

    (A) 9 m/s   (B) 6 m/s   (C) 27 m/s   (D) 48 m/s   (E) 12 m/s

GO ON TO THE NEXT PAGE

51. A cylindrical container with a moveable piston at one end is completely filled with water and held horizontal. A force is applied to the piston, and when the fluid pressure in the container reaches 3×10^5 Pa, a small hole develops at the other end of the cylinder. At the instant the hole develops, the speed of the water emerging from the cylinder is closest to which one of the following? (Assume atmospheric pressure is 1×10^5 Pa, and the density of water is $1,000 \, \frac{\text{kg}}{\text{m}^3}$.)

    (A) 10 m/s   (B) 20 m/s   (C) 30 m/s   (D) 40 m/s   (E) 50 m/s

Questions 52–54

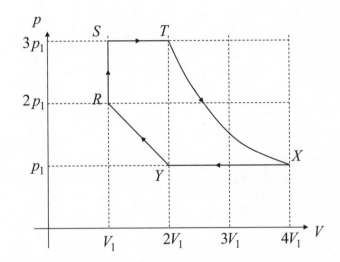

One mole of ideal gas is the working substance for a heat engine with a pV diagram shown in the figure.

52. The change in internal energy in the process RS is

    (A) 0   (B) $\frac{1}{2}p_1V_1$ (C) $\frac{3}{2}p_1V_1$ (D) $3p_1V_1$ (E) $\frac{5}{2}p_1V_1$

53. The work done by the gas during the process ST is

    (A) 0   (B) p_1V_1 (C) $2p_1V_1$ (D) $3p_1V_1$ (E) $6p_1V_1$

54. The total work done over the entire cycle is closest to

    (A) 0   (B) p_1V_1 (C) $2p_1V_1$ (D) $3p_1V_1$ (E) $4p_1V_1$

GO ON TO THE NEXT PAGE

55. A ray of light with wave speed v and wavelength λ is incident on a surface where the index of refraction is less than in the incident medium. Which of the following is true for the refracted beam having wave speed v' and wavelength λ'?

   (A) The ray bends toward the normal, $\lambda' < \lambda$, $v' < v$.
   (B) The ray bends away from the normal, $\lambda' < \lambda$, $v' < v$.
   (C) The ray bends toward the normal, $\lambda' > \lambda$, $v' > v$.
   (D) The ray bends away from the normal, $\lambda' > \lambda$, $v' > v$.
   (E) The ray bends away from the normal, $\lambda' > \lambda$, $v' < v$.

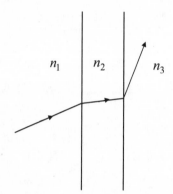

56. A light ray moves across two interfaces as shown in the figure. Which of the following relations is true for the three indices of refraction?

   (A) $n_1 > n_2$, $n_2 > n_3$, $n_1 > n_3$
   (B) $n_1 < n_2$, $n_2 > n_3$, $n_1 < n_3$
   (C) $n_1 > n_2$, $n_2 > n_3$, $n_1 < n_3$
   (D) $n_1 < n_2$, $n_2 > n_3$, $n_1 > n_3$
   (E) $n_1 < n_2$, $n_2 < n_3$, $n_1 < n_3$

57. A prism with index of refraction $\frac{3}{2}$ is illuminated with white light and the emerging rays exhibit dispersion, with the red separated from the violet by an angle of 2°. The prism is now placed under water having index of refraction $\frac{4}{3}$ and illuminated in exactly the same way. Which of the following is true?

   (A) There is no dispersion in this case.
   (B) The order of the colors is the same, but the angular separation is greater.
   (C) The order of the colors is the same, but the angular separation is smaller.
   (D) The order of the colors is reversed, and the angular separation is greater.
   (E) The order of the colors is reversed, and the angular separation is smaller.

GO ON TO THE NEXT PAGE

58. At a height of 1 km above the Earth, an object has a weight of 100 N. If this object is then brought to a height of 10 km above the Earth, its weight would be closest to

    (A) 10 N   (B) 1 N   (C) 100 N   (D) 0.1 N   (E) 50 N

Questions 59 and 60
A 2 kg mass moving at 4 m/s over a smooth horizontal surface collides with an identical mass attached to a spring with spring constant 64 N/m. The two masses stick together.

59. The period of the resulting oscillations is closest to

    (A) 1 s   (B) 1.5 s   (C) 2 s   (D) 2.5 s   (E) 3 s

60. The amplitude of the resulting oscillations is closest to

    (A) $\frac{\sqrt{2}}{2}$ m   (B) $\frac{1}{2}$ m   (C) $\sqrt{2}$ m   (D) 2 m   (E) $\frac{2}{\sqrt{2}}$ m

61. An electron moves in a region of uniform magnetic field with a velocity that currently makes an angle of 45° with the field. Which of the following is true?

    (A) The electron will move in a circle at constant speed.
    (B) The electron will move in a circle, gradually increasing in speed.
    (C) The electron will move in a helix at constant speed.
    (D) The electron will move in a helix, gradually increasing in speed.
    (E) The electron will move in a straight line at constant speed.

62. A square loop is placed near a long current-carrying wire that's carrying current to the right in the figure. The current is decreased to 0 over a time t. Which of the following is true while the current is changing?
    I. The loop will experience a net force toward the long wire.
    II. A clockwise current is induced in the loop.
    III. An electric field is created around the long wire.

    (A) I only   (B) I and II only   (C) I and III only   (D) II and III only   (E) III only

GO ON TO THE NEXT PAGE

63. A fluid with density ρ and speed v flows through a horizontal pipe system. If the radius of the pipe increases by a factor of 2, the change in pressure is closest to which of the following?

(A) $\frac{1}{2}\rho v^2$ (B) ρv^2 (C) $\frac{3}{2}\rho v^2$ (D) $2\rho v^2$ (E) $\frac{5}{2}\rho v^2$

64. When the temperature of an ideal gas is doubled,

(A) the volume must increase
(B) the pressure must increase
(C) the molecular speeds double
(D) the molecular speeds increase by a factor of 4
(E) the molecular speeds increase by a factor of $\sqrt{2}$

65. A Carnot engine operates between hot and cold reservoirs of temperatures 600 K and 200 K, respectively. Every hour, 100 MJ is expelled from the engine to the cold reservoir. The useful work performed by the engine every hour is

(A) 100 MJ   (B) 150 MJ   (C) 200 MJ   (D) 250 MJ   (E) 300 MJ

66. A mass moves in an elliptical orbit about the Sun. Which property of the mass remains the same as it executes its orbit?

(A) kinetic energy   (B) angular momentum   (C) acceleration
(D) potential energy   (E) linear momentum

67. An acceptable unit for torque is

(A) $\dfrac{\text{kg} \cdot \text{m}}{\text{s}}$ (B) $\text{N} \cdot \text{s}$ (C) $\dfrac{\text{J}}{\text{s}}$ (D) $\dfrac{\text{kg} \cdot \text{m}^2}{\text{s}^2}$ (E) $\text{N} \cdot \text{J}$

68. A mass m slides across a smooth horizontal table, moving at speed v. It collides head on with an identical stationary mass attached to a spring with spring constant k. The two masses stick together after the collision. The time it takes for the spring to reach its maximum compression is most nearly

(A) $\dfrac{\pi}{2}\sqrt{\dfrac{m}{k}}$ (B) $2\pi\sqrt{\dfrac{m}{k}}$ (C) $\dfrac{\pi}{2}\sqrt{\dfrac{2m}{k}}$ (D) $2\pi\sqrt{\dfrac{2m}{k}}$ (E) $\dfrac{\pi}{2}\sqrt{\dfrac{k}{m}}$

GO ON TO THE NEXT PAGE

69. In a nuclear fusion reaction, 2 $^3_2$He nuclei combine to form another nucleus, and 2 energetic protons are also produced. The other nucleus is

(A) $^1_1$H   (B) $^2_1$H   (C) $^2_2$He   (D) $^4_2$He   (E) $^4_3$Li

70. If the masses of the neutron and proton are m_n and m_p, respectively, which of the following is true for the mass of the helium nucleus $^3_2$He?

(A) $m_{He} = 2m_p - m_n$ (B) $m_{He} = 2m_p + m_n$ (C) $m_{He} = 2m_n + m_p$
(D) $m_{He} < 2m_p + m_n$ (E) $m_{He} > 2m_p + m_n$

STOP
END OF SECTION I

IF YOU FINISH BEFORE TIME IS CALLED,
YOU MAY CHECK YOUR WORK ON THIS SECTION.

DO NOT GO ON TO SECTION II UNTIL YOU ARE TOLD TO DO SO.

STOP

AP PHYSICS B TEST I

SECTION II—FREE RESPONSE

Time: 90 minutes

7 Questions

Directions: Answer all 7 questions, which are weighted according to the points indicated. The suggested time is about 15 minutes for answering each of questions 1–4, and about 10 minutes for answering each of questions 5–7. The parts within a question may not have equal weight.

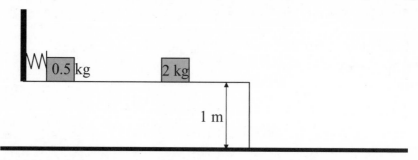

1. (15 points)
   A 0.5 kg mass, resting on a smooth tabletop 1 m high, is pushed into a spring with spring constant 200 N/m as shown in the figure. With the spring compressed 0.5 m, the mass is released, and after it loses contact with the spring it collides with a stationary 2 kg mass. A graph of the force exerted on the 2 kg mass during the collision is shown below.

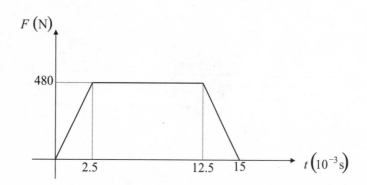

   (a) Determine the speed of the 0.5 kg mass after it has left the spring, but before it has hit the 2 kg mass.
   (b) Determine the speed of the 2 kg mass after the collision.
   (c) Determine the energy lost in the collision.
   (d) Determine the distance between the impact points of each object when they finally strike the ground.

GO ON TO THE NEXT PAGE

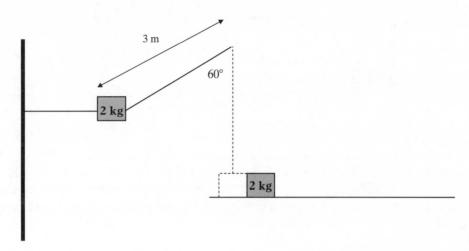

2. (15 points)
    A 2 kg mass is suspended by two ropes, one horizontal and one—3 m in length—at an angle of 60° with the vertical, as shown in the figure.
    (a) Find the tension in each rope.

    The horizontal rope is cut, and the mass swings down and collides with an identical mass resting on a smooth horizontal surface. At the instant the two masses collide, the rope breaks.

    (b) Find the speed of the swinging mass just before the collision.
    (c) Find the tension in the rope just before it breaks.

    The two masses stick together after the collision.
    (d) Find the speed of the masses after the collision, assuming they stick together.
    (e) Is kinetic energy conserved as a result of the collision? Justify your answer.

GO ON TO THE NEXT PAGE

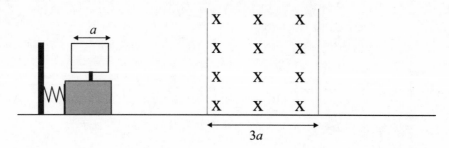

3. (15 points)
A square wire loop of side $a = 0.4$ m and resistance 2 Ω is secured to the top of a block so that their total mass is 0.25 kg. The block is pushed 0.3 m into a spring with $k = 100$ N/m and released, causing the block to slide across a smooth horizontal table. Eventually, the block enters a region of constant magnetic field with strength 0.2 T directed into the page. The width of the field region is 3 times the width of the loop.

(a) Determine the speed of the loop just before it enters the field region.
(b) What is the value of the induced voltage in the loop when the loop first enters the field region?
(c) On the axes below, sketch the magnetic flux through the loop as a function of position. Begin when the front edge of the loop is about to enter the field region and end after the loop has just left the field region.

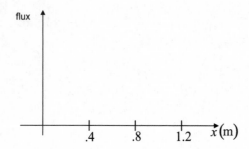

(d) On the axes below, sketch the induced current as a function of position. Follow the convention that counterclockwise currents are positive.

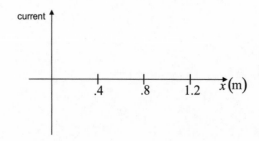

GO ON TO THE NEXT PAGE

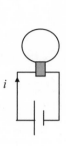
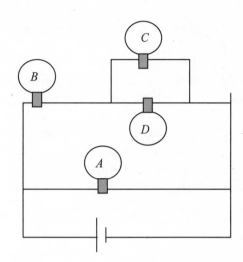

4. (15 points)
When a single light bulb of resistance R is connected to a battery as in the figure, a current i flows in the bulb. An identical battery is connected to a circuit consisting of four bulbs identical to the single bulb. Assume the bulbs behave as ideal resistors.
(a) How much energy is supplied to the single bulb by the battery in a time t?
(b) In terms of i, determine the current in each bulb in the larger circuit.
(c) Describe the brightness of each bulb in the larger circuit, expressing it as a fraction of the brightness of the single bulb in the smaller circuit.
(d) In each of the following cases, one bulb of the larger circuit fails. Describe the brightness of the remaining bulbs as in part c.
   (i) Bulb A fails.
   (ii) Bulb C fails.

GO ON TO THE NEXT PAGE

5. (10 points)
   In a photoelectric experiment, 480 nm light incident upon a metal surface requires a stopping potential of 1.85 eV.
   (a) What is the work function of the material?
   (b) Determine the threshold wavelength for the experiment.
   (c) What wavelength of incident radiation would be needed so that a stopping potential of 3 V is required?
   (d) What is the De Broglie wavelength of the ejected electrons in part c?
   (e) Describe an experiment that could be performed with the electrons in part c that would demonstrate their wave properties.

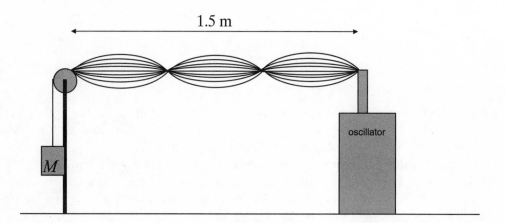

6. (10 points)
   A string of length 1.5 m is connected at one end to a mechanical oscillator with a variable frequency. The other end runs over a pulley to a mass M that hangs vertically. When the oscillator frequency is set to 100 Hz, the standing wave in the figure is set up on the string.
   (a) What is the wavelength of the standing wave?
   (b) What is the wave speed on the string?
   (c) What is the lowest frequency of the oscillator that will produce a standing wave?
   (d) With the oscillator fixed at 100 Hz, the mass M is slowly increased. Describe qualitatively the features of the standing wave as the mass is increased.

GO ON TO THE NEXT PAGE

7. (10 points)
    You have been given a pen laser of unknown wavelength and a diffraction grating that is 2.5×10^{-3} m wide, containing 80 equally spaced slits. You have also been given another diffraction grating of unknown slit spacing. Using only passive, nonelectronic equipment, you are to devise a method for measuring the wavelength of the laser and determining the spacing of the unknown grating.
    (a) List the equipment you will need.
    (b) Draw a diagram showing how the apparatus is set up.
    (c) Describe what your apparatus does.
    (d) Show how your measurements will give the desired wavelength and spacing.

END OF EXAM

STOP

Physics B
Practice Exam

PHYSICS B TEST II

SECTION I—MULTIPLE CHOICE

Time: 90 minutes

70 Questions

Directions: Each of the questions or incomplete statements below is followed by 5 suggested answers or completions. Select the one that is best in each case.

Note: To simplify calculations, you may use $g = 10$ m/s^2 in all calculations

1. An object is moving in a straight line at a constant speed. Which of the following is true?
   I. There are no forces acting on the object.
   II. The object has 0 acceleration.
   III. The object has a constant velocity.

   (A) I only (B) II only (C) I and II only (D) II and III only (E) I, II, and III

Questions 2 and 3

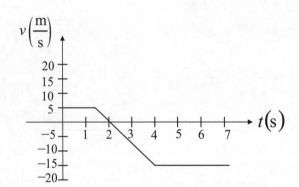

An object moves in one dimension with a velocity vs. time graph as shown.

2. The instantaneous acceleration of the object at $t = 2$ s is most nearly

   (A) $0 \frac{m}{s^2}$ (B) $-15 \frac{m}{s^2}$ (C) $-10 \frac{m}{s^2}$ (D) $-7.5 \frac{m}{s^2}$ (E) $-4 \frac{m}{s^2}$

3. The object returns to its initial position at a time

   (A) $t = 2$ s (B) $t = 3$ s (C) $t = 4$ s
   (D) between $t = 3$ s and $t = 4$ s (E) between $t = 4$ s and $t = 5$ s

GO ON TO THE NEXT PAGE

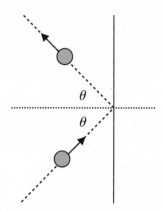

4. A ball strikes a wall and rebounds with the same speed as shown in the figure. The impulse delivered by the wall to the ball is best represented by

    (A) ↑   (B) →   (C) ←   (D) ↘   (E) ↘

5. Two equal mass objects are set into motion at the same time from the same height above the Earth. One is released from rest, and the other is projected horizontally with an initial speed v_0. Which one of the following is true?

    (A) The objects hit the ground simultaneously with horizontal velocity components that differ from their initial values.
    (B) The objects hit the ground at different times with different horizontal velocity components.
    (C) The objects hit the ground simultaneously with different vertical velocity components.
    (D) The objects hit the ground at different times with the same vertical velocity components.
    (E) The objects hit the ground simultaneously with the same horizontal velocity components.

6. A 10 kg mass is being pulled across a horizontal surface by a rope held parallel to the surface. While the tension in the rope is maintained at 20 N, the mass accelerates uniformly at 0.5 m/s^2. The magnitude of the friction force is most nearly

    (A) 0.15 N   (B) 5 N   (C) 100 N   (D) 10 N   (E) 15 N

7. Two teams square off in a tug-of-war on a horizontal field, using a rope held parallel to the surface. Which of the following is true?
    I.   The winning team was stronger.
    II. The winning team exerted a greater force on the rope.
    III. The winning team exerted a greater force on the ground.

    (A) I only   (B) II only   (C) III only   (D) I and III only   (E) II and III only

GO ON TO THE NEXT PAGE

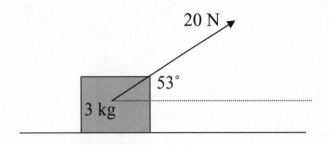

8. A 3 kg mass is sliding across a horizontal surface at a constant speed while being pulled by a rope with tension 20 N held at 53° above the horizontal. The force of friction is most nearly

   (A) 30 N   (B) 12 N   (C) 16 N   (D) 20 N   (E) 1 N

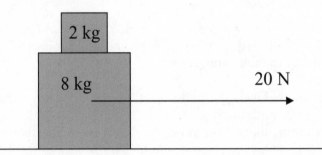

9. Two masses accelerate without slippage across a smooth horizontal surface as a result of a 20 N force applied to the bottom mass. From the information given, what can you determine about the coefficient of static friction between the masses?

   (A) $\mu = 0.2$ (B) $\mu \leq 0.2$ (C) $\mu \geq 0.2$ (D) $\mu = 0.25$ (E) $\mu \leq 0.25$

10. A uniform plank with mass 20 kg and length 12 m extends 2 m over the edge of a building. A 40 kg crate is slid out onto the plank. How far can it be pushed out without toppling the plank?

    (A) 0.5 m   (B) 1 m   (C) 1.25 m   (D) 1.5 m   (E) 2 m

11. A 2 kg mass moving at 10 m/s slows to a speed of 4 m/s while sliding across a rough horizontal surface. The work done by friction is most nearly

    (A) 116 J   (B) −116 J   (C) 84 J   (D) −84 J   (E) −16 J

GO ON TO THE NEXT PAGE

12. A mass m is accelerated from rest across a smooth horizontal surface by a rope held parallel to the surface. The tension T in the rope is constant. After a time t, the instantaneous power delivered to the mass by the rope is

(A) $\dfrac{T}{m}t$ (B) $\dfrac{T^2}{m}t$ (C) $\dfrac{T}{m}t^2$ (D) $\dfrac{T^2}{m}t^2$ (E) $\dfrac{T^2}{m}t$

13. Two identical conducting spheres have a center separation of D. One sphere carries a net charge of $-Q$, and the other carries a charge of $+3Q$. The two spheres attract each other with a force F. The two spheres are brought together so that they touch, and then they are returned to a separation D. The force they experience now is

(A) F, repulsive   (B) $\dfrac{1}{3}F$, repulsive   (C) F, attractive   (D) $\dfrac{1}{3}F$, attractive   (E) $2F$, repulsive

Questions 14 and 15

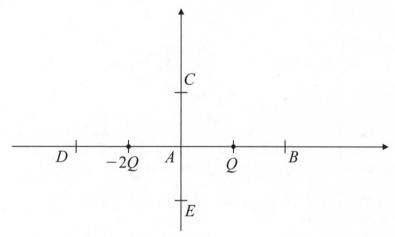

Two charges are fixed on the x-axis equidistant from the origin A. Points C and E are the same distance from the origin, and B and D are twice this distance.

14. The electric has its largest magnitude at

(A) A (B) B (C) C (D) D (E) E

15. The value of the electric potential is a minimum at

(A) A (B) B (C) C (D) D (E) E

GO ON TO THE NEXT PAGE

16. A cylindrical piece of conducting material with resistance R has length L, radius r, and resistivity ρ. If it's drawn out to twice its length, the resistance becomes

    (A) R (B) $2R$ (C) $\sqrt{2}R$ (D) $2\sqrt{2}R$ (E) $4R$

17. Which of the following will increase the capacitance of a parallel plate capacitor?
    I.   Increase the supply voltage.
    II. Decrease the plate separation.
    III. Increase the plate area.

    (A) I and III only   (B) I and II only   (C) II and III only   (D) I only   (E) I, II, and III

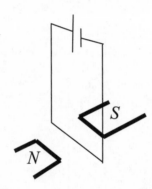

18. A segment of wire is connected by long leads to a battery. The segment runs between north and south magnetic poles as shown. The magnetic force on the segment is

    (A) up, toward battery   (B) down, away from battery   C) 0
    (D) left, toward north pole   (E) right, toward south pole

19. Cylindrical container S has a height H and cross-sectional area A. A second cylindrical container T has a height $2H$ and area $\frac{1}{2}A$. Both containers are filled with water, and it is determined that the fluid pressure at the bottom of S is p. The fluid pressure at the bottom of T is

    (A) p (B) $\frac{1}{2}p$ (C) $\frac{1}{4}p$ (D) $2p$ (E) $4p$

20. A mass with density ρ is hung vertically from a spring and is found to stretch it a distance x. With the spring still attached, the mass is lowered into a fluid with density 2ρ. The stretch of the spring will now be

    (A) x (B) $2x$ (C) 0 (D) $\frac{1}{2}x$ (E) $\frac{1}{4}x$

GO ON TO THE NEXT PAGE

Questions 21 and 22

A child is watering a garden with a hose of cross-sectional area A. By placing her finger over the end of the hose, she reduces the area to $\frac{1}{8}A$.

21. By what factor will the mass flow rate increase?

(A) 0   (B) 8   (C) $\sqrt{8}$ (D) $8\sqrt{8}$ (E) 64

22. If the hose is held horizontal at the same height before and after she puts her finger over the end, by what factor will the horizontal distance of the water stream increase?

(A) 0   (B) 8   (C) $\sqrt{8}$ (D) $8\sqrt{8}$ (E) 64

23. A gas performs 200 J of work on its surroundings while 400 J of heat flows from the surroundings into the gas. Which of the following is correct?

(A) The internal energy of the gas increased by 400 J.
(B) The internal energy of the gas increased by 200 J.
(C) The internal energy of the gas increased by 600 J.
(D) The internal energy of the gas decreased by 400 J.
(E) The internal energy of the gas decreased by 600 J.

24. Which of the following statements is <u>not</u> true about fluid pressure?

(A) For a fluid at rest, it increases in direct proportion to the depth of the fluid.
(B) For a fluid at rest, differences in fluid pressure give rise to the buoyant force.
(C) It has the units of $\frac{J}{m^3}$.
(D) In a horizontal pipe, it's greatest where the fluid is moving the fastest.
(E) It is a scalar.

25. A cube at rest in a fluid floats so that $\frac{3}{4}$ of it is submerged. If ρ_f is the density of the fluid, then the density of the cube is

(A) ρ_f (B) $\frac{4}{3}\rho_f$ (C) $\frac{3}{4}\rho_f$ (D) $\frac{1}{4}\rho_f$ (E) $\frac{1}{3}\rho_f$

GO ON TO THE NEXT PAGE

26. A portion of a soap bubble appears red when illuminated with white light and viewed in the reflected light. Which of the following statements follows from this observation?
    I. Light can exhibit wave behavior.
    II. The reflected red light is interfering constructively.
    III. Other parts of the spectrum are not reflected.

    (A) I only   (B) II only   (C) I and II only   (D) II and III only   (E) I, II, and III

27. Two identical flat glass plates are placed on top of each other, and a thin piece of paper is partially inserted between the plates. When the plates are illuminated with monochromatic light of known wavelength, a series of parallel fringes is observed in the reflected light. Which of the following is <u>not</u> true?

    (A) You could use this experiment to determine the thickness of the paper.
    (B) The fringes result from interference of reflected rays.
    (C) Only one of the interfering rays experiences a phase shift.
    (D) The fringe pattern begins at V with a bright band.
    (E) If a slightly thicker piece of paper is used, more fringes appear.

28. Light consisting of a mixture of red and violet is incident upon two closely spaced slits, producing a characteristic pattern on a screen 2 m behind the slits. Which of the following will occur on the screen as the spacing of the slits is decreased?

    (A) The first order maxima of each color will move toward the central maximum by the same amount.
    (B) The first order maxima of each color will move toward the central maximum by the different amounts.
    (C) The first order maxima of each color will move away from the central maximum by the same amount.
    (D) The first order maxima of each color will move away from the central maximum by the different amounts.
    (E) The first order maxima of each color will not move.

GO ON TO THE NEXT PAGE

29. Monochromatic light is incident on a Young's two slit apparatus. Which of the following occurs if the slit spacing is increased by 20 percent?

    (A) The central maximum shrinks.
    (B) The number of visible fringes decreases.
    (C) The distance between consecutive maxima on the same side of the central maximum increases.
    (D) The distance between the same order maxima on the opposite sides of the central maximum increases.
    (E) The interference pattern disappears.

30. In a photoelectric experiment, it's found that a certain wavelength of light does cause electrons to be ejected. To increase the number of ejected electrons, what could be done?

    (A) Increase the intensity of the light.
    (B) Increase the wavelength of the light.
    (C) Increase the potential on the collector.
    (D) Decrease the frequency of the light.
    (E) Place the metal surface in a uniform electric field.

Questions 31 and 32

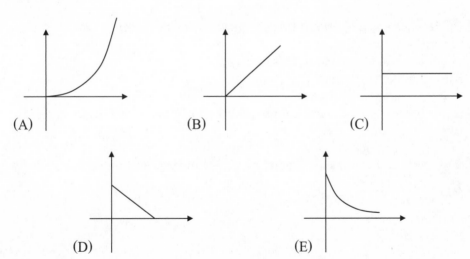

(A)   (B)   (C)

(D)   (E)

31. Which graph would accurately depict the maximum kinetic energy of ejected electrons in a photoelectric experiment with the intensity of the incident light at a fixed wavelength plotted on the horizontal axis?

    (A) A   (B) B   (C) C   (D) D   (E) E

GO ON TO THE NEXT PAGE

32. Which graph would depict the momentum of a photon plotted as a function of wavelength, with wavelength on the horizontal axis?

(A) A   (B) B   (C) C   (D) D   (E) E

33. Which of the following is true of the Compton effect?
   I. Scattered X-rays exhibit a shift in wavelength.
   II. There is a threshold energy.
   III. It provides evidence for the particle nature of light.

(A) I only   (B) II only   (C) III only   (D) I and II only   (E) I and III only

34. Which of the following provides evidence for the wave nature of electrons?

(A) photoelectric effect
(B) Compton effect
(C) X-ray diffraction
(D) electron diffraction
(E) Faraday's law

35. Which of the following is true about the two nuclei $_{26}^{56}Fe$ and $_{26}^{57}Fe$?
   I. They are isotopes.
   II. One mole of each type has a mass of 26 g.
   III. Each contains 26 neutrons.

(A) I only   (B) II only   (C) I and II only   (D) I and III only   (E) I, II, and III

36. A proton reacts with a $_{6}^{13}C$ nucleus, producing a $_{7}^{14}N$ nucleus and one other particle. The other particle is a
(A) neutron   (B) proton   (C) photon   (D) electron   (E) $_{2}^{4}He$

GO ON TO THE NEXT PAGE

Questions 37 and 38

A 3 kg mass is attached to the end of a light rod and made to move clockwise in a vertical circle of radius 2 m at a constant speed of 6 m/s.

37. The pair of vectors that best represent the velocity and acceleration at the highest point is given by

$$\text{(A)} \quad \overset{v}{\uparrow}\ \overset{a}{\rightarrow} \qquad \text{(B)} \quad \overset{v}{\rightarrow}\ \overset{a}{\uparrow} \qquad \text{(C)} \quad \overset{v}{\rightarrow}\ \overset{a}{\downarrow} \qquad \text{(D)} \quad \overset{v}{\leftarrow}\ \overset{a}{\downarrow} \qquad \text{(E)} \quad \overset{v}{\leftarrow}\ \overset{a}{\rightarrow}$$

38. The tension in the rod at the lowest point is most nearly

    (A) 54 N   (B) 84 N   (C) 30 N   (D) 24 N   (E) 39 N

39. A simple pendulum of mass m connected to a string of length L is set into motion so that it rises to a maximum height h above the lowest point. The tension in the string at the lowest point is

    (A) mg (B) $mg\left(\dfrac{2h}{L} + 1\right)$ (C) $mg\left(\dfrac{2h}{L} - 1\right)$ (D) $mg\dfrac{2h}{L}$ (E) 0

40. A 2 kg mass slides across a smooth horizontal surface, moving at 5 m/s. It collides with a stationary 3 kg mass, and the two masses stick together. The mechanical energy lost as a result of the collision is closest to

    (A) 25 J   (B) 20 J   (C) 15 J   (D) 10 J   (E) 5 J

41. A projectile is moving above the Earth with negligible air resistance. Which of the following is true for the object while it remains a projectile?

    (A) Energy and momentum are both conserved.
    (B) Energy is not conserved, but momentum is conserved. The energy lost appears as thermal energy in the object.
    (C) Energy is conserved, but momentum is not conserved. The change in the momentum will equal the impulse delivered by gravity.
    (D) Energy is conserved, but momentum is not conserved. The change in the momentum can be accounted for by the random motion of the molecules in the object.
    (E) Neither energy nor momentum is conserved.

GO ON TO THE NEXT PAGE

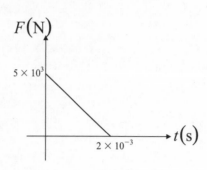

42. A 2 kg mass moving with a velocity of + 10 m/s in one dimension is acted upon by the force shown for 2×10^{-3} s. At the end of this time, the velocity of the mass is

    (A) $20 \dfrac{m}{s}$　(B) $5 \dfrac{m}{s}$　(C) $12.5 \dfrac{m}{s}$　(D) $15 \dfrac{m}{s}$　(E) 0

Questions 43–45

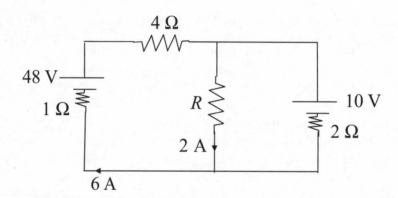

The figure shows two batteries with internal resistances of 1 Ω and 2 Ω. Currents are depicted by arrows.

43. The terminal voltage of the 10 V battery is

    (A) 10 V　(B) 12 V　(C) 8 V　(D) 2 V　(E) 18 V

44. The value of R is

    (A) 5 Ω　(B) 9 Ω　(C) 24 Ω　(D) 10 Ω　(E) 1 Ω

45. The power supplied by the 48 V battery to the external circuit is

    (A) 48 W　(B) 42 W　(C) 252 W　(D) 228 W　(E) 276 W

GO ON TO THE NEXT PAGE

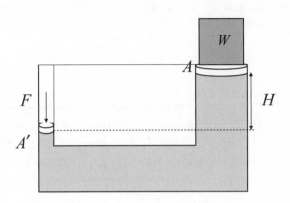

46. In a hydraulic lift, a weight W sitting on a light platform of area A is held in place by a force F applied to a smaller area A' at a height H below the level of the platform. Which of the following is true?

(A) $F = W$ (B) $F = W\dfrac{A'}{A}$ (C) $F = W\dfrac{A}{A'}$ (D) $F > W\dfrac{A'}{A}$ (E) $F < W\dfrac{A'}{A}$

Questions 47 and 48

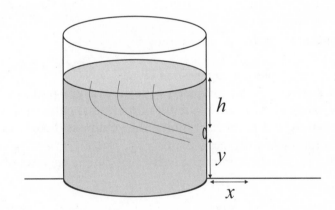

A large cylindrical container water tank open to the air on top develops a small hole at a distance $h = 4$ m below the surface of the water.

47. Assuming atmospheric pressure is 1×10^5 Pa and the density of water is $1{,}000 \ \frac{\text{kg}}{\text{m}^3}$, the speed of the water exiting the hole is closest to

(A) $5 \ \dfrac{\text{m}}{\text{s}}$ (B) $6 \ \dfrac{\text{m}}{\text{s}}$ (C) $7 \ \dfrac{\text{m}}{\text{s}}$ (D) $8 \ \dfrac{\text{m}}{\text{s}}$ (E) $9 \ \dfrac{\text{m}}{\text{s}}$

GO ON TO THE NEXT PAGE

48. The leaking water lands a distance x from the base of the tank. If the same situation occurred on the Moon, where the acceleration of gravity is $\frac{1}{6}g$, at what distance would the leaking water land?

(A) x (B) $\frac{1}{6}x$ (C) $6x$ (D) $\frac{1}{\sqrt{6}}x$ (E) $\sqrt{6}x$

49. A cylindrically shaped piece of material with resistivity ρ has electrical resistance 0.1 Ω. It is heated by applying a potential difference across the ends of the material causing an electric current of 2 A to be established in the material. If the same potential difference is applied across a material with the same dimensions but with resistivity $\frac{1}{2}\rho$, the power consumed by this material will be closest to

(A) 0.2 W   (B) 0.4 W   (C) 0.5 W   (D) 0.8 W   (E) 0.1 W

50. Which of the following is always true when heat is transferred between two systems?

(A) One system does work on the other.
(B) The internal energy of each system changes.
(C) The two systems are at different temperatures.
(D) The transfer is achieved through conduction and convection.
(E) The process was adiabatic.

51. Which of the following is not true of an ideal gas?

(A) Collisions between molecules are elastic.
(B) The molecules are very small compared with the average space between them.
(C) The pressure exerted by the gas is a result of molecular collisions.
(D) For a fixed pressure and number of moles, the volume is directly proportional to the temperature expressed in degrees Celsius.
(E) The internal energy is the sum of the individual kinetic energies of all the molecules.

52. A child is hiding behind a stone wall 2 m high when her mother calls her for dinner. Which property of sound is responsible for the fact that the child can hear her mother?

(A) interference   (B) diffraction   (C) dispersion   (D) refraction   (E) beats

GO ON TO THE NEXT PAGE

53. Monochromatic light is passed through a single narrow slit. Which of the following is <u>not</u> true of the pattern produced on a screen 2m behind the slit?

    I. It is produced by the interference of light arriving at the screen from different points within the slit.

    II. It consists of a bright central maximum and less intense secondary maxima.

    III. The property of diffraction isn't needed to explain the pattern.

(A) I only   (B) III only   (C) I and II only   (D) I and III only   (E) II and III only

54. Which of the following is true for the diffraction pattern produced by a single narrow slit when visible light is incident upon it?

(A) The central maximum broadens as the incident wavelength gets smaller.

(B) Scattering of light off the slit edges is an important consideration in explaining the pattern.

(C) The central maximum broadens if the slit is narrowed and the wavelength doesn't change.

(D) The intensity of the central maximum increases if the slit is made more narrow.

(E) Changing the slit size has no effect on the pattern as long as the slit size is comparable to the wavelength of the light.

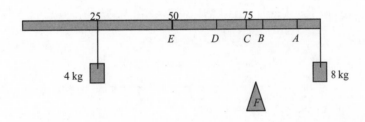

55. A light meter stick has stationary masses hanging by light strings as shown. At what point must the fulcrum *F* be placed so that the stick will remain horizontal?

(A) *A*   (B) *B*   (C) *C*   (D) *D*   (E) *E*

56. A 0.5 kg mass is moving in a horizontal circle of radius 2 m at a constant speed of 4 m/s, subject to a tension force of 16 N. The magnitude of the angular momentum of the mass about the center of the circle is

(A) $4 \dfrac{\text{kg} \cdot \text{m}^2}{\text{s}}$ (B) $8 \dfrac{\text{kg} \cdot \text{m}^2}{\text{s}}$ (C) $2 \dfrac{\text{kg} \cdot \text{m}^2}{\text{s}}$ (D) $64 \dfrac{\text{kg} \cdot \text{m}^2}{\text{s}}$ (E) $16 \dfrac{\text{kg} \cdot \text{m}^2}{\text{s}}$

GO ON TO THE NEXT PAGE

57. A 4 kg object is to be taken to a planet that has 3 times the mass of the Earth but only $\frac{1}{2}$ the Earth's radius. On this planet, the mass of the object would be

(A) 12 kg   (B) 3 kg   (C) 48 kg   (D) 4 kg   (E) 24 kg

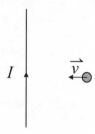

58. An electron moves toward a long wire carrying current I as shown in the figure. The magnetic force on the electron is

(A) 0   (B) toward the top of the page   (C) toward the bottom of the page
(D) toward the left of the page   (E) toward the right of the page

Questions 59 and 60
A rail is pulled across a pair of fixed rails separated by 2 m and connected by a 4 Ω resistor. A uniform magnetic field of 0.1 T is directed into the page

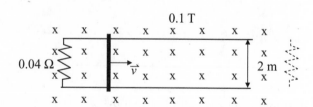

59. To produce a current of 0.3 A and maintain a constant speed for the moving rail, what force must be applied to it?

(A) 0.06 N   (B) 0.6 N   (C) 0.15 N   (D) 3 N   (E) 1.5 N

60. A second 4 Ω resistor is added at the other end of the rails. If the moving rail is maintained at the same speed, what will be the effect of the second resistor?

(A) The magnetic force on the moving rail will decrease.
(B) The induced voltage will increase.
(C) The induced voltage will decrease.
(D) The power consumed by the original resistor will remain the same.
(E) The power consumed by the original resistor will decrease.

GO ON TO THE NEXT PAGE

61. A particle of mass m and charge q moves through a potential difference, causing its De Broglie wavelength to decrease by $\frac{1}{2}$. The energy of the particle can best be described by which of the following?

(A) increase by a factor of 2
(B) increase by a factor of 4
(C) increase by a factor of $\sqrt{2}$
(D) decrease by a factor of 2
(E) decrease by a factor of $\sqrt{2}$

62. Which of the following particles can exhibit wave-particle duality?
    I. electron
    II. photon
    III. neutron

(A) I and II   (B) I and III   (C) II and III   (D) II only   (E) I, II, and III

Questions 63–65

A hypothetical atom has an electron energy level diagram as shown in the figure.

63. If a gas of these atoms is excited, what energy photon will <u>not</u> be emitted?

(A) 1 eV   (B) 2 eV   (C) 3 eV   (D) 4 eV   (E) 9 eV

GO ON TO THE NEXT PAGE

64. A collection of these atoms in their ground state is illuminated with electromagnetic radiation spanning a continuous energy range from 2 eV to 4 eV. The absorption spectrum for this radiation will consist of

   (A) no lines   (B) 1 line   (C) 2 lines   (D) 3 lines   (E) 4 lines

65. Which of the following is not true for an electron at the − 5 eV level?

   (A) It can jump to the ground state directly, emitting a 5 eV photon.
   (B) It can absorb a 3 eV photon.
   (C) It can absorb a 4 eV photon.
   (D) It can absorb a 6 eV photon.
   (E) It can absorb a 1 eV photon.

66. A mass m is moving with speed v in a circular orbit of radius R about the Earth. For an object of twice the mass to be placed into the same circular orbit, it would have to have what speed?

   (A) v (B) $2v$ (C) $\frac{1}{2}v$ (D) $\sqrt{2}\,v$ (E) $4v$

67. The period of a simple pendulum with mass m and length L on Earth is 1 s. To make a simple pendulum with the same period on the Moon, where the acceleration of gravity is $\frac{1}{6}g$, which of the following would work?

   (A) Increase the mass to $6m$ and leave L the same.
   (B) Decrease the mass to $\frac{1}{6}m$ and leave L the same.
   (C) Keep m and L the same.
   (D) Keep m the same and decrease length to $\frac{1}{6}L$.
   (E) Keep m the same and decrease length to $\frac{1}{\sqrt{6}}L$.

GO ON TO THE NEXT PAGE

68. An acceptable unit for power is

(A) $\dfrac{\text{kg} \cdot \text{m}}{\text{s}}$ (B) $\dfrac{\text{kg} \cdot \text{m}^2}{\text{s}^3}$ (C) $\dfrac{\text{N}}{\text{s}}$ (D) $\dfrac{\text{kg} \cdot \text{m}^2}{\text{s}^2}$ (E) $\text{J} \cdot \text{s}$

69. Consider the following nuclear reaction:
$^{4}_{2}\text{He} + {}^{b}_{a}X \rightarrow {}^{30}_{15}\text{P} + {}^{1}_{0}\text{n}$
How many neutrons are in the X nucleus?

(A) 12   (B) 13   (C) 14   (D) 26   (E) 27

70. In the nuclear reaction $A + B \rightarrow X + Y$, the sum of the product masses is 1.5×10^{-27} kg less than the sum of the reactant masses. The energy released in this reaction is closest to

(A) 10^0 MeV   (B) 10^1 MeV   (C) 10^2 MeV   (D) 10^3 MeV   (E) 10^4 MeV

STOP
END OF SECTION I

IF YOU FINISH BEFORE TIME IS CALLED,
YOU MAY CHECK YOUR WORK ON THIS SECTION.

DO NOT GO ON TO SECTION II UNTIL YOU ARE TOLD TO DO SO.

STOP

PHYSICS B TEST II

SECTION II—FREE RESPONSE

Time: 90 minutes

7 Questions

Directions: Answer all 7 questions, which are weighted according to the points indicated. The suggested time is about 15 minutes for answering each of questions 1–4, and about 10 minutes for answering each of questions 5–7. The parts within a question may not have equal weight.

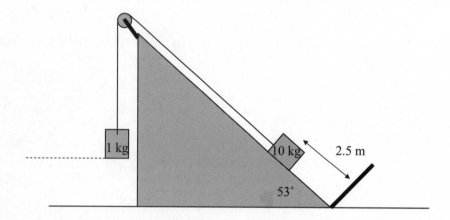

1. (15 points)
    A 10 kg mass, at rest on a 53° incline, is connected by a light string over an ideal pulley to a 1 kg mass. The coefficient of kinetic friction between the mass and the incline is 0.25. The masses are released, and the motion of the 10 kg mass is eventually stopped by a barrier at the bottom of the incline, 2.5 m from the starting point.
    (a) Determine the acceleration of the masses before the barrier is hit.
    (b) Find the tension in the rope before the barrier is hit.
    (c) The 10 kg mass stops as soon as it hits. Find the total energy change in the system from the start of the motion to the time just after the 10 kg mass has stopped.
    (d) How high will the 1 kg mass go above its initial position, indicated by the dotted line in the figure?

GO ON TO THE NEXT PAGE

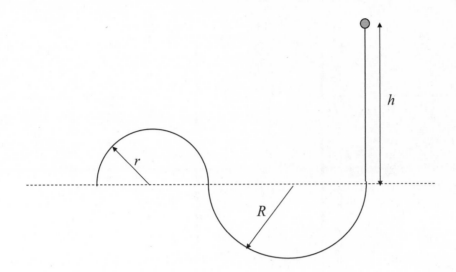

2. (15 points)
A small bead of mass m is designed to slide on a wire track that consists of a straight, vertical section of length h and two semicircular sections of different radii R and r. The bead is released from rest at the beginning of the track and is assumed to slide without friction. Answer the following in terms of R, r, h, m, and g.
(a) Find the speed of the bead at the low point of the track.
(b) Find the force exerted by the track on the bead at the low point.
(c) Find the force exerted by the track on the bead at the high point of the track.

It is determined that the first loop of the track is not frictionless and that the bead loses half its energy as it travels through the first loop.
(d) Assuming the second loop is frictionless, what must be the radius of the second loop so that the track will exert 0 force on the bead at the highest point?

GO ON TO THE NEXT PAGE

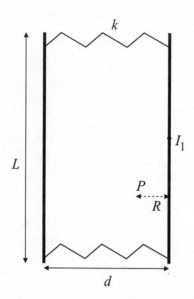

3. (15 points)
    Two identical long wires of length L run parallel to each other. One of them carries a current I_1 directed up as shown in the figure. When a current $I_2 < I_1$ is established in the other wire, the two wires move closer until the separation is d. Two identical springs with constants k keep the wires from getting closer than d.
    (a) Which way does the current I_2 flow?
    (b) Determine the distance moved by each wire as equilibrium is established. In the current configuration, an electron moving toward the top of the page with speed v passes through the point P located a distance $R < \frac{d}{2}$.
    (c) Determine the magnitude and direction of the force exerted on the electron as it passes through P.
    (d) A uniform electric field is introduced into the region such that an electron passing through P experiences no deflection. Determine the magnitude and direction of this field.

GO ON TO THE NEXT PAGE

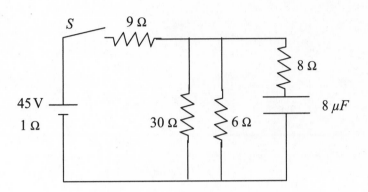

4. (15 points)
The 45-volt battery in the preceding circuit has an internal resistance of 1 Ω. The switch S is closed, and after a long time, the currents reach steady values.
   (a) What is the current in the 8 Ω resistor after a long time?
   (b) Determine the current in the 9 Ω resistor.
   (c) Determine the terminal voltage of the battery.
   (d) Determine the current in the 30 Ω resistor.
   (e) Find the charge on one of the capacitor plates.
   (f) Determine the energy stored in the capacitor.

5. (10 points)
1 mole of ideal gas is to be used as a working substance in a heat engine. Initially, the gas is at a pressure p_0 and volume V_0. It then undergoes the following set of processes.
   I.   The gas is heated at constant volume, increasing the pressure to $3p_0$.
   II. With the addition of $Q = 3.3p_0V_0$ of heat, the gas is allowed to expand isothermally to a volume $3V_0$.
   III. The gas is compressed at constant pressure back to its initial state.

   (a) On the figure on the following page, draw the pV diagram for this cycle. Label each vertex with the appropriate temperature.

GO ON TO THE NEXT PAGE

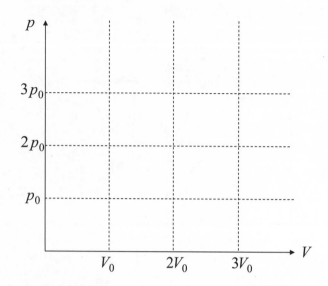

(b) Determine the heat added in process I.
(c) Determine the work done on the gas in process II.
(d) Determine the change in internal energy for the entire cycle.
(e) Determine the efficiency of the engine.

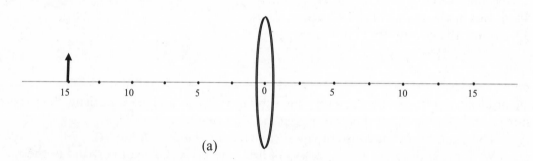

(a)

6. (10 points)
   A single converging thin lens of focal length 5 cm has an object placed 15 cm from it.
   (a) Draw a ray diagram on the figure to determine the approximate position and size of the image.
   (b) Calculate the exact position and magnification of the image. State whether the image is real or virtual, and explain your reasoning.
   (c) Describe qualitatively what happens to the image as the object is moved slowly from its current position to a point 2 cm in front of the lens.
   (d) On the figure below, draw a ray diagram to determine the approximate position and magnification of the image.

GO ON TO THE NEXT PAGE

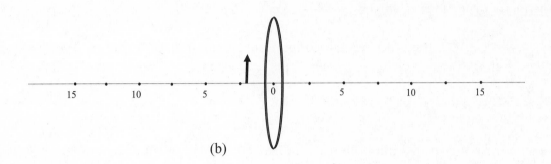

(b)

7. (10 points)
You're given two tuning forks, one with known frequency f_0 and the other with an unknown frequency. You're also given several hollow glass tubes 5 cm in diameter. Your task is to determine the speed of sound and the frequency of the unknown tuning fork. You can use what has been given and any common lab apparatus that is passive in nature. For example, you can use a meter stick or clamps, but not a frequency meter or a voltmeter.
(a) List the apparatus you will need.
(b) Draw a diagram showing how the apparatus is set up.
(c) Describe what your apparatus does.
(d) Show how your measurements will give the desired speed and frequency.

END OF EXAMINATION

STOP

GO ON TO THE NEXT PAGE

1 B MULTIPLE-CHOICE EXPLANATIONS

1. The answer is A. Uniformly accelerated motion from rest means $\Delta x = \frac{1}{2}at^2$, the graph of which is a concave up parabola.

2. The answer is D. The velocity decreases linearly, $v = v_0 - gt$, and so does the momentum, since $p = mv$.

3. The answer is D. Newton's third law tells you that the force exerted by the book on the Earth will equal the weight of the book. This is the reaction force to the weight, not the normal force. Since the book isn't accelerating, the normal force and weight have equal magnitudes.

4. The answer is D. The acceleration due to gravity is constant and directed down the entire trip.

5. The answer is E. Applying the second law to the entire system, you have
$$m_1g = (m_1 + m_2)a$$

6. The answer is D. Gravity and the spring force are in equilibrium.
$$k(0.05) = (0.25)(10)$$

7. The answer is B. Momentum is conserved, but there is more kinetic energy after the collision than before, so it must have come from some stored potential energy. Elastic collisions conserve KE, and this obviously does not.

8. The answer is B. There must be a component forward to accelerate the 4 kg mass, and a component upward to balance gravity.

9. The answer is E. The normal force between the two masses is the only force accelerating the 4 kg mass, so $N = ma = 4(15) = 60$ N. The static friction provided is less than or equal to the maximum value, but it must equal the weight to keep from slipping.
$$f = mg = 40 \leq f_{max} = \mu N = 60\mu$$

$$\mu \geq \frac{2}{3}$$

10. The answer is A. Taking torques about the pivot, you have
$$net\tau = 0 \Rightarrow 40\sin30(2) - F(0.5) = 0$$

11. The answer is E. The work done by friction will equal the change in mechanical energy.

$$\Delta E = mgh - \frac{1}{2}mv^2 = 40(3) - \frac{1}{2}(4)(10^2) = -80 \text{ J}$$

12. The answer is C. The average power is the increase in PE divided by the time it takes.

$$P = \frac{mgh}{t} = \frac{(600)(12)}{10} = 720 \text{ W}$$

13. The answer is B. Both N and mg act down, so the second law gives you

$$N + mg = \frac{mv^2}{R}$$

14. The answer is B. The normal force at P is supplied by the normal force because gravity has no component to the center. The normal force here depends on the speed, so there's no reason for a relation between the weight and the normal force.

15. The answer is E. The electrons on the neutral conductor will move toward the nonconducting sphere. While the conducting sphere remains overall neutral, the closer negative charges will lead to a net attractive force.

16. The answer is B. The horizontal component to the right from $+Q$ is larger than the horizontal component to the left from $-Q$. The $-Q$ creates an upward vertical component.

17. The answer is D. The center is equidistant from the two equal but opposite charges:

$$U = k\frac{qQ}{a\frac{\sqrt{2}}{2}} - k\frac{qQ}{a\frac{\sqrt{2}}{2}} = 0$$

18. The answer is A. The field will be greatest where the surfaces are closest, since

$$E = \frac{\Delta V}{\Delta x}$$

19. The answer is C. It takes no work to move through 0 potential difference.

20. The answer is E. At C, the field is perpendicular to the surface and directed toward lower potential. Electrons will accelerate opposite the field direction.

21. The answer is D. Current is charge per time, and the charge on an electron is 1.6×10^{-19} C.

$$I \cong \frac{10^8 \cdot 10^{-19}}{10}$$

22. The answer is A. The fluid pressure is $\rho gh = \rho(50) = 3 \times 10^4$.

23. The answer is D. By Archimedes' principle, the mass of the solid equals the mass of the displaced fluid: $m = \rho_f hA$. The volume V of the solid is just tA, so $\rho_{solid} = \frac{m}{V} = \rho_f \frac{h}{t}$.

24. The answer is B. The weight of the displaced fluid will be the difference in the two spring force readings: $k(x_1 - x_2) = \rho_f g V$. Solving for V gives the result.

25. The answer is B. Pascal's principle tells you that any change in pressure applied to an enclosed static fluid is transferred undiminished throughout the fluid.

26. The answer is E. Adiabatic means no heat transfer, so the first law gives you $\Delta U = Q + W = W$. The internal energy has increased, and for an ideal gas, this means the temperature must increase as well, since $\Delta U = \frac{3}{2} nR\Delta T$.

27. The answer is E. By Archimedes' principle you know that an object placed in a fluid and allowed to reach equilibrium will displace an amount of water having a weight equal to the object's weight, so II is true. If the object had a greater density than the fluid, then even when completely submerged the weight of the displaced water would be less than the weight of the object and the buoyant force would not be great enough to keep it afloat. Thus I is true. If the object is completely submerged, for example by pushing it under the surface, it must displace a volume of water equal to its own volume, so III is true.

28. The answer is A. Bernoulli's principle, $\frac{1}{2}\rho v^2 + \rho g h + p = $ constant, follows from energy conservation.

29. The answer is A. Number I is heating by radiation, and III is by conduction. Number II is a work process.

30. The answer is D. In an ideal gas, after the molecules separate they exert no force on each other. Clearly, charged electrons will exert repulsive forces on each other.

31. The answer is B. Since $U = \frac{3}{2} nRT$, isothermal—no change in temperature—means the internal energy stays the same as well.

32. The answer is D. Once the object is inside the focal length, a converging mirror cannot bring the rays together to form a real image. The image will always be larger than the object. A couple of test sketches would convince you of this without the need for algebraic details.

33. The answer is B. A diverging mirror will produce only a virtual image smaller than the object, as you could see with a couple of test sketches.

34. The answer is D. The image equation at the first position gives you

$$\frac{1}{f} = \frac{1}{2f} + \frac{1}{s_i} \Rightarrow s_i = 2f \Rightarrow m = -1$$

At the second position, you get

$$\frac{1}{f} = \frac{2}{3f} + \frac{1}{s_i} \Rightarrow s_i = 3f \Rightarrow m = -2$$

There is no change of image type until the focal point is passed.

35. The answer is C. A single diverging lens can produce only a virtual image. A quick sketch can convince you of the size change, or you could do the little bit of algebra using the image equation, as in question 34.

36. The answer is E. To reach threshold, you must increase the energy of the incident photons, which means decrease λ.

37. The answer is A. Since the De Broglie wavelength is much smaller than the slit size, there is very little diffraction and the electrons behave as particles, producing the particle pattern on the screen.

38. The answer is A. Writing the equation, you have

$$^{10}_{5}B + ^{A}_{Z}? \rightarrow ^{7}_{3}Li + ^{4}_{2}He$$

Balancing top and bottom gives you $Z = 0$, $A = 1$.

39. The answer is C. Since neutrons are $^{1}_{0}n$, you need 2 to balance the top numbers.

40. The answer is B. Since power is $P = Fv$, you have $P = (mg)(gt) = mg^2t$. This is a linearly increasing graph.

41. The answer is D. The falling object will have a speed of $v = gt = 10(1) = 10 \frac{m}{s}$ after 1 second. Momentum conservation then gives you $2(10) = 5v$

42. The answer is A. Use kinematics to find a and the second law to find F.

$$v = v_0 + at \Rightarrow 3 = 10 + 2a \Rightarrow a = -3.5 \frac{m}{s^2}$$
$$F = ma = 4(-3.5) = -14 \text{ N}$$

43. The answer is B. Use momentum conservation for each component.

$$4(10) = 5v_x \Rightarrow v_x = 8 \frac{m}{s}$$

$$1(40) = 5v_y \Rightarrow v_y = 8 \frac{m}{s}$$

$$v = \sqrt{8^2 + 8^2}$$

44. The answer is E. The center of mass will remain stationary. Since the 6 kg mass is 3 times the mass of the 2 kg mass, it must travel $\frac{1}{3}$ the distance that the 2 kg mass travels.

45. The answer is D. The angular momentum is given by $l = mvr_{\perp} = 2(7)(3)$. If you extend the line of the velocity, $r_{\perp}$ is the closest distance to the origin of the line.

46. The answer is A. You could work out the math or recognize that the two 4 Ω in parallel will give 2 Ω, and adding a 100 Ω in parallel won't change it much.

47. The answer is B. The overall resistance of the circuit is 10 Ω, so a current of 5 A flows. The battery has a terminal voltage of $V_T = 50 - 5(2)$.

48. The answer is A. The 5 A will split into a 4:1 ratio at the junction with 4 A going through the 5 Ω resistor, so $P = i^2 R = 4^2(5) = 80$ W.

49. The answer is E. Starting at A, you go up 40 V through the battery, its terminal voltage, then down $V_{12} = 1(12) = 12$ V through the 12 Ω resistor, which carries 1 A.

50. The answer is D. The continuity equation tells you that $v' = v\dfrac{A}{A'} = 3\dfrac{4^2}{1^2} = 48\ \dfrac{m}{s}$.

51. The answer is B. Use Bernoulli's principle on opposite sides of the hole.

$$\left(\frac{1}{2}\rho v^2 + \rho gh + P\right)_{out} = \left(\frac{1}{2}\rho v^2 + \rho gh + P\right)_{in}$$

$$\frac{1}{2}(1,000)v^2 + 10^5 = 3 \times 10^5 \quad \Rightarrow \quad v = 20\ \frac{m}{s}$$

52. The answer is C. Since $\Delta U = \dfrac{3}{2}R\Delta T$, you can use the gas law to find ΔT.

$$\Delta T = \frac{\Delta p V_1}{R} = \frac{p_1 V_1}{R}$$

53. The answer is D. It is the area under the ST segment.

54. The answer is D. Each box has an area of $p_1 V_1$, and there are about 3 boxes contained inside the cycle.

55. The answer is D. When a ray of light goes from a lower index region to a higher index region, like air to glass, the light slows down and the wavelength decreases as it bends toward the normal line. Just the opposite happens as the ray exits the glass back into air.

56. The answer is D. At first interface, light bends toward normal, so $n_2 > n_1$. At second interface, it bends away from normal, so $n_3 < n_2$. If $n_1 = n_3$, the outgoing ray would be parallel to the original ray. Since it is bent beyond parallel, $n_3 < n_1$.

57. The answer is C. Since the difference in the index of refraction at the interface has decreased, there is less refraction and the angular spread is less, but the order stays the same.

58. The answer is C. The distance from the center of the Earth has changed by less than 1 percent, and this is the important distance in determining the force exerted by the Earth on the object.

59. The answer is B. The oscillating system is 4 kg, so the period formula gives you

$$T = 2\pi\sqrt{\frac{m}{k}} = 2\pi\sqrt{\frac{4}{64}} = \frac{\pi}{2}$$

60. The answer is B. Use momentum conservation to find the speed after the collision, then energy conservation to find the maximum compression, which is the amplitude.

$$P_i = P_f \qquad\qquad E_i = E_f$$

$$2(4) = 4v \qquad\qquad \frac{1}{2}(4)(2)^2 = \frac{1}{2}(64)x^2 \;\Rightarrow\; x = \frac{1}{2}\,\text{m}$$

$$v = 2\,\frac{\text{m}}{\text{s}}$$

61. The answer is C. The magnetic field does no work, so the speed is constant. The motion path is a helix because there are velocity components both parallel and perpendicular to the field.

62. The answer is C. The flux out of the page through the loop is decreasing, so a counterclockwise current must flow to try to keep it from changing. The segment closest to the long wire then feels an attractive force. Since you have a changing magnetic field, an electric field is created as well.

63. The answer is A. Use the continuity equation to determine the speed in the wider pipe, and then use Bernoulli's equation to find the pressure.

$$v' = v\frac{A}{A'} = v\frac{r^2}{r'^2} = \frac{v}{4}$$

$$\frac{1}{2}\rho v^2 + P = \frac{1}{2}\rho v'^2 + P'$$

$$P' - P = \frac{1}{2}\rho v^2\left(1 - \frac{1}{16}\right)$$

64. The answer is E. For an ideal gas, $\frac{1}{2}mv^2 = \frac{3}{2}kT$, so doubling T increases v by $\sqrt{2}$.

65. The answer is C. The efficiency is $e = 1 - \frac{200}{600} = \frac{2}{3}$. One-third of the input energy is expelled, so 300 MJ must be the input, and 200 J of work are performed every hour.

66. The answer is B. For an elliptical orbit, the radius changes, so all the other quantities will change. The gravitational force exerts no torque since it acts toward the origin (the Sun), so angular momentum will stay the same.

67. The answer is D. Torque has dimensions of (force) $\times$ (distance), the same as energy. D has dimensions of (mass) $\times$ (velocity)^2—energy.

68. The answer is C. There will be a mass $2m$ oscillating on a spring with constant k. The time to reach maximum compression will be $\frac{1}{4}T$.
$$\frac{1}{4}T = \frac{1}{4}2\pi\sqrt{\frac{2m}{k}}$$

69. The answer is D. The reaction equation is
$$^{3}_{2}\text{He} + {}^{3}_{2}\text{He} \rightarrow 2^{1}_{1}\text{p} + {}^{A}_{Z}?$$

Balancing the top and bottom gives $Z = 2$, $A = 4$.

70. The answer is D. The nucleus consists of 2 protons and 1 neutron. The binding energy of the nucleus lowers its mass to be less than the sum of the individual components.

1 B FREE-RESPONSE EXPLANATIONS

1. (a) Use energy conservation to find the KE and the velocity of the mass after it leaves the spring.
$$E_i = E_f$$
$$E_i = \frac{1}{2}kx^2 = \frac{1}{2}(200)(0.5)^2 = 25 \text{ J}$$
$$\frac{1}{2}kx^2 = \frac{1}{2}mv^2$$
$$v = \sqrt{\frac{k}{m}}x = \sqrt{\frac{200}{0.5}}(0.5) = 10 \ \frac{\text{m}}{\text{s}}$$

(b) The impulse delivered to the 2 kg mass will equal its change in momentum and can be determined from the area under the F vs. t graph given. There are two equal triangles and a rectangle.
$$\Delta p = J = \text{area}$$
$$mV - 0 = 2\left[\frac{1}{2}(2.5 \times 10^{-3})(480)\right] + (10 \times 10^{-3})(480) = 6 \text{ N} \cdot \text{s}$$
$$2V = 6$$
$$V = 3 \ \frac{\text{m}}{\text{s}}$$

(c) To find the final energy of the system, you need to use momentum conservation to find the final velocity of the smaller mass.
$$P_i = P_f$$
$$0.5(10) = 2(3) + 0.5v' \quad \Rightarrow \quad v' = -2 \ \frac{\text{m}}{\text{s}}$$
$$\Delta E = E_f - E_i$$
$$\Delta E = \left[\frac{1}{2}(0.5)(-2)^2 + \frac{1}{2}(2)(3)^2\right] - 25 = -15 \text{ J}$$

(d) The 2 kg mass will go directly over the edge of the table. The 0.5 kg mass rebounds first into the spring, but since the spring force is conservative, the mass will leave the spring with the same speed, 2 m/s, and eventually go over the edge as well. Both masses take the same time to hit the ground after they leave the table, since they have no initial vertical velocity.

$$\Delta y = \frac{1}{2}gt^2 \qquad\qquad \Delta y = 1 \text{ m}$$

$$t = \sqrt{\frac{2\Delta y}{g}} = 0.45 \text{ s}$$

$$\Delta x_{2kg} = Vt = 3(0.45) = 1.35 \text{ m}$$

$$\Delta x_{0.5kg} = v't = 2(0.45) = 0.90 \text{ m}$$

They hit 0.45 m apart.

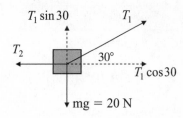

2. (a) Since this is an equilibrium situation, $netF = 0$. Therefore the net force in the x-direction equals zero and the net force in the y-direction equal to zero. Using the figure, you find:

x-component $\qquad\qquad\qquad$ y-component
$T_1\cos30 = T_2$ $\qquad\qquad\qquad$ $T_1\sin30 = 20$

From the y-component, you get $T_1 = 40$ N. Substituting T_1 in the first equation, you get $T_2 = 34.6$ N.

(b) Use energy conservation, since the tension does no work on the mass as it descends. The initial height is $h = 3 - 3\cos60 = 1.5$ m.

$$E_i = mgh = E_f = \frac{1}{2}mv^2$$

$$v = \sqrt{2gh} = \sqrt{30} = 5.5 \frac{\text{m}}{\text{s}}$$

(c) The mass is moving in a circular arc, so use Newton's second law and the centripetal acceleration formula.

$$netF = ma = m\frac{v^2}{R} = 2\frac{30}{3} = 20 \text{ N}$$

$$T - mg = 20$$

$$T = 40 \text{ N}$$

(d) Use momentum conservation.

$$2(5.5) = 4v' \qquad \Rightarrow v' = 2.75 \, \frac{m}{s}$$

(e) Kinetic energy is not conserved. One can explicitly calculate the KE before and after and see that they are different. The KE just before collision will equal the initial PE since the string does no work.

$$\Delta K = \frac{1}{2}(2m)v'^2 - mgh = 2(2.75)^2 - 20(1.5) = -14.9 \, J$$

The loss of energy occurs because work is done by internal forces within the bodies producing thermal energy, deformation, and sound.

3. (a) Use energy conservation.

$$\frac{1}{2}kx^2 = \frac{1}{2}mv^2$$

$$v = \sqrt{\frac{k}{m}}x = \sqrt{\frac{100}{0.25}}(0.3) = 6 \, \frac{m}{s}$$

(b) For the moving rail, the induced voltage is

$$V = BLv = (0.2)(0.4)(6) = 0.48 \, V$$

(c) The flux rises linearly from 0 to B (area) $= 0.032$ weber over the first 0.4 m. It then remains constant at this value for the next 0.4 m, and finally decreases linearly to 0 over the last 0.4 m.

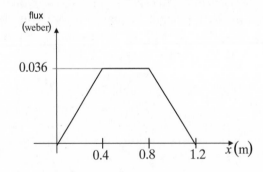

(d) While the loop is entering the field region, the current will be given by Ohm's law.

$$i = \frac{V}{R} = \frac{0.48}{2} = 0.24 \, A$$

Since the flux is increasing, the current will make its own field to oppose this, creating a field out of the page. The loop right-hand rule then tells you that the current flows counterclockwise. There is no flux change over the second 0.4 m, so no current is induced. As the loop leaves the field region, the same magnitude of current is induced. Now the flux is decreasing, so the induced current will flow to make a field that points into the page, implying a clockwise current.

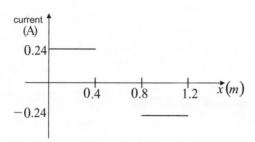

4. (a) Since the power supplied equals the power consumed by the bulb, you have

$$P = i^2 R \qquad \Rightarrow E_{supplied} = i^2 Rt$$

(b) Bulb A, connected in parallel with the battery, will have the same current i. The other three bulbs can be treated as a separate loop. Their effective resistance is $\frac{3}{2}R$ since the two in parallel have resistance $\frac{1}{2}R$. That means the current in bulb B is $\frac{2}{3}i$, and both C and D will have $\frac{1}{3}i$.

(c) The brightness will be proportional to the power consumed by the bulbs. The power dissipation of each bulb is

A	B	C	D
$i^2 R$	$\left(\frac{2}{3}i\right)^2 R = \frac{4}{9}i^2 R$	$\left(\frac{1}{3}i\right)^2 R = \frac{1}{9}i^2 R$	$\left(\frac{1}{3}i\right)^2 R = \frac{1}{9}i^2 R$

A has the same brightness, B is $\frac{4}{9}$ as bright, and both C and D are $\frac{1}{9}$ as bright.

(d) (i) If A fails, there is no effect on the other bulbs because they have the same voltage applied across them.

(ii) If C fails, A is unaffected. Now B and D are in series in the outer loop. Since their resistance is now effectively $2R$, the current in these bulbs will be $\frac{1}{2}i$, and the power they consume will be $\left(\frac{1}{2}i\right)^2 R = \frac{1}{4}i^2 R$. They will be $\frac{1}{4}$ as bright as the single bulb circuit.

5. (a) You can use the photoelectric effect energy equation in eV energy units.

$$KE = \frac{hc}{\lambda} - \phi$$

$$1.85 = \frac{1,240}{480} - \phi \quad \Rightarrow \phi = 0.73 \text{ eV}$$

(b) At threshold, the photon energy equals the work function.

$$\frac{hc}{\lambda_{th}} = \phi$$

$$\lambda_{th} = \frac{1,240}{0.73} \quad \Rightarrow \lambda_{th} = 1,698 \text{ nm}$$

(c) Now that you know the work function, you can use the energy relation again.

$$KE = \frac{hc}{\lambda} - \phi$$

$$3 = \frac{1,240}{\lambda} - 0.73 \quad \Rightarrow \lambda = 332 \text{ nm}$$

(d) The energy of the ejected electrons will be 3 eV. To find the De Broglie wavelength, rearrange the De Broglie formula (be careful of units).

$$E_{electron} = \frac{p^2}{2m} \quad \Rightarrow p = \sqrt{2mE_{electron}}$$

$$E_{electron} = 3(1.6 \times 10^{-19}) = 4.8 \times 10^{-19} \text{ J}$$

$$\lambda = \frac{h}{p} = \frac{6.6 \times 10^{-34}}{\sqrt{2(9 \times 10^{-31})(4.8 \times 10^{-19})}} = 7.1 \times 10^{-10} \text{ m}$$

(e) To see the effects of the electron wavelength, you need a "grating" with spacing on the order of the wavelength. This is comparable to the spacing in salt crystals, so you could direct this beam at such a crystal and look for the interference pattern, clear evidence of wave properties.

6. (a) There are 6 N-A intervals, each $\frac{1}{4}\lambda$, so

$$6\left(\frac{\lambda}{4}\right) = 1.5 \qquad \lambda = 1 \text{ m}$$

(b) Since the wave is periodic and its frequency is the same as the oscillator, you have

$$v_w = \lambda f = (1)(100) = 100 \ \frac{\text{m}}{\text{s}}$$

(c) Since the endpoints are fixed, the fundamental mode with the lowest frequency will have a single antinode, and the wavelength will be 3 m. The wave speed will be the same, since it's determined by the string mass and tension. Then for this standing wave, you have

$$f = \frac{v_w}{\lambda} = \frac{100}{3} = 33.3 \text{ Hz}$$

(d) Increasing the mass will increase the wave speed on the string. As the mass is increased holding the frequency fixed, the standing wave pattern will disappear fairly quickly since it's a resonance; as you change the wave speed, you change the natural frequencies of the string. Since $v_w = \lambda f$, the wavelength of the string wave will increase as well. As you continue to increase the mass, you eventually increase the wavelength enough so that 4 N-A intervals are set up on the string, and you're back at a resonance condition.

7. (a) stand for mounting laser, meter stick, paper or screen

(b)

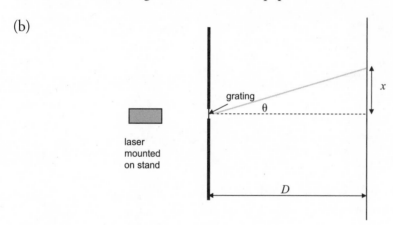

(c) Align the laser so that light can pass through the known grating. Set up a screen a distance D behind the grating. Make D large enough so that the first order maxima have separated appreciably from the central maximum. Measure x, the distance from the central maximum to the first order maximum. This will allow you to determine θ, and you can then use the interference equation to determine λ, since the spacing can be determined from the given data. Once λ has been determined, replace the known grating with the unknown one. Make the same measurements of the interference pattern, determine θ, and now use the interference equation to determine the unknown spacing.

(d) For the known grating, $a = \dfrac{2.5 \times 10^{-3}}{80} = 3.13 \times 10^{-5}$ m. Determine the angle from

$$\tan\theta = \frac{x}{D}$$

The interference equation for the first order maximum then yields

$$a\sin\theta = \lambda \qquad\qquad \text{solve for } \lambda$$

Once λ is known, you can insert the unknown grating and obtain measurements of D' and x' with your meter stick. Then find θ' using:

$$\tan\theta' = \frac{x'}{D'}.$$

Then the interference equation gives you

$$a' = \frac{\lambda}{\sin\theta'}$$

2 B MULTIPLE-CHOICE EXPLANATIONS

1. The answer is D. The net force is 0, but there can be forces that add up to 0.

2. The answer is D. Acceleration is the slope of the v vs. t graph.

3. The answer is D. Displacement is the area under the v vs. t graph, and you need the time for total displacement to be 0. Over the first 2 s, the area is about $+ 8.8$ m from the rectangle and triangle. From 2 s to 3 s the area is less than $- 5$ m, but from 2 s to 4 s the area is $- 15$ m. The $+$ and $-$ contributions thus add to 0 between 3 s and 4 s.

4. The answer is C. Only the horizontal momentum of the ball changes, so the impulse can only be horizontal. B is in the wrong direction for the ball to bounce back.

5. The answer is E. Horizontally projected objects hit at the same time if they're projected from the same height. The horizontal velocity component doesn't change.

6. The answer is E. $netF = ma \Rightarrow 20 - f = 10(0.5) \Rightarrow f = 15$ N

7. The answer is C. The third law tells you that each team exerts the same force on the rope. Strength doesn't matter. A children's team could beat a football team if the latter were on roller skates.

8. The answer is B. Since there's no acceleration, the friction force must equal the horizontal component of the tension, $20\cos53 = 12$ N.

9. The answer is C. Since there's no friction on the bottom and the system moves without slippage, the second law tells you that $20 = 10a \Rightarrow a = 2 \frac{m}{s^2}$. Only static friction accelerates the top mass, so $f = ma = 2(2) = 4$ N. The maximum value of static friction is greater than or equal to this. $f_{max} = \mu N = \mu(20) \geq 4 \Rightarrow \mu \geq 0.2$

10. The answer is E. Taking torque about the edge, the plank weight acts at a point 4 m from this axis, so $net\tau = 0 \Rightarrow 200(4) - 400x = 0 \Rightarrow x = 2$ m.

11. The answer is D. The work done by friction will equal the change in KE, $\frac{1}{2}(2)(4^2 - 10^2) = - 84$ J.

12. The answer is B. Since the only accelerating force is the tension, $a = \frac{T}{m}$ and $v = at = \frac{T}{m}t$. Using the power relation, you have $P = Fv = T\left(\frac{T}{m}t\right)$.

13. The answer is B. The initial force is proportional to $3Q^2$. The total charge of the two spheres is $+ 2Q$, and when they touch, each will end up with $+ Q$. The final force is repulsive, proportional to Q^2.

14. The answer is A. Here the two contributions are both directed to the left, and the distance is the smallest of the possible choices.

15. The answer is D. To get the smallest (most negative) potential, you get as close to the $-2Q$ and as far away from the $+Q$ as possible.

16. The answer is E. Since the volume of the material stays the same, as L doubles, the area must halve. Then $\rho\frac{L}{A}$ increases by 4.

17. The answer is C. The capacitance is proportional to $\frac{A}{d}$, independent of supply voltage.

18. The answer is A. The field points from north to south. The current flows counterclockwise, so the force right-hand rule gives the up direction.

19. The answer is D. The pressure depends on only the depth.

20. The answer is C. Since the density of the fluid is greater than the mass, the mass floats and the spring doesn't have to support the mass.

21. The answer is A. Conservation of mass tells you that the mass passing any point in a given time is the same.

22. The answer is B. The continuity equation $Av = A'v'$ tells you that the speed of the water is 8 times greater. Since it's a horizontal projectile, it takes the same time to hit in each case, so $\Delta x' = v't$ is 8 times larger than Δx.

23. The answer is B. The first law of thermodynamics tells you that

$$\Delta U = Q + W = 400 - 200 = 200 \text{ J}$$

24. The answer is D. Hydrostatic pressure is given by $\rho g h$ where h is the fluid depth, so the pressure and depth are in direct proportion. When an object is immersed in a static fluid, it is the differences in pressure above and below the object that give rise to the buoyant force. From Bernoulli's principle, $\frac{1}{2}\rho v^2 + \rho g h + p = $ constant, we can see that pressure has the units of energy density since $\frac{1}{2}\rho v^2$ has these units, and it also tells us that the pressure is *least* where the fluid moves fastest, so D is not correct.

25. The answer is C. From Archimedes' principle, the weight of the displaced fluid will equal the weight of the object. Since $\frac{3}{4}$ of the volume of the object is displaced, we can write:

$$W_{object} = \rho_{object}V_{object} = \rho_f\left(\frac{3}{4}V_{object}\right) \Rightarrow \rho_{object} = \frac{3}{4}\rho_f$$

26. The answer is C. The red light is interfering constructively, demonstrating an important wave property. While there may be a particular value of wavelength that isn't reflected, this cannot be true for all other wavelengths.

27. The answer is D. At the vertex there's no path difference in the reflected rays, but there is a phase shift, causing these two rays to interfere destructively.

28. The answer is D. From the equation $\sin\theta = \frac{\lambda}{a}$, you can see that the angle gets larger and depends on the wavelength.

29. The answer is A. The width of the central maximum is determined by the positions of the first order minimum: $\sin\theta = \frac{\lambda}{2a}$, and as a increases, this gets smaller. Note that the number of visible fringes is given when $\theta = 90°$, so $N = \frac{a}{\lambda}$ increases.

30. The answer is A. Above threshold, every photon absorbed will eject an electron, and increasing intensity increases the number of photons.

31. The answer is C. While more electrons are ejected as intensity increases, the maximum KE of the ejected electrons stays the same.

32. The answer is E. $p = \frac{h}{\lambda}$

33. The answer is E. The wavelength shift in the scattered X-rays can be explained if you think of the process as a photon electron elastic collision. No minimum energy is required of the photon before it will exhibit this effect.

34. The answer is D. Diffraction is the quintessential wave property.

35. The answer is A. Each contains 26 *protons*. The mass of a mole of each is 56 g and 57 g, respectively.

36. The answer is C. From the reaction $_1^1\text{p} + {_6^{13}\text{C}} \rightarrow {_7^{14}\text{N}} + {_Z^A}?$, you can see that $Z = 0$ and $A = 0$, so the particle has no charge and isn't a nucleon.

37. The answer is C. At the highest point, it must be moving to the right. The centripetal acceleration is toward the center, so it must point down.

38. The answer is B. At the lowest point, the tension is directed up. From the second law and the centripetal acceleration formula, you have

$$T - 30 = 3\frac{6^2}{2}$$

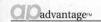

39. The answer is B. Energy conservation gives the speed at the bottom:

$$mgh = \frac{1}{2}mv^2 \Rightarrow v = \sqrt{2gh}$$

The second law and centripetal acceleration then give

$$T - mg = m\frac{(\sqrt{2gh})^2}{L}$$

40. The answer is C. Momentum conservation gives the final speed:

$$P_i = P_f \Rightarrow 2(5) = 5v \Rightarrow v = 2\,\frac{m}{s}$$

The change in energy is then

$$\frac{1}{2}(5)(2)^2 - \frac{1}{2}(2)(5)^2 = -15\ \text{J}$$

41. The answer is C. Energy is conserved because gravity is a conservative force. But it's an external force for the projectile, so the change in momentum of the projectile will equal the impulse delivered by this force.

42. The answer is C. The impulse delivered is the area of the triangle, 5 N • s. This will equal the change in momentum.

$$2v' - 2(10) = +5 \Rightarrow v' = 12.5\,\frac{m}{s}$$

43. The answer is E. Kirchhoff's first law tells you that the current in the 10 V battery is 4 A. It's recharging, so $V_T = 10 + 2(4) = 18$ V.

44. The answer is B. Apply the loop equation to the left loop.

$$-(6)(1) + 48 - (6)(4) - 2R = 0$$

45. The answer is C. The terminal voltage of the 48 V battery is 42 V, and the power it supplies will be $P = IV_T = 6(42) = 252$ W.

46. The answer is D. If the force were applied at the same level, Pascal's principle would give you $F = W\frac{A'}{A}$. Since F must also support the weight of the water above the dotted line, D follows.

47. The answer is E. Apply Bernoulli's principle between the top of the water level, where you assume atmospheric pressure and negligible speed, and just outside the hole, where the pressure is atmospheric again.

$$\left(\frac{1}{2}\rho v^2 + \rho gh + P\right)_{top} = \left(\frac{1}{2}\rho v^2 + \rho gh + P\right)_{hole}$$

$$\rho gh = \frac{1}{2}\rho v^2 \Rightarrow v = \sqrt{2gh} = \sqrt{80}$$

48. The answer is A. The time it takes to hit after exiting is $t = \sqrt{\frac{2y}{g}}$.

Then, using the result of question 47, you have for the projected water:

$$x = vt = \sqrt{2gh}\sqrt{\frac{2y}{g}} = \sqrt{4hy} \qquad \text{independent of } g$$

49. The answer is D. The applied voltage can be found from Ohm's law, $V = IR = 2(0.1) = 0.2A$. Since the dimensions of the new material are the same but the resistivity is halved, the resistance is also halved, so $R' = 0.05\Omega$. The power consumed is then

$$P = \frac{V^2}{R'} = \frac{(0.2)^2}{0.05} = 0.8\,W$$

50. The answer is C. Heat is defined as energy transferred due to temperature differences only.

51. The answer is D. The volume is directly proportional to the temperature expressed in kelvins.

52. The answer is B. The sound must bend around the wall to reach the child's ears.

53. The answer is B. The interference of each Huygens emitter produces the pattern of a central maximum and less intense secondary maxima. The pattern is larger than the slit, so clearly the light has moved into the shadow region and has diffracted.

54. The answer is C. Diffraction is more pronounced when the wavelength gets smaller relative to the slit size, and this means the central maximum must get larger, spreading more into the shadow region.

55. The answer is C. To get a net 0 torque, you need the 4 kg mass twice as far from the fulcrum as the 8 kg mass.

56. The answer is A. For an object moving in a circle, the angular momentum about the circle's center is $l = mvR = 0.5(4)(2)$.

57. The answer is D. Mass doesn't change when it's repositioned.

58. The answer is B. The field due to the wire is into the page at the electron position. The force right-hand rule then indicates that the force is up, remembering that the electron is negative.

59. The answer is A. The magnetic force on the induced current is $F = iLB = 0.3(2)(0.1) = 0.06$ N. An external force just equal to this will have to be supplied to the right to keep the speed the same.

60. The answer is D. The second resistor is in parallel with the first. Since the speed is the same, the voltage drop across each resistor is the same, so the power consumed by each will be equal and will be the same as the original power consumption.

61. The answer is B. You can write the kinetic energy as $E = \frac{p^2}{2m} \Rightarrow p = \sqrt{2mE}$. Then, from the De Broglie formula, you have

$$\lambda = \frac{h}{p} = \frac{h}{\sqrt{2mE}}$$

For the wavelength to be halved, the energy must increase by a factor of 4.

62. The answer is E. Modern experiments have demonstrated wave properties for particles as large as molecules.

63. The answer is B. There is no energy difference between levels of 2 eV.

64. The answer is A. Ground state electrons would need to absorb 5 eV to reach the next level, and this isn't available.

65. The answer is E. There is no level 1 eV higher than the -5 eV level. It can absorb 6 eV and get ionized.

66. The answer is A. The orbit radius speed $v = \sqrt{\dfrac{GM_e}{R}}$ is independent of the satellite mass.

67. The answer is D. Since $T = 2\pi\sqrt{\dfrac{l}{g}}$, it follows that for equal periods

$$\frac{L}{g} = \frac{L'}{\frac{g}{6}} \Rightarrow L' = \frac{L}{6}$$

68. The answer is B. Power is energy per time. Think in terms of $\dfrac{mv^2}{t} \approx \dfrac{\text{kg}\left(\frac{\text{m}}{\text{s}}\right)^2}{\text{s}}$.

69. The answer is C. Balancing top and bottom numbers gives you $a = 13$, $b = 27$. The number of neutrons is $27 - 13 = 14$.

70. The answer is D. The mass converted to energy is very close to 1 u, which will yield 931 MeV.

2 B FREE-RESPONSE EXPLANATIONS

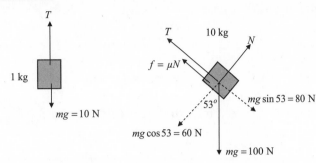

1. (a, b) The diagram shows the various forces. For the 10 kg mass, the components perpendicular to the incline determine the normal force and the friction force.

$$N - mg\cos53 = 0$$

$$N = 60\text{ N} \quad \Rightarrow f = 15\text{ N}$$

Applying the second law to each mass along the direction of motion, you have

1 kg   10 kg
$$T - 10 = 1a \qquad 80 - T - 15 = 10a$$

Adding the two equations eliminates T, yielding

$$55 = 11a \quad \Rightarrow a = 5\,\frac{\text{m}}{\text{s}^2}$$

Substituting yields $T = 15$ N.

(c) The system will lose all the KE of the 10 kg mass as well as the work done by friction as the 10 kg mass slid 2.5 m. Since the 10 kg mass accelerated at 5 m/s² traveling 2.5 m, you can use kinematics to find v.

$$v^2 = v_0^2 + 2a\Delta x = 0 + 25$$

$$v = 5\,\frac{\text{m}}{\text{s}} \qquad\qquad KE = \frac{1}{2}(10)(25) = 125\text{ J}$$

$$|W_{fric}| = 15(2.5) = 37.5\text{ J}$$

The system loses 162.5 J.

(d) The 1 kg mass will be moving at 5 m/s when the 10 kg mass hits. It will then move upward under the influence of gravity until it reaches 0 velocity.

$$v^2 = v_0^2 + 2a\Delta y$$

$$0 = 5^2 + 2(-10)\Delta y \qquad \Rightarrow \Delta y = 1.25 \text{ m}$$

Then the 1 kg mass will ascend a total of $2.5 + 1.25 = 3.75$ m.

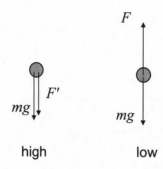

high   low

2. (a) Use energy conservation.

$$mg(h + R) = \frac{1}{2}mv_{low}^2 \qquad \Rightarrow v_{low}^2 = \sqrt{2g(h + R)}$$

(b) Use Newton's second law applied to circular motion at the low point. The forces are shown in the figure.

$$F - mg = m\frac{v_{low}^2}{R}$$

$$F = mg + m\frac{2g(h + R)}{R} = mg\left(3 + \frac{2h}{R}\right)$$

(c) Use a similar approach. Energy conservation applied to the high point yields

$$mg(h - r) = \frac{1}{2}mv_{high}^2 \qquad \Rightarrow v_{high}^2 = \sqrt{2g(h - r)}$$

$$F + mg = m\frac{v_{high}^2}{r}$$

$$F = m\frac{2g(h - r)}{r} - mg = mg\left(\frac{2h}{r} - 3\right)$$

(d) The kinetic energy at the top loop will now be

$$\frac{1}{2}mv^2 = mg(h - r) - \frac{1}{2}mgh$$

$$v^2 = g(h - 2r)$$

Now apply the second law as before.

$$F' + mg = m\frac{v^2}{r} = m\frac{g(h - 2r)}{r}$$

$$F' = mg\left(\frac{h}{r} - 3\right)$$

Thus, $r = \frac{1}{3}h$ for 0 force exerted by the track.

3. (a) Since the two wires attract, the currents must flow parallel to each other, so I_2 flows up.

(b) When equilibrium is established, the spring forces just counterbalance the magnetic attraction between the two wires.

$$2kx = k'\frac{I_1 I_2}{d}L$$

$$x = k'\frac{I_1 I_2}{2kd}L$$

Since the wires are identical, each wire will move $\frac{1}{2}x$.

(c) To find the force on the electron, you need to find the resultant magnetic field at P. The long wire right-hand rule tells you that the field created by I_1 is out of the page at P, and that the one created by I_2 is into the page. Since P is closer to the larger current, the net field will be out of the page.

$$B_{net} = k'\frac{I_1}{R} - k'\frac{I_2}{d - R}$$

The magnetic force on the electron will be directed to the right with magnitude

$$F = qvB_{net} = qv\left(k'\frac{I_1}{R} - k'\frac{I_2}{d - R}\right)$$

(d) The electric force on the electron must point to the left, so the field must point to the right. The magnitude of the field is given by

$$qE = qvB_{net} = qv\left(k'\frac{I_1}{R} - k'\frac{I_2}{d - R}\right)$$

$$E = v\left(k'\frac{I_1}{R} - k'\frac{I_2}{d - R}\right)$$

4. (a) After a long time, the capacitor is fully charged, and no current will flow through the 8 Ω resistor.

(b) With no current in the 8 Ω resistor, you can analyze the rest of the circuit as a simple circuit. The equivalent resistance of the 30 Ω and the 6 Ω is

$$\frac{1}{R_p} = \frac{1}{30} + \frac{1}{6} = \frac{1}{5} \qquad \Rightarrow R_p = 5 \ \Omega$$

Then the equivalent resistance of the circuits is

$$R_{eq} = 1 + 9 + 5 = 15 \ \Omega$$

since the 9 Ω and the internal resistance are in series with the two parallel resistors. The current in the battery and the 9 Ω resistor will be

$$i = \frac{V_B}{R_{eq}} = \frac{45}{15} = 3 \ \text{A}$$

(c) The battery is operating in its normal mode, so the terminal voltage will be

$$V_T = V_B - ir = 45 - 3(1) = 42 \ \text{V}$$

(d) The 3 A will divide into a 5-to-1 ratio because of the resistor values. If you let x represent the current in the 30 Ω resistor, the junction law tells you that

$$3 = x + 5x \qquad \Rightarrow x = 0.5 \ \text{A}$$

(e) The capacitor has the same voltage drop across it as the 30 Ω resistor. From Ohm's law, you get

$$V_{30\Omega} = 0.5(30) = V_{cap} = \frac{q}{C}$$

$$q = CV_{cap} = (8 \times 10^{-6})(15) = 120 \ \mu\text{C}$$

(f) Use the basic formula for energy in a capacitor.

$$U_{cap} = \frac{1}{2}CV^2_{cap} = \frac{1}{2}(8 \times 10^{-6})(15)^2 = 9 \times 10^{-4} \ \text{J}$$

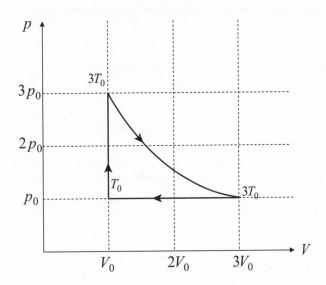

5. (a) The initial temperature follows from the gas law.

$$p_0 V_0 = nRT_0 \qquad \Rightarrow T_0 = \frac{p_0 V_0}{R}$$

At the end of process I, you can use the gas law again.

$$(3p_0) V_0 = nRT_1 \qquad \Rightarrow T_1 = \frac{3p_0 V_0}{R} = 3T_0$$

Since process II is isothermal, the temperature at the end of this process is still $3T_0$. The gas law then tells you that the pressure after this process will be p_0.

$$(3p_0) V_0 = p'(3V_0) \qquad \Rightarrow p' = p_0$$

(b) Process I is a constant volume process so no work is done on the gas. You can use the first law to find the heat added.

$$\Delta U = Q_I = \frac{3}{2} nR \Delta T = (1)\left|\frac{3}{2}R\right|(3T_0 - T_0) = 3RT_0 = 3p_0 V_0$$

(c) The first law of thermodynamics tells you that

$$\Delta U = Q_{II} + W_{II}^{on} = Q_{II} - W_{II}^{by}$$

Here the superscripts refer to work done on or by the gas. Since $\Delta U = 0$ for an isothermal process, you have immediately

$$W_{II}^{by} = Q_{II} = 3.3 p V_0$$

(d) Since the system ends back in its initial state, there's no change in the internal energy over a complete cycle.

(e) To find the efficiency, you need to find the net work done by the gas and divide by the overall heat added: $e = \dfrac{W_{total}}{Q_{added}}$. Heat is added in processes I and II:

$$Q_{added} = Q_I + Q_{II} = 3p_0V_0 + 3.3p_0V_0 = 6.3p_0V_0$$

The net work done by the gas is the sum of the works done in processes II and III, since no work is done in process I (constant volume). For process III, the work done by the gas is just the negative area of the rectangle under that part of the cycle diagram:

$$W_{III}^{by} = -2p_0V_0$$

The total work done by the gas is

$$W_{total} = W_{II}^{by} + W_{III}^{by} = 1.3p_0V_0$$

The efficiency is then

$$e = \frac{1.3}{5.2} = 0.25$$

6. (a)

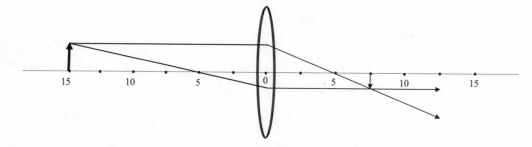

(b) Use the image equation.

$$\frac{1}{f} = \frac{1}{s_o} + \frac{1}{s_i}$$

$$\frac{1}{5} = \frac{1}{15} + \frac{1}{s_i} \qquad \Rightarrow s_i = 7.5 \text{ cm}$$

The magnification equation gives you

$$m = -\frac{s_i}{s_o} = -\frac{7.5}{15} = -\frac{1}{2}$$

The image is real because the rays actually come together. A screen 7.5 cm behind the lens would display an inverted image $\frac{1}{2}$ the size of the original.

(c) As the object is moved closer to the lens, a real image will continue to form behind the lens. It will move farther and farther away from the lens, and the magnification will get larger and larger. As the object approaches the focal point, the image distance approaches infinity. Passing through the focal point, virtual images are now formed that get closer and closer to the lens as the object gets closer and closer to the lens.

(d)

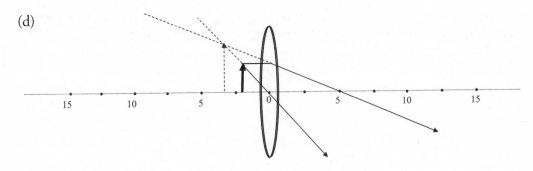

7. (a) Large graduated cylinder, water, meter stick

(b)

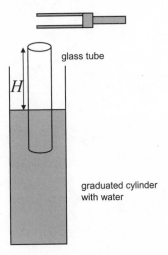

(c) Fill the graduated cylinder with water and insert one of the glass tubes into the water, leaving a portion of the tube above water. Strike the tuning fork with frequency f_0 and place it near the top of the glass tube. Raise the tube out of the water slowly until a resonance is achieved. Measure the height H of the air column above the water. This information will determine the speed of sound.

Repeat the procedure with the unknown tuning fork, obtaining a different height H'. With the speed of sound known, this will determine the unknown frequency.

(d) The air column will have an antinode at the open end and a node at the water surface. Since you're finding the first resonance as you raise the tube out of the water, the column is excited in its fundamental mode. Because $\frac{1}{4}\lambda$ is in the tube (one N-A distance), the wavelength is $4H$, and the wave speed is

$$V_{sound} = \lambda f = 4Hf_0$$

The same analysis will then yield for the unknown fork:

$$f = \frac{v_w}{\lambda'} = \frac{4Hf_0}{4H'} = \frac{H}{H'}f_0$$

Glossary

absorption spectrum The set of electromagnetic wave wavelengths that can be absorbed by a collection of a given type of atom.

acceleration The time rate of change of velocity. There are two types of acceleration: **average acceleration**, given by the change in velocity over an interval, divided by the size of the time interval, and **instantaneous acceleration**, the limit of the average acceleration over an infinitesimally small interval.

adiabatic A process that occurs without an exchange of heat energy.

amplitude The maximum value of the disturbance in a wave or the magnitude of the largest displacement of an oscillating system.

angular momentum A measure of the motion of an object about an axis. When no torques are exerted about this axis, the angular momentum is conserved.

angular momentum conservation law A law stating that the total angular momentum of a system won't change if no external torques are acting on the system.

antinodes The points in a standing wave where the maximum disturbance occurs.

apparent weight The reading of a bathroom scale that's in the same state of motion as the object resting on it.

Archimedes' principle A principle stating that for any object completely immersed or partially immersed in a fluid, the buoyant force will be equal in magnitude to the weight of the fluid displaced by the object.

atomic energy levels The discrete values of energy that an electron bound to a nucleus may possess.

atomic number The number of protons in a nucleus.

beats The oscillations that occur when two waves of slightly different frequencies interfere. The beat frequency is the difference of the two frequencies interfering.

Bernoulli's equation An equation that relates the work done by gravity and pressure to the change in kinetic energy of a fluid element.

binding energy The energy that must be added to a nucleus to completely separate all the nucleons.

boundary condition A constraint placed on the properties of a standing wave by the boundaries that reflect the component waves.

buoyant force The force on an object in a static fluid due to pressure differences between the top and bottom of the object.

capacitance The ratio of the charge separated per potential drop for a capacitor. Capacitance measures the ability to store charge; it increases when the conductors get larger or closer together.

capacitor A circuit device that consists of two separated conductors.

Carnot cycle A sequence of four processes that ends in returning the working substance to its initial state. On a pV diagram, there are two isothermal processes connected by two adiabatic processes.

Carnot efficiency The maximum efficiency that any heat engine can achieve. It depends only on the temperatures of the two reservoirs, not on the details of the engine mechanism.

cascade A process by which an excited atomic electron makes several transitions, emitting a single photon in each transition.

center of mass The average coordinate of a system of particles, with the average weighted by the mass at each coordinate. The CM obeys the dynamic equation of a point particle moving under the influence of only the external forces acting on the system.

central maximum A region of constructive interference at the center of an interference pattern. For a two-slit apparatus, it corresponds to a zero-path difference between the rays interfering.

centripetal acceleration For a circularly moving object, the component of the acceleration directed toward the center.

centripetal force For a circularly moving object, the component of the net force directed toward the center.

Compton effect A phenomenon associated with the scattering of x-rays off electrons. The wavelength shift of the scattered x-rays could be explained only by treating the light as a collection of photons.

conduction In thermodynamics, a mechanism of heat transfer that relies on molecular collisions to distribute the energy. In conduction, the molecules themselves don't move far.

conductor A material that contains many mobile charges within it that can partake in an electric current if a local electric field is established.

conservation laws Principles that state that under certain conditions, some physical quantities don't change; they are conserved. Examples include the conservation laws for energy, momentum, angular momentum, and electric charge.

conservation of mechanical energy A principle that states that if only conservative forces act on a system, the total mechanical energy won't change.

conservation of momentum principle A statement that when no external forces act on a system, its total linear momentum won't change.

conservative force A force with the property that the work done by the force is independent of path. Only for conservative forces can a potential energy be meaningfully defined.

constructive interference A condition that occurs when two waves superpose to produce an amplitude that is the sum of the individual amplitudes of each wave.

contact force A force exerted between two systems as a result of their actually touching each other.

continuity equation An equation that expresses the condition that fluid mass is neither lost nor gained in a flow without sources or sinks.

convection A mechanism of heat transfer characterized by the transfer of the more energetic molecules from one place to another.

conventional current The electric current produced by imagining positive charges are moving instead of electrons. It flows in the opposite direction to the electron flow.

coulomb The SI unit of electric charge.

Coulomb's law The inverse square law that describes the force exerted between two point charges.

critical angle The minimum angle that incident light must have to be totally reflected at an interface as light moves from a medium with a larger index of refraction to a smaller one.

cross product A type of vector multiplication that results in a third vector perpendicular to each of the two vectors in the product. The direction is determined by the right-hand rule. Parallel vectors produce a cross product of 0.

De Broglie wavelength The wavelength of a material particle.

destructive interference A condition that occurs when two waves superpose to produce an amplitude that is the difference of the individual amplitudes of each wave.

diffraction A property of a wave that describes a wave's tendency to bend around an obstacle into what would be called the shadow region of the obstacle.

diffraction grating An optical device consisting of many closely spaced slits.

dispersion A phenomenon that results from the variation of the index of refraction of a material with frequency. White light entering a material will emerge in separated colors.

displacement The change in position of an object.

Doppler effect The frequency change of a wave due to the motion of the wave source or the observer of the wave.

dot product A type of vector multiplication that results in a scalar. It's maximized when the two vectors in the product are parallel, and it's 0 when they are perpendicular.

drift speed The slow speed acquired by conduction electrons as a result of an impressed electric field within the conductor.

efficiency For a heat engine, the ratio of the useful work done to the heat flowing into the engine.

elastic collision A collision where the total kinetic energy doesn't change.

electric charge A fundamental property possessed by many of the basic constituents of matter. The basic unit of charge is 1.6×10^{-19} C. Electrons carry 1 negative unit, and protons carry 1 positive unit.

electric current The rate at which charge flows across a given cross-sectional area.

electric field A vector quantity defined at every point in space as the electric force per unit charge. The direction of the electric field is determined by its effect on a positive charge. Electric fields are created by charges and changing magnetic fields.

electric field lines A representation of the electric field. The electric field is tangential to the field lines, and the strength of the field is directly proportional to the density of the lines in space. For electrostatic fields, field lines begin on positive charges and end on negative charges. For induced fields, the field lines close on themselves.

electric potential difference The work per unit charge needed to move a charge between two points.

electric potential energy (difference) The negative of the work done by the electric field as a charge is slowly repositioned.

electrical resistance The property of a conductor or other electrical device that determines how much current will be established in the material or device for a given potential drop.

electromagnetic wave A wave that propagates through the mutual interactions of electric and magnetic fields.

electron-volt A unit of energy corresponding to the amount of energy gained by an electron as it moves through a 1-volt potential difference.

electrostatic equilibrium The condition achieved when all mobile charges have ceased moving in response to an imposed electric field.

electrostatic field An electric field created by stationary charges.

electrostatics The study of the properties of charges at rest.

emission spectrum The set of electromagnetic wave wavelengths that can be emitted by a collection of a given type of atom.

energy of assembly The work needed to construct a charge distribution from scratch with all elements initially at infinity.

entropy A measure of the number of ways that a system can be reorganized at the molecular level without changing the macroscopic properties. It specifically measures the number of microstates that manifest the same macrostate.

equilibrium position For an oscillating system, the position where the restoring force is 0.

equipotential surface A connected surface that has zero potential difference between any two points on the surface. The electric field will be perpendicular to the equipotential surfaces. It takes zero work to move a charge along such a surface.

farad The SI unit of capacitance corresponding to 1 coulomb per volt.

Faraday's law A law that relates the voltage induced in a loop to the change in the flux through the loop. More generally, it relates an induced electric field to a changing magnetic field.

first law of thermodynamics A particular statement of the conservation of energy principle. For systems consisting of many particles, it states that any change in internal energy can be accounted for by work done on the system and heat flow into the system.

first order maximum The first region of constructive interference outside the central maximum of an interference pattern. For a two-slit apparatus, it corresponds to a 1-wavelength path difference between the rays interfering.

fluid A substance in which constituent molecules or atoms don't have fixed positions. A fluid can "flow"—that is, undergo continuous deformations in response to forces that act on the fluid.

focal point The point at which rays parallel to the axis will be brought to convergence by a concave mirror or a convex lens. The point where rays parallel to the axis will appear to diverge from for a convex mirror or a concave lens.

freebody diagram An abstract representation of an interacting system. The system is usually depicted in a simplified form, and forces acting on it are shown as arrows with an organized labeling scheme.

frequency The number of repetitions per second for an oscillating system.

friction force The component of the force between two surfaces that is parallel to the surfaces. It is called kinetic friction when the two surfaces slide past each other, and static friction when the two surfaces don't move with respect to each other.

gas A fluid with very weak intermolecular forces. A gas fills any volume that contains it.

geosynchronous Having a period of 1 day. A satellite in geosynchronous orbit over the equator always remains over the same point on the Earth's surface.

ground state The lowest energy that an atomic electron may possess.

heat An energy transfer between systems that occurs because of the temperature differences between the systems. The heat transferred to or from a system is the result of random motions in the surroundings of the system.

heat engine Any mechanism that extracts energy from a hot reservoir, converting some to useful work, then expelling the remainder into a cold reservoir.

Huygens emitter A point along a wave front that can be thought of as emitting spherical wavelets.

Huygens' principle A conceptual principle for determining the position and shape of a new wave front, given the old wave front. Each point on the old wave front acts as a Huygens emitter. The envelope of the wavelets emitted determines the new wave front.

hydrostatic pressure The force per unit area exerted equally in all directions at a fixed depth by a fluid at rest.

ideal fluid An incompressible fluid that flows without viscous effects.

ideal gas A model for describing a gas. In the model, you assume that the molecules occupy a negligible space, that they interact with each other only upon direct contact, and that all molecular collisions are elastic.

ideal gas law A mathematical statement of the relation between temperature, pressure, volume, and amount of substance for an ideal gas.

impulse A vector quantity that, for constant forces, is equal to the product of a force and the time over which it acts. The impulse delivered by the net force will equal the change in momentum of the system.

incompressible fluid A fluid that doesn't change density when subjected to pressure variations.

index of refraction The ratio of the speed of light in a medium to the speed in vacuum. The index of refraction varies slightly with the frequency of the light.

induced voltage An electric potential difference created in a circuit by changing magnetic flux through the circuit.

inelastic collision A collision in which kinetic energy is transformed into some other form of energy. In a totally inelastic collision, the colliding objects move as one after the collision.

inertia The property of all matter manifested by its persistence in its current state of motion, either at rest or with constant speed in a straight line, unless an unbalanced force is present.

intensity A measure of the rate at which light energy crosses a unit area.

internal energy The sum of the kinetic and potential energies associated with the atomic and molecular motions and positions within a substance.

internal resistance The effective resistance added to a circuit by a battery.

inverse square law A force law between two objects where the force varies inversely with the square of the separation between the objects. Newton's law of gravity and Coulomb's law of electrostatics are both inverse square laws.

inverted An image that has the opposite orientation to the object.

ionization energy The energy that must be acquired by a ground state electron to remove it from the atom.

irrotational flow A condition met when a small paddlewheel placed within a fluid will not rotate.

isobaric A process that occurs at constant pressure.

isothermal A process that occurs at constant temperature.

isotopes Nuclei with the same atomic number but different mass numbers. Isotopes differ in the number of neutrons present in the nucleus.

junction law The first of Kirchhoff's laws, stating that current entering a junction equals current leaving a junction. The junction law is a manifestation of the conservation of charge principle.

kinematics That part of Mechanics that deals with the description of motion without addressing the causes of motion.

kinetic energy The energy associated with the motion of an object. For an object moving so that all parts have the same velocity vector, it's referred to as **translational** kinetic energy.

kinetic molecular theory A model that uses the microscopic behavior of a gas to explain macroscopic properties of the gas. In its simplest form, it assumes an ideal gas undergoing elastic collisions that can be analyzed using Newton's laws of mechanics.

Kirchhoff's laws Rules that determine what currents will be established in a given connection of circuit elements.

law of reflection A law that says the incident and reflected angles are equal when light is reflected off a smooth surface.

Lenz's law A law stating that an induced current will always flow in such a way as to oppose the change that caused it.

line spectra The collective name for the emission and absorption spectra of atoms and molecules.

linear momentum A vector quantity equal to the product of an object's mass and velocity. The linear momentum of a system of particles is equal to the product of the total mass and the system center of mass velocity. Linear momentum of a system will be conserved if no external forces act on the system.

liquid A fluid that has a definite volume but takes on the shape of its container. Intermolecular forces are strong enough to keep molecules fairly close to each other.

long wire rule A right hand rule used to determine the magnetic field direction in a region surrounding a long wire.

longitudinal wave A wave in which the oscillations occur along the same line as the direction of wave travel.

loop law The second of Kirchhoff's laws, stating that the sum of the potential drops around a closed circuit loop must add to 0. It's a result of the conservative nature of the electric force.

macrostate The large scale state of a system that isn't concerned with the particular behaviors of individual molecules. Typically, there will be many ways the molecules can behave and produce the same macrostate.

magnetic field A vector quantity defined at every point in space. The field exerts forces on moving charges and is created by moving charges and changing electric fields.

magnetic field lines A representation of the magnetic field. The field is tangential everywhere to the field lines, and the strength of the field is proportional to the density of field lines.

magnetic flux A measure of how much of a magnetic field cuts through a given area.

mass number The total number of nucleons in a nucleus.

mass-energy equivalence principle The quantitative relation between the change in mass of a system and the amount of energy released or increased in the process.

mechanical wave A wave whose propagation characteristics are determined by Newton's laws of mechanics.

microstate One particular arrangement of molecular positions and velocities in a system. Typically, there are many microstates that produce the same large-scale manifestations of the system.

mole A counting unit. One mole is 6×10^{23} objects.

net force The vector sum of all forces acting on a system.

neutrino A very low-mass, neutral quantum particle involved in nuclear reactions.

Newton's first law The law that describes the property of inertia.

Newton's law of gravity The quantitative statement that relates the properties of two masses to their mutual gravitational attraction. For point masses, this force is proportional to the product of the masses, inversely proportional to the square of their separation, and directed along the line connecting the two masses.

Newton's second law The law that quantitatively defines force in terms of mass and acceleration.

Newton's third law The law that recognizes the equal but opposite nature of all forces exerted between interacting systems.

nodes The points in a standing wave where the disturbance is always 0.

noncontact force A force exerted between two systems when they aren't actually touching each other.

normal force The component of the force exerted between two surfaces that is perpendicular to the surfaces.

normal line An imaginary line perpendicular to the interface between two media.

nuclear fission A nuclear process that involves the splitting of a large nucleus by a neutron.

nuclear fusion A nuclear process that involves two smaller nuclei reacting to form a larger nucleus.

nucleon The collective name for a proton or a neutron.

ohm The SI unit of electrical resistance corresponding to 1 volt per ampere.

Ohm's law A statement of the linear relation between voltage and current for a conductor.

parallel A connection condition in a circuit. Two devices in parallel always have the same potential drop across them.

Pascal's principle Any change in pressure applied to an enclosed incompressible static fluid is transmitted undiminished throughout the fluid.

path difference The extra distance a ray travels compared with another ray that it will eventually interfere with. Path difference is usually discussed in terms of multiples of a wavelength.

period The time it takes for a repetitive motion to repeat itself once.

periodic wave A wave in which the disturbance oscillates with a regular frequency.

phase The current state of the oscillation in a wave. The phase is determined by the current value of the disturbance and by how it is changing.

phase shift A change in the phase of a wave as a result of a reflection.

photoelectric effect A phenomenon associated with the ejection of electrons from a metal surface as they absorb light energy. The photoelectric effect is historically important for its manifestation of the particle nature of light.

photon A particle of light, first introduced in the explanation of the photoelectric effect. Photons carry both energy and momentum.

Planck's constant A fundamental constant of nature whose size determines the strength of quantum effects.

plane wave A periodic wave in which the wave fronts are geometric planes.

position The specific place where an object resides. It is given quantitatively by the coordinates of the point in some coordinate system.

potential energy The energy an object has as a result of its position. PE is measured with respect to a zero point that can be arbitrarily chosen.

power The rate at which work is done. Its SI units are watts.

principle of superposition A principle stating that a complex interaction of several systems can be analyzed in terms of individual components of the interaction as if the others weren't present. The complete analysis of the complex interaction is then obtained by putting together the individual contributions in an additive manner, taking their scalar or vector natures into account.

principle rays In geometrical optics, a ray that is especially easy to draw in determining image formation.

projectile An object moving near the Earth's surface solely under the influence of gravity.

quantized A property is said to be quantized if there is a basic unit of the quantity that cannot be subdivided. Electric charge and photon energy are quantized properties.

quantum The smallest unit of a physical quantity. Since the properties of quantum particles are so different from those at the macroscopic scale, these particles and their interactions are called the quantum world.

rays Imaginary lines perpendicular to the wave fronts of a wave.

real image An image formed by the actual convergence of light rays at a point.

reference circle The circle and its accompanying uniform circular motion associated with the simple harmonic motion of a real system. The reference circle has a radius equal to the amplitude of the SHM, and a period equal to the period of the SHM. Vector quantities on the reference circle project only one component onto the SHM.

refraction The bending of light at an interface between two media due to the difference in wave speed in the two media.

reservoir A large system that can absorb or expel heat without changing its temperature.

resistor A circuit element obeying Ohm's law.

resonance A condition that occurs when a large disturbance is produced in a system by the repeated application of small impulses applied at a frequency equal to a natural frequency of the system.

restoring force The generic name given to the force that tends to bring an oscillating system back to its equilibrium position.

resultant The sum of two or more vectors.

right-hand rule A rule that determines the direction of the cross product of two vectors. You curl the fingers of your right hand from the first vector in the product into the second, with the thumb then pointing in the appropriate direction.

rotational equilibrium That state of a system with 0 net torque acting upon it.

rotational kinetic energy The energy associated with the rotational motion of an object.

scalar A physical quantity that can be completely quantified by a single number.

second law of thermodynamics A principle that describes the spontaneous flow of energy between systems. In its most fundamental form, it states that the entropy of a closed system can never decrease.

series A connection condition in a circuit that requires that the two devices in series always have the same current established within them.

simple circuit A circuit consisting of batteries and resistors, with the batteries in series and the resistors connected in such a way that the equivalent resistance of the entire circuit can be determined using the series and parallel rules for resistor combinations.

simple harmonic motion A repetitive motion caused by a restoring force that's directly proportional to the displacement.

Snell's law A law that relates the incident and refracted angles when light moves from one medium to another.

spring constant A parameter that indicates the stiffness of a spring. It's the proportionality constant in the equation that relates the force exerted by a spring and the amount of extension or compression the spring has acquired.

standing wave A disturbance produced when two waves of the same frequency interfere with each other.

steady state A nonequilibrium state of a system that doesn't change. A battery connected across a conductor will create a steady state in which a constant current flows in the conductor.

steady-state flow A condition met when the density, pressure, and velocity at an arbitrary point in the flow don't change in time.

stopping potential The minimum voltage that must be applied to the collector in a photoelectric experiment to prevent electrons from reaching the collector.

streamlines The trajectories of fluid particles in steady-state fluid flow. The velocity of the fluid at any point is tangent to the streamline passing through that point.

strong nuclear force A short-range force responsible for holding the nucleus together. The strong force is much stronger than the electric force.

temperature On the macroscopic scale, the parameter that describes the direction of spontaneous energy flow. At the microscopic level, temperature is proportional to the average translational kinetic energy of the molecules or atoms of the substance.

tension The force exerted by a rope or rod.

terminal speed The limiting speed approached by an object experiencing a resistive force that increases as the speed increases.

terminal voltage The potential difference across a battery when current is established within it. Terminal voltage can be less than or greater than the battery's ideal voltage, depending on how the battery is connected.

tesla The SI unit for magnetic field, equal to $1\frac{N \cdot s}{C \cdot m}$.

test charge A small positive charge.

thermal equilibrium A condition reached between two or more systems when there's no longer any tendency for energy to flow spontaneously from one system to another. It's characterized by all systems being at the same temperature.

thermal radiation A mechanism of heat transfer that involves an emission of infrared radiation from a warmer object and the subsequent absorption of this radiation by the cooler object. Thermal radiation doesn't require a material medium between the systems exchanging heat energy.

threshold The discontinuity in the number of ejected electrons in a photoelectric experiment as the wavelength is varied.